Gerard Newson

Elementary Structural Design in Concrete to CP 110

GW00775813

A. W. Astill and L. H. Martin
University of Aston in Birmingham

Edward Arnold

First published in 1975 by
Edward Arnold (Publishers) Ltd.
25 Hill Street, London W1X 8LL

Reprinted with corrections 1977
(including Amendments 1 and 2 to CP 110)

ISBN 0 7131 3357 0

Printed in Great Britain by The Pitman Press, Bath

Preface

The authors, for some time, have felt the need for a book which presents
the theories of reinforced and prestressed concrete in a simple and unified
manner and at the same time shows, as far as possible, how these theories
are developed into the formulae given in Codes of Practice and their use in
practical design offices.   The publication of CP110:1972:The Structural
Use of Concrete presents the opportunity since it is not so much a revision
of earlier codes but the result of a complete re-appraisal of the
philosophy of the design of concrete structures.   CP110 is based on the
principles of Limit State Design rather than the working load design of
earlier codes.

The aim of this book is to provide students with a clear and simple
exposition of the principles of Limit State Design as applied to reinforced
concrete and in particular to lead the student through the stages of
reinforced concrete design using the methods set out in CP110.
Consequently there are frequent references to CP110 throughout the text
some of the most commonly used tables and clauses being reproduced where
they are first needed.

No previous knowledge of reinforced concrete design is assumed making the
book suitable for the use of students of architecture, building, civil and
structural engineering either in conjunction with a course of lectures or
as a self-instruction text.   The book will also be useful to those
practising designers who have little or no knowledge of Limit State Design
and who are in need of an introduction to CP110.   In order to achieve
maximum understanding of the subject it is important that the problems
given are solved as soon as they appear in the text.

A parallel course on Structural Analysis is necessary for the full
understanding of Chapters 2, 3 and 4, consequently some readers may find
it more convenient to omit these chapters initially returning to them when
their knowledge of analysis of structures is more complete.

Acknowledgements

The following extracts from CP110: 1972 The Structural Use of Concrete, Part 1, Design, materials and workmanship, Part 2, Design charts for singly reinforced beams, doubly reinforced beams and rectangular columns, and Part 3, Design charts for circular columns and prestressed beams, are reproduced by permission of the British Standards Institution, 2 Park Street, London W1A 2BS (from whom copies of the complete Code of Practice may be obtained):

List of Symbols

The symbols listed below are those occurring frequently in the text.
Other symbols used in one place only are defined where they occur and not
included here.

A	cross sectional area of member
A_c	Area of concrete
A_{ps}	Area of prestressing tendons
A'_s	Area of compression reinforcement
A_s	Area of tension reinforcement
A_{sc}	Area of longitudinal reinforcement (for columns)
A_{sd}	Area of tensile reinforcement corresponding to M_{ud}
A_{sl}	Cross-sectional area of longitudinal reinforcement provided for torsion
$A_{s.prov.}$	Area of tension reinforcement provided
$A_{s.req.}$	Area of tension reinforcement required
A_{ss}	Area of tensile reinforcement corresponding to M_{us}
A_{sv}	Cross-sectional area of the two legs of a link
a	Deflection
a_b	Distance between bars
a_e	Elastic deflection
a_c	Creep deflection
a_v	Distance between the line of action of the load and the face of the supporting member
b	Width of section
b_c	Breadth of compression face
b_t	Breadth of section at level of tension reinforcement
b_w	Breadth of web or rib of a member
b_s	Breadth of beams at soffit
C	Torsional constant

d	Effective depth of tension reinforcement
d'	Depth to compression reinforcement
d_t	Effective depth in shear
d_2	Depth to reinforcement
E_c	Static secant modulus of elasticity of concrete
E_s	Modulus of elasticity of steel
e	eccentricity of prestressing force from the centroidal axis (+ve below the axis)
e	Base of Napierian logarithms
e_1	Eccentricity of prestressing force at the lowest cable position
e_2	Eccentricity of prestressing force at the highest cable position
F	Ultimate Load
F_{bst}	Tensile bursting force
F_k	Characteristic load
f_{bs}	Bond stress
f_c	Stress in the concrete adjacent to the steel
f'_c	Cylinder crushing strength of concrete
f_{ci}	Concrete strength at (initial) transfer
f_{co}	Stress in concrete at the level of the tendon due to initial prestress and dead load
f_{cp}	Compressive stress at the centroidal axis due to prestress
f_{cu}	Characteristic concrete cube strength
f_{ec}	Allowable service compressive stress in the concrete
f_{et}	Allowable service tensile stress in the concrete
f_{e1}	Final effective stress on the tension side
f_{e2}	Final effective stress on the compression side
f_k	Characteristic strength
f_{pb}	Tensile stress in tendons at (beam) failure
f_{pe}	Effective prestress (in tendon)
f_{pi}	Initial stress in the prestressing steel
f_{pt}	Stress due to prestress
f_{pu}	Characteristic strength of prestressing tendons
f_s	Service stress
f_{su}	Stress in the steel at the ultimate limit state which may be less than or equal to $0.87 f_y$

f_{s2}	Stress in reinforcement
f_t	Maximum principal tensile stress
f_{tc}	Allowable compressive stress in the concrete at transfer
f_{tt}	Allowable tensile stress in the concrete at transfer
f_{t1}	Final stress on the tension side at transfer
f_{t2}	Final stress on the compression side at transfer
f_u	$0.87f_y$
f_y	Characteristic strength of reinforcement
f_{yi}	Characteristic strength of inclined bars
f_{yl}	Characteristic strength of longitudinal reinforcement
f_{yv}	Characteristic strength of link reinforcement
G	Shear modulus
G_k	Characteristic dead load
g_k	Characteristic dead load per unit area or per unit length
h	Overall depth of section in plane of bending
h_{agg}	Maximum size of aggregate
h_c	Diameter of column head
h_t	Thickness of flange
h_{max}	Larger dimension of section
h_{min}	Smaller dimension of section
I	Second moment of area
i	Radius of gyration
j	Number of joints
K	Stiffness of member (EI/L)
K_b	Stiffness of beam
K_1	Stiffness of lower column length
K_u	Stiffness of upper column length
k	A constant (with appropriate subscripts)
L,l	Distance from face of support at the end of a cantilever or effective span of a simply supported beam or slab
l_e	Effective height of a column or wall
l_{ex}	Effective height for bending about the major axis
l_{cv}	Effective height for bending about the minor axis
l_o	Clear height of column between end restraints

l_x — Length of the shorter side (of rectangular slab)

l_y — Length of the longer side (of rectangular slab)

ℓ — Bond length

ℓ_g — Length of gap between welds

ℓ_w — Length of weld

M — Bending moment due to ultimate loads

M_{add} — Maximum additional moment

M_i — Maximum initial moment in a column due to ultimate loads (but not less than 0.05 Nh)

M_{min} — Minimum bending moment (generally due to self weight for simply supported beams)

M_s — Bending moment due to service load i.e. dead load + imposed load

M_{sx}, M_{sy} — The bending moments at midspan on strips of unit width and spans l_x and l_y respectively

M_t — Total moment in a column due to ultimate loads

M_u — Ultimate resistance moment

M_{ud} — Moment of resistance due to the additional compression and tension steel in a reinforced concrete beam

M_{us} — Maximum moment of resistance of a singly reinforced concrete beam

M_{ux} — Maximum moment capacity in a short column assuming ultimate axial load and bending about the major axis only

M_{uy} — Maximum moment capacity in a short column assuming ultimate axial load and bending about the minor axis only

M_x, M_y — Moments about the major and minor axes of a short column due to ultimate loads

M_o — Moment necessary to produce zero stress

N — Ultimate axial load at section considered

N_{bal} — Axial load on a column corresponding to the balanced condition

N_{uz} — Axial load capacity of a column ignoring all bending

n — Total ultimate load per unit area ($1.4g_k + 1.6q_k$)

P_e — Prestressing force after losses (effective)

P_k — Characteristic load in tendon

P_o — Prestressing force in the tendon at the jacking end (or at tangent point near jacking end)

P_t — Prestressing force at transfer

P_{t1} — Prestressing force corresponding to the lowest cable position

P_{t2} — Prestressing force corresponding to the highest cable position

P_x	Prestressing force at distance x from jack
Q_k	Characteristic imposed load
q	Distributed imposed load
q_k	Characteristic imposed load per unit area
r	Internal radius of bend
r_{ps}	Radius of curvature (of a prestressing tendon)
$\dfrac{1}{r_b}$	Curvature of a beam at midspan or, for cantilevers, at the support section
s_b	Spacing of bars
s_i	Spacing of inclined bars along the member
s_v	Spacing of links along the member
T	Torsional moment due to ultimate loads
u	Perimeter
V	Shear force due to ultimate loads
V_c	Ultimate shear resistance of concrete
V_{co}	Ultimate shear resistance of a section uncracked in flexure
V_{cr}	Ultimate shear resistance of a section cracked in flexure
v	Shear stress
v_c	Ultimate shear stress in concrete
v_i	Shear stress resisted by inclined bars
v_s	Shear stress resisted by vertical links
v_t	Torsional shear stress
v_{tmin}	Allowable torsional shear stress without torsion reinforcement
v_{tu}	Ultimate torsional shear stress
V_u	Ultimate shear resistance of a reinforced concrete section
W	Total load on a beam
W_k	Characteristic wind load
x	Neutral axis depth
x_1	Smaller dimension of a link centre to centre of bars
y_o	Half the side of end block
y_{po}	Half the side of loaded area
y_1	Larger dimension of a link centre to centre of bars
$\bar{y}$	Distance to centroid of cross section
Z	Elastic section modulus
Z'	Theoretical optimum elastic section modulus

z	Lever arm
α_c	A ratio of the sum of column stiffnesses to the sum of beam stiffnesses
α_{c1}	Value of α_c at lower end of column
α_{c2}	Value of α_c at upper end of column
α_{cmin}	Minimum value of α_{c1} and α_{c2}
α_e	Modular ratio
α_n	Coefficient as a function of column axial loading
α_{sx}, α_{sy}	Bending moment coefficients for slabs with no provision to resist torsion at the corners or to prevent the corners from lifting
β_b	Ratio of the resistance moment at mid-span obtained from the redistributed maximum moment diagram to that obtained from the maximum moment diagram before redistribution.
β_{red}	Ratio of the reduction in resistance moment
β_{sx}, β_{sy}	Bending moment coefficients for slabs with provision to resist torsion and to prevent corners from lifting
β_1	Ratio of the longer to shorter base sides
γ_f	Partial safety factor for load
γ_m	Partial safety factor for strength
ε_{cs}	Shrinkage strain
ε_{c1}	Strain in concrete at the level of the tendon at time of loading
ε_{c2}	Strain in concrete at the centroid of the section at time of loading
ε_s	Strain in the steel or shear factor
η	Loss of prestress coefficient $\left[P_e/P_t \right]$
μ	Coefficient of friction
ρ	$\rho = \dfrac{A_s}{bd}$
ΣA_{sv}	Area of shear reinforcement
Σu_s	Sum of the effective perimeters of the tension reinforcement
σ	Soil stress
ϕ	Bar size

Contents

1 Materials and Loads

1.A. THE OBJECT OF STRUCTURAL DESIGN (cl.2.1 (CP110))

The object of structural design is to achieve a structure which fulfills the requirements of the client at reasonable cost.

These requirements may include any or all of the following:

(a) the structure shall not collapse.

(b) it shall not be so flexible that the appearance of the structure or the motion of the structure causes alarm or discomfort to the users.

(c) it shall not require excessive repair due to accidental overload nor because of the action of the weather.

(d) in the case of a building the structure shall be sufficiently fire resistant to allow the occupants to escape in the case of fire.

Throughout the design process the designer should be conscious of the costs involved. These include:

(a) the initial cost - site preparation, cost of materials, and construction.

(b) maintenance costs - decoration, structural repair.

(c) insurance - chiefly against fire damage.

It could be argued that the cost of the eventual demolition of the structure should also be included in some cases.

1.B. THE OBJECT OF LIMIT STATE DESIGN (cl.2.1 (CP110))

The object of limit state design is to achieve an acceptable probability that a structure will not become unserviceable in its lifetime. It, therefore, sets out to examine all the ways in which a structure may become unfit for use.

The condition of a structure when it becomes unserviceable is called a "limit state". The most important of these limit states which must be examined in design are:-

(a) the ultimate limit state - neither the whole structure nor any part of the structure should collapse under forseeable overload.

(b) the serviceability limit state of deflection - the deflection of the

1

structure should not adversely affect the appearance of the structure.

(c) the serviceability limit state of cracking - the cracking of the concrete should not adversely affect the appearance or the durability of the structure e.g. excessive cracks allow ingress of water with subsequent corrosion and frost damage.

(d) the serviceability limit state of vibration - vibration should not be such as to cause alarm or discomfort.

QUESTION 1.1

Are there any other considerations which should be taken into account in the design of a structure?

(*Answer.   Fatigue, durability, fire resistance, watertightness, excessive noise, excessive gain or loss of heat.*)

1.C. VARIATION OF MATERIAL PROPERTIES (cl.2.3.2(CP110))

A knowledge of the properties (i.e. strength, elasticity, durability etc) of a material is necessary in order to determine the size of a member in a structure, or to determine the proportions of the materials in a composite section.   The material properties most usually considered are:

(a) the stress or strain at which a material will fail.

(b) the stress-strain relationship determined from a simple test.

It is found that not only do the properties vary within a particular batch of material but the stress-strain relationships are complex.   In design it is necessary to derive "idealised" design criteria which take account of the actual situation but enable practical methods of analysis to be used.

It is found by experiment that the strength of samples taken from a batch of material approximates to the normal distribution shown in Fig. 1.1.

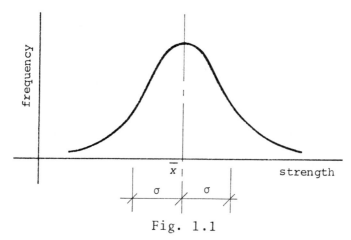

Fig. 1.1

where: x = the strength of a sample

$\overline{x}$ = the arithmetic mean of the sample strengths.

n = the number of samples.

σ = the standard deviation = $\sqrt{\left[\dfrac{\Sigma(x-\overline{x})^2}{n-1}\right]}$ This is a measure of the variation of the test results.

QUESTION 1.2

Determine the arithmetic mean and the standard deviation for the set of cube strengths listed. 34, 40, 42, 44, 50, 56, 60, 66, N/mm^2.

(Answer. $\overline{x}$ = 49 N/mm^2, σ = 11 N/mm^2).

1.D. CHARACTERISTIC STRENGTH (cl.2.3.2(CP110))

In specifying a strength of a material either the average strength or the minimum strength could be used.   The average strength however takes no account of the range of strengths in a batch.   The distribution curve shows that it would not be realistic to specify a minimum strength because there is always the probability that some samples would fail to satisfy this.

The unified code adopts the criterion that no more than 5% of the sample should have less than a certain strength.   This strength is called the "characteristic strength" and is shown as f_k on the distribution curve.

It can be shown that this criterion is satisfied if $f_k = \overline{x} - 1.64\sigma$ as shown in Fig. 1.2.

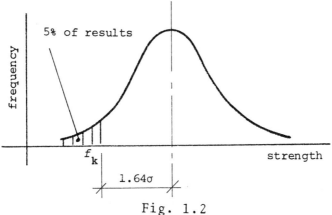

Fig. 1.2

The test results used in specifying the characteristic strengths for the materials of reinforced concrete are:

Concrete ·   -   the cube strength (cl.3.1.4.2(CP110))

Steel reinforcement   -   the yield stress or proof stress (cl.3.1.4.3(CP110))

Prestressing steel   -   the proof stress (cl.4.1.4.3(CP110))

QUESTION 1.3

Samples are taken from two batches of concrete A and B and made into test cubes.   The crushing strengths of the cubes are as follows:

(a) 25, 30, 34, 40, 47, 49, 55 N/mm^2

(b) 30, 35, 37, 40, 42, 46, 50 N/mm^2

Determine the average strength and characteristic strength for each batch.

(Answer.   (a) $\bar{x}$ = 40, f_k = 22.1;   (b) $\bar{x}$ = 40, f_k = 28.9 N/mm^2)

1.E. DESIGN STRENGTH - PARTIAL SAFETY FACTOR FOR STRENGTH
    (cls. 2.3.2, 2.3.3.2 (CP110))

The characteristic strength refers to the strength of the set of test pieces, i.e. cubes for concrete and tensile test pieces for steel.   It is found however that the variation of strength in the actual structure may be greater than at the supply point.   This is due to local variations and deterioration in transit.   For example the concrete test cubes are usually taken at the mixer and compacted and cured under ideal conditions whereas the strength of the concrete in the structure may be reduced by:

(a) segregation in transport

(b) dirty casting conditions

(c) bad curing conditions due to the effects of heat, rain, frost, wind, etc

(d) inadequate compaction

These effects are allowed for in design by dividing the characteristic strength by a partial safety factor for strength γ_m.   In general the partial safety factor adopted for concrete is 1.5.   The value for steel is 1.15 since there is less variation in strength.

QUESTION 1.4

Suggest reasons for the introduction of the partial safety factor for steel.

(Answer.   Corrosion and variation of cross sectional area)

1.F. STRESS-STRAIN RELATIONSHIP FOR CONCRETE

The mechanical properties of concrete and hence the shape of the stress strain curve are influenced by a number of factors such as :-

(a) creep (increase in strain under constant load)
(b) type of aggregate
(c) strength of the concrete
(d) age of the concrete
(e) curing conditions

Fig. 1.3 shows the effect of creep on the shape of the stress-strain curve for a particular concrete mix.

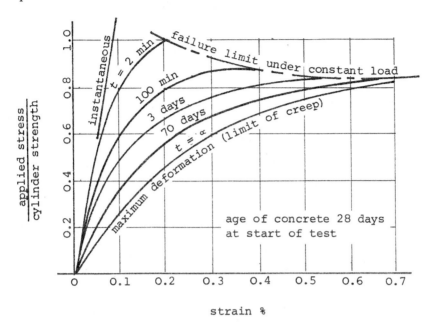

Fig. 1.3

QUESTION 1.5

A stress equal to 0.6 of the cylinder strength is applied to a specimen. Using Fig. 1.3:

(a) what is the instantaneous strain?

(b) what is the maximum strain?

(c) what is the maximum strain due to creep?

(d) what is the maximum stress that could be applied for an indefinite period without failure?

(*Answer.*   (a) 0.06%, (b) 0.30%, (c) 0.24%, (d) 0.82 times the cylinder strength)

1.G. IDEALISED STRESS-STRAIN RELATIONSHIP FOR CONCRETE (Fig. 1(CP110))

The experimental stress-strain relationship for concrete is clearly too complicated for use in design and is therefore idealised and modified in CP110 as shown in Fig. 1(CP110).   It should be noted that the graph gives a value of instantaneous modulus, maximum stress, and maximum strain.

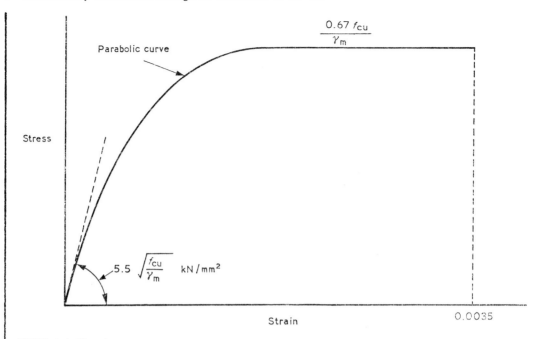

NOTE. f_{cu} in N/mm².

Fig. 1. Short term design stress–strain curve for normal weight concrete

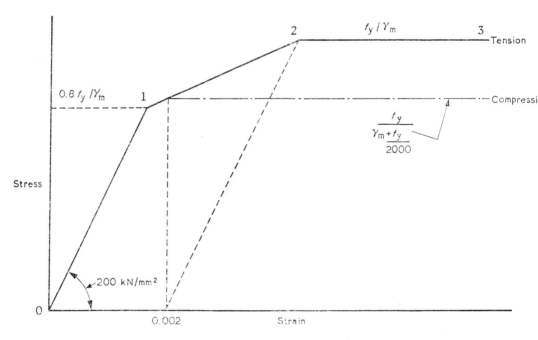

Note. f_y in N/mm².

Fig. 2. Short term design stress–strain curve for reinforcement

The maximum stress is shown as $(0.67f_{cu}/Y_m)$. The 0.67 is introduced to allow for the difference in strength indicated by a cube crushing test and the strength of the concrete in the structure. A cube is crushed between two parallel steel plates which restrain the lateral expansion of the concrete by friction and leads to an artifically high result, whereas the area which crushes in a structure is bounded by concrete which does not give the same restraint. The length of the test specimen also enters into this, since a short specimen will always give a higher result than a longer one. The values for Youngs modulus to be used in calculations for the serviceability limit states are given in tabular form in Table 1 cl.2.4.2.2(CP110).

2.4.2.2 *Elastic modulus: concrete.* In the absence of better information, for normal weight concrete the short term elastic modulus, relevant to the serviceability limit states, may be taken from Table 1.

Table 1. Values of modulus of elasticity of concrete

Cube strength of concrete at the appropriate age or stage considered	Modulus of elasticity of concrete
N/mm²	kN/mm²
20	25
25	26
30	28
40	31
50	34
60	36

For lightweight aggregate concrete having a density between 1400 kg/m³ and 2300 kg/m³ the values given in Table 1 should be multiplied by $\left(\dfrac{D_c}{2300}\right)^2$, where D_c is the density of the lightweight aggregate concrete in kg/m³.

Further information on the elastic modulus of concrete is given in Appendix D. For sustained loading conditions, appropriate allowance for shrinkage and creep should be made.

QUESTION 1.6

What important variable is omitted from the stress-strain relationship as given in CP110?

(Answer. *time variation which produces creep*)

1.H. STRESS-STRAIN RELATIONSHIP FOR STEEL   (Fig.2 (CP110))

Typical stress-strain curves for various types of steel are shown in Fig.1.4.

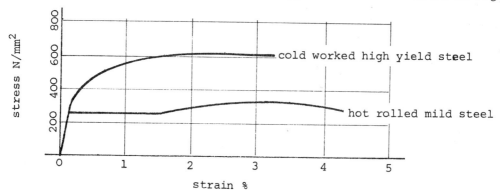

Fig. 1.4

In both curves shown the initial curve, which represents the elastic behaviour of the material, is linear and Young's modulus is given by its slope.   The change from elastic to plastic conditions appears to be abrupt for mild steel and gradual for high yield steel and prestressing wire. However it can happen that a gradual change occurs with mild steel particularly for small bars.   Because of this variation in the shapes of the curves an idealised curve, which will give safe results, must be used. Therefore for design purposes the tri-linear stress-strain curves shown in Figs. 2 & 3 (CP110) are used.   The graphs incorporate the partial safety factor of 1.15.

The characteristic strengths of reinforcement are given in Table 3 (CP110)

Table 3. Strength of reinforcement

Designation	Nominal sizes	Specified characteristic strength f_y
	mm	N/mm^2
Hot rolled mild steel (BS 4449)	All sizes	250
Hot rolled high yield (BS 4449)	All sizes	410
Cold worked high yield (BS 4461)	Up to and including 16	460
	Over 16	425
Hard drawn steel wire (BS 4482)	Up to and including 12	485

QUESTION 1.7

(a) What is the value of Young's modulus for steel given in Fig.2(CP110)?

(b) The maximum stress in the compression steel is expressed as a factor times f_y in Fig.2 (CP110).   Determine the value of the factor for
$$f_y = 410 \text{ and } 460 \text{ N/mm}^2.$$

(Answers.   (a) 200 kN/mm^2, (b) 0.74, 0.72)

1.I. CHARACTERISTIC LOADS (cl.2.3.1(CP110))

The loads on a structure are classified as:

(a) dead loads - the weight of the structure (G_k).

(b) imposed loads - due to furniture, occupants, machinery, vehicles etc (Q_k).

(c) wind loads (W_k).

Ideally these loads should be considered statistically and a characteristic
load determined.   For example the characteristic load could be defined as
the load above which not more than 5% of the loads fall, when all the loads
likely to be applied to the structure during its working life are considered.

It can be shown that:

$$\text{characteristic load} = \text{mean load} + 1.64\sigma$$

as shown in Fig.1.5.

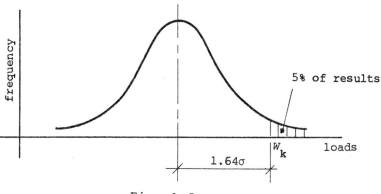

Fig. 1.5

The complete statistical information on loads, however, is not available
and designers are recommended to use:

BS648 - Schedule of Weights of Building Materials.

CP3 Ch. V Pt. 1 - Dead Loads and Imposed Loads.

CP3 Ch. V Pt. 2 - Wind Loads.

In calculating the weight of the structure the density of reinforced concrete
may be taken as 2400 kg/m^3.   The weight of a member of dimensions b x h x l
in metre units is 2400 x b x h x l x 9.81 x 10^{-3} kN

CP3 usually gives a uniformly distributed load and an alternative
concentrated load.   The characteristic load selected should be that which
produces the worst effect.   The concentrated load is more likely to be used
for beams and slabs of short span and the distributed load will be used for
longer spans.   It is not possible to give a span below which the
concentrated load will always be used since there is not a fixed relationship
between the concentrated and uniformly distributed loads.

EXAMPLE 1.1

For a billiard room, CP3 Chap V gives a distributed load of 2.0 kN/m^2 and a concentrated load of 2.7 kN on a square of 300 mm side.   The uniformly distributed load allows for the total load which may occur on the floor and includes allowances for the tables, floor coverings, furniture and persons using the room, but it does not allow directly for the effect of concentration of the load due to the billiard tables being applied to the floor through the table legs.

If the billiard room has a simply supported floor of 4m span, because the concentrated load is 300mm wide consider a strip of floor 0.3m wide ignoring lateral distribution of load.   The uniformly distributed load gives a bending moment of

$$M = \frac{2.0 \times 0.3 \times 4^2}{8} = 1.2 \text{ kNm}$$

The concentrated load applied over a length of 0.3m at the centre of the span gives a bending moment of

$$M = \frac{QL}{4} - \frac{Q}{2} \times \frac{l}{4} = \frac{2.7 \times 4.0}{4} - \frac{2.7}{2} \times \frac{0.3}{4}$$

$$= 2.7 - 0.1 = 2.6 \text{ kNm}$$

In this case if all the assumptions* are correct the concentrated load will control the design.   The bending moment obtained must be increased by the partial safety factor for imposed loads and added to the bending moment due to self weight which is also increased by the appropriate partial safety factor in order to arrive at the bending moment to be used for design.

QUESTION 1.8

For a garage CP3 recommends a uniformly distributed load of 2.5 kN/m^2 or a concentrated load of 9.0 kN acting on any square of 300 mm side.   If a simply supported beam spans 3m and supports a section of the floor 1.5m wide on each side of the beam determine the magnitude of (a) the maximum bending moment, and (b) the maximum shear force in the beam from the uniformly distributed load and the concentrated load.

(Answers.   (a) *8.44 kNm due to udl on the whole span and 6.41 kNm due to the concentrated load applied at the centre of the span.*

(b) *11.25 kN for the udl on the whole span and 8.55 kN for the concentrated load applied at the end of the beam.*

For this case the uniformly distributed load will control the design for both bending and shear.)

---

* *Note - the width of floor which can be considered to resist concentrated loads will depend on the form of construction and is further discussed in Chapter 13.*

1.J DESIGN LOAD (cl.2.3.3.1(CP110))

The characteristic load is determined from the normal variation in load. In practice the design load may be larger than the characteristic load for the following reasons:

(a) there is no pretence that the characteristic load is an absolute maximum, reference to Fig. 1.5 shows that 5% of all probable values are greater than the characteristic load.

(b) the effect of some limit states can be more disastrous than others.

(c) the lack of dimensional accuracy of construction can lead to larger or smaller loads.

(d) there may be inaccuracies in the assessment of the loading and stress redistribution within the structure.

(e) there may be unusual increases in load beyond those envisaged when deriving the characteristic load.

Each characteristic load (dead, imposed or wind) is therefore multiplied by a partial safety factor and the loads are added to produce a design load. Therefore, for any limit state, the design load is given by the sum of the characteristic loads each multiplied by its own partial safety factor.

i.e.
$$F = \gamma_{fg}\, G_k + \gamma_{fq}\, Q_k + \gamma_{fw}\, W_k$$

At the ultimate limit state the partial safety factors for load are much greater than 1.0 (with one important exception). At this limit state the important consideration is one of strength. At the servicability limit states the partial safety factors will be equal to 1.0 or less since deflection and cracking are the most important factors to consider at normal working loads. Values of the design loads are given in cl.2.3.3.1 and cl.2.3.4.1(CP110).

2.3.3 Values for the ultimate limit state

2.3.3.1 Loads. The design loads for the ultimate limit state referred to in Section 3 as the ultimate loads should be taken as

(1) Dead and imposed load
  design dead load $= 1.4G_k$
  design imposed load $= 1.6Q_k$

(2) Dead and wind load
  design dead load $= 0.9G_k$
  design wind load $= 1.4W_k$

(3) Dead, imposed and wind load
  design dead load $= 1.2G_k$
  design imposed load $= 1.2Q_k$
  design wind load $= 1.2W_k$

where G_k is the characteristic dead load,
  Q_k is the characteristic imposed load,
  W_k is the characteristic wind load,
  and the numerical values are the appropriate γ_f factors.

2.3.4 Values for a serviceability limit state

2.3.4.1 *Loads.* The design loads for a serviceability limit state should be taken as

(1) Dead and imposed load
  design dead load $= 1.0G_k$
  design imposed load $= 1.0Q_k$

(2) Dead and wind load
  design dead load $= 1.0G_k$
  design wind load $= 1.0W_k$

(3) Dead, imposed and wind load
  design dead load $= 1.0G_k$
  design imposed load $= 0.8Q_k$
  design wind load $= 0.8W_k$

It will be noticed that the values given for the ultimate limit state are considerably higher than the values for the servicability limit state, as would be expected and the values for both the servicability limit states are the same.   It will also be noticed that the values of partial safety factor are different for different combinations of load.   This difference is to allow for the different probabilities of all the loads within a load combination reaching their maximum at the same time.   It is also stated in CP110 that the arrangement of loads considered should be that which causes the most severe condition of stress, stability, deflection etc. When considering dead and imposed load on a continuous beam system at the ultimate limit state the worst stresses at the centre of the span will occur when alternate spans are loaded with dead load $1.0G_k$ only and the full combined load $F = 1.4\ G_k + 1.6\ Q_k$.   Where stability, i.e. overturning, is a criterion then the load combination of $0.9\ G_k + 1.4\ W_k$ should be considered. The partial safety factor of 0.9 is applied to the dead load to allow for the possibilities of (a) the sizes of all members being slightly smaller than the nominal and (b) the densities of all the materials being lower than those used in the calculations.   To ensure stability under horizontal forces a lower limit is placed on the value of design wind force considered at any level.   Thus, at the ultimate limit state the value of $1.4W_k$ or $1.2W_k$ depending on whether load combination 2 or 3 is being used, should not be le than 1½% of the total characteristic dead load above that level.   The application of each of the load combinations is discussed further in Chapter 2 and 3.

EXAMPLE 1.2

For the column shown in Fig. 1.6 determine the maximum and minimum values of axial force N shear force V and bending M for each load combination listed in CP110.   Both the ultimate limit state and the servicability limit states should be considered.

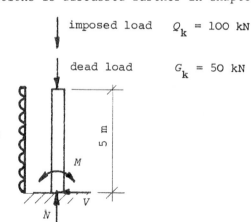

imposed load $Q_k = 100$ kN

dead load $G_k = 50$ kN

Fig. 1.6

(a) Ultimate limit state

   (i) Load combination 1, dead and imposed load.

   N_{max} = 1.4 x 50 + 1.6 x 100 = 230 kN

   N_{min} = 1.0 x 50 + 0 x 100 = 50 kN

   V and M are caused by wind forces which are not included in this load combination.

   (ii) Load combination 2, dead and wind load

   N_{min} = 0.9 x 50   = 45.0 kN

   M = 1.4 x 5 x $\dfrac{5^2}{2}$ = 87.5 kNm

   V = 1.4 x 5 x 5 = 35.0 kN

   N_{max} = 1.4 x 50   = 70.0 kN

   M and V may be combined with either N_{min} or N_{max} depending which gives the worst condition.   If M and V are reduced to a minimum of zero this load combination will revert to load case 1.

   (iii) Load combination 3, dead and imposed and wind load.

   N_{max} = 1.2 x 50 + 1.2 x 100 = 180 kN

   M_{max} = 1.2 x 5 x $\dfrac{5^2}{2}$ = 75 kNm

   V_{max} = 1.2 x 5 x 5   = 30 kN

(b) Serviceability limit states

   (i) Load combination 1, dead and imposed load

   N_{max} = 1.0 x 50 + 1.0 x 100 = 150 kN

   N_{min} = 1.0 x 50 + 0 x 100 = 50 kN

   Note: in a continuous beam maximum load on alternate spans and minimum load on the others will cause maximum downward deflection of the loaded span and maximum upward deflection of the unloaded span.

   (ii) Load combination 2, dead and wind load

   N = 1.0 x 50   = 50.0 kN

   M = 1.0 x 5 x $\dfrac{5^2}{2}$ = 62.5 kNm

   V = 1.0 x 5 x 5   = 25.0 kN

   (iii) Load combination 3, dead and imposed and wind load

   N = 1.0 x 50 + 0.8 x 100 = 130.0 kN

   M = 0.8 x 5 x $\dfrac{5^2}{2}$ = 50.0 kNm

   V = 0.8 x 5 x 5   = 20.0 kN

QUESTION 1.9

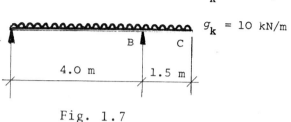

For the beam shown in Fig. 1.7
determine the maximum bending
moments and shear forces at the
supports A and B, and in the span
AB for the ultimate limit state.
Consider three loading cases.
Maximum loading on ABC.   Maximum
loading on AB, minimum on BC.
Maximum loading on BC, minimum on
AB.

Fig. 1.7

(Answers.   Bending moment M_B = 37.35 kNm Max Load on BC only or on AB
and BC

M_{span} = 60.91 kNm 1.92m from A Max Load on AB
min load on BC

Shear V_{BC} = 49.8 kN Max Load on BC only or on AB and
BC

V_{BA} = 75.74 kN Max Load on AB and BC

V_{AB} = 63.59 kN Max Load on AB min load on BC.)

1.K STRUCTURAL SAFETY

From earlier sections of this chapter it can be seen that, for the ultimate
limit state, the loads used in design are greater than the characteristic
loads and the stresses are lower than the characteristic stresses.   The
loads and stresses are modified in this way to allow for the possibility
of a section at which the strengths of the materials are at a minimum
occurring at a point where the forces and moments due to overload are at
a maximum.   The effect of modifying the actual loads and stresses in this
way is to give an acceptable factor of safety against collapse.
Nevertheless absolute safety cannot be completely ensured and beyond a
certain point, attempts to reduce risk of collapse will cause
disproportionate increases in cost.

2 Frame Analysis for Vertical Loads

2.A. METHOD OF ANALYSIS

Ideally the forces in the members should be computed for both the
serviceability limit states (elastic or working load condition) and for the
ultimate limit state (partial or complete collapse). Further experimental
and theoretical work is required before a reliable analysis can be made for
the ultimate limit state. Meanwhile elastic analysis is used, but
adjustments are made by redistribution of moments so as to achieve an
approximation to an ultimate load analysis (see Chapter 4 for redistribution).

Because elastic analysis is used for the determination of moments and forces
section sizes must be assumed so that the stiffness of each member can be
calculated. Secondly, the structure is often too large for analysis as a
complete structure, even by computer, so that it is usually necessary to
break down the structure into suitable sub-frames for analysis. Thirdly,
in order to ensure that the section is designed for the worst condition
which can be reasonably expected, a number of different load cases must be
considered for each sub-frame. For this chapter each load case will be
within load combination (1) (cl.2.3.3.1(CP110)).

This chapter therefore considers stiffness, frame analysis and alternative
load cases.

2.B. STIFFNESS OF A MEMBER (cl.3.2.1,cl.2.4.3.1(CP110))

All methods of elastic analysis involve the member stiffness which may be
defined as $\frac{EI}{L}$ where:-

E = Youngs Modulus for the material

I = second moment of area of the cross section about the centroidal axis

L = actual length of the member between the joint centres.

The flexural rigidity (EI) should be based on the actual properties of the
materials and the actual cross section of the member. Because for concrete
both E and I are dependent on the state of stress, E is assumed to have the
constant value given in Table 1(CP110). (see Chapter 1)

The values for I may be based on any one of the following sections
(cl.2.4.3.1(CP110)):-

(1) The concrete section: the entire concrete cross section, ignoring
                             the reinforcement.

(2) The gross section: the entire concrete cross section including
                             the reinforcement on the basis of the modular
                             ratio.

(3) The transformed section: the compression area of the concrete cross
                             section combined with the reinforcement on
                             the basis of the modular ratio.

The concrete section (1) is the most commonly used.   Occasionally it is
advisable to use the transformed section.

QUESTION 2.1

Determine the stiffness ($^{EI}/L$) about both axes, of a concrete member 8 m
in length between joint centres.   It has a rectangular cross section of
300 mm x 400 mm.   Use the concrete section and assume f_{cu} = 25 N/mm^2.

(Answers: 5.2 x 10^6 KNmm;   2.93 x 10^6 KNmm)

2.C. SUB FRAMING (cl.3.2.2.1(CP110))

All structures are three dimensional so that even with quite small
structures there can be a large number of joints each with six degrees of
freedom.   The number of simultaneous equations to be formed and solved is
therefore 6j which leads to very expensive computer runs in order to get a
solution for the whole structure.   It is usual to adopt some form of
simplification to reduce the work.

The most common simplification is to
divide the structure into a series of
plane frames (Fig. 2.1a) which can
usually be analysed by computer
without difficulty.   The number of
equations now being reduced to 3j,
and j the number of joints is also
reduced.   If hand computation is to
be used however, even a complete
plane frame is usually too large and
further subframing is necessary.

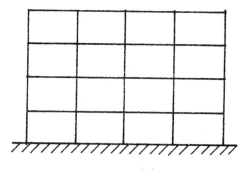

Fig. 2.1(a)

The commonest method is to treat the plane frame as a beam and column structure.   The beams are analysed as simply supported continuous beams and the columns as sub-frames with one free joint as shown in Fig. 2.1b and described in detail in 2D and 2E.

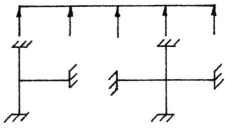

Fig. 2.1(b)

Another method suggested in CP110 uses the two free joint subframe illustrated in Fig. 2.1c and described in detail in 2F.

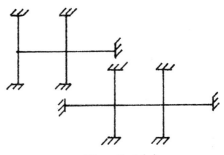

Fig. 2.1(c)

Finally, and probably the best after the complete structure is the one floor level sub-frame illustrated in Fig. 2.1d and described in detail in 2G.

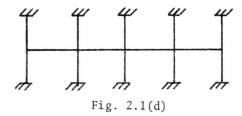

Fig. 2.1(d)

QUESTION 2.2

For the plane frame shown in Fig. 2.2 sketch all the subframes which might be used for hand computation.

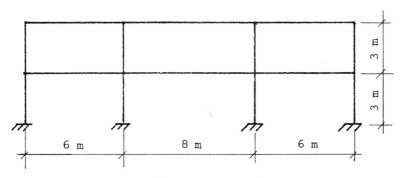

Fig. 2.2

(Answer: given in Fig. 2.3)

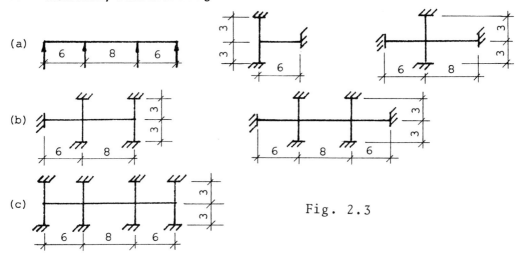

Fig. 2.3

2.D. CONTINUOUS BEAM (BEAM AND COLUMN STRUCTURE)

ACCURATE METHOD (cl.3.3.3(CP110)

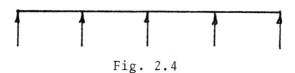

Fig. 2.4

The continuous beam structure shown in Fig. 2.4 is analysed quite normally
using the actual lengths and stiffnesses of the members.   The loading
cases must, however, be carefully considered so as to obtain the most
critical values of bending moment and shear.

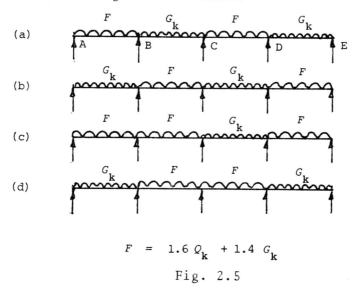

$$F = 1.6 Q_k + 1.4 G_k$$

Fig. 2.5

(a) The loading arrangement given at Fig. 2.5a i.e. alternate spans carrying maximum load and the remaining spans carrying dead load only, gives the maximum sagging moment near the centre of the spans carrying maximum load. The minimum sagging moment (it may actually be negative i.e. hogging) is in the spans carrying dead load only. This will also give the maximum shear at support A.

(b) The loading arrangement of Fig. 2.5b is similar to that of Fig. 2.5a. It will give maximum and minimum bending moments in the alternate spans to that shown in Fig. 2.5a and maximum shear at support E.

(c) Two adjacent spans loaded and the two remaining spans loaded alternatively as shown in Fig. 2.5c gives maximum hogging bending moment over the support B near the centre of the two adjacent loaded spans. The maximum shear in the beams adjacent to the support B, and the maximum reaction at support B are also obtained from this load case.

(d) The loading condition shown in Fig. 2.5d is similar to that in Fig. 2.5c.

The bending moment diagram should be drawn for each load case and all superimposed on the same drawing, as shown in Fig. 2.6, so that the most critical condition for all sections may be seen. The curve which encloses all bending moment curves is called the Bending Moment Envelope, shown by solid lines in Fig. 2.6. The Shear Force Envelope may be obtained in the same way.

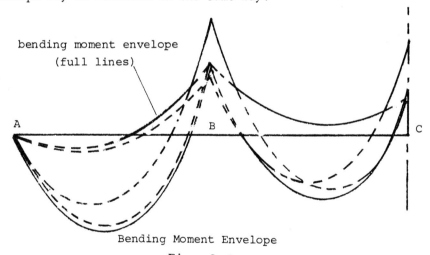

Bending Moment Envelope

Fig. 2.6

EXAMPLE 2.1

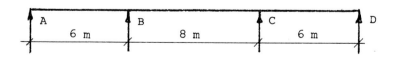

Fig. 2.7

If g_k = 40 kN/m and q_k = 32 kN/m draw the bending moment and shear force envelopes for the beam shown in Fig. 2.7 and calculate the maximum reactions at the supports.   Assume EI constant.

6m span   max. load = 6(1.4 x 40 + 1.6 x 32) = 643.2 kN

$$\text{F.E.M}_{BA} = {}^{WL}/8 = \frac{643.2 \times 6}{8} = 482.4 \text{ kNm}$$

min. load = 6 x 40 = 240 kN

$$\text{F.E.M}_{BA} = {}^{WL}/8 = \frac{240 \times 6}{8} = 180 \text{ kNm}$$

8m span   max. load = 8(1.4 x 40 + 1.6 x 32) = 857.6 kN

$$\text{F.E.M}_{BC} = {}^{WL}/12 = \frac{857.6 \times 8}{12} = 571.73 \text{ kNm}$$

min. load = 8 x 40 = 320 kN

$$\text{F.E.M}_{BC} = {}^{WL}/12 = \frac{320 \times 8}{12} = 213.33 \text{ kNm}$$

Load Case (1) - maximum load on the centre span.

Determine the moments at the ends of the members using moment distribution or some other method if preferred.

Distribution factors:

$$\text{D.F.}_{BA} = \frac{\text{stiffness BA}}{\text{stiffness (BA+BC)}} = \frac{\frac{3}{4} \times EI/6}{\frac{3}{4} \times EI/6 + \frac{1}{2} \times EI/8} = \frac{2}{3}$$

$$\text{D.F.}_{BC} = \frac{\text{stiffness BC}}{\text{stiffness (BA+BC)}} = \frac{\frac{1}{2} \times EI/8}{\frac{3}{4} \times EI/6 + \frac{1}{2} \times EI/8} = \frac{1}{3}$$

Note: to avoid carry over of moments, the centre span stiffness is halved since the structure and the load is symmetrical. $\frac{3}{4}$ x stiffness is taken for the end span since it is pinned at A.

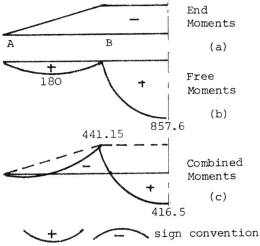

| | $\frac{2}{3}$ | $\frac{1}{3}$ |
	AB	BA	BC
F.E.M.	0	+180.00	-571.73
Balance		+261.15	+130.58
End M.	0	+441.15	-441.15
			kNm

Fixed end moments clockwise positive

(d)

Fig. 2.8

The final bending moment diagram shown in Fig. 2.8c is obtained by combining the end moments shown in Fig. 2.8a with the free moments shown in Fig. 2.7b.   The end moments are shown in the distribution table Fig. 2.8d.   The free moments are obtained from considering each span as simply supported with a maximum moment of $FL/8$ or $G_k L/8$ at the centre of the span.

REACTIONS AT SUPPORTS

span AB (Fig. 2.9)

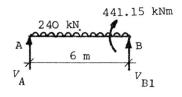

Fig. 2.9

Taking moments about B, clockwise positive

$+ 441.15 + 6V_A - 240 \times 3 = 0$

$V_A = 46.475$ kN

Taking moments about A clockwise positive

$+ 441.15 - 6V_{B1} + 240 \times 3 = 0$

$V_{B1} = 193.525$ kN

span BC (Fig. 2.10)

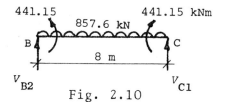

Fig. 2.10

Taking moments about B, clockwise positive

$- 441.15 + 441.15 - 8V_{C1} + 857.6 \times 4 = 0$

$V_{C1} = 428.8$ kN $= V_{B2}$

$V_B = V_{B1} + V_{B2} = 622.325$ kN

Final check $V_A + V_B + V_C + V_D$ = total vertical load.

SHEAR FORCE DIAGRAMS

span AB

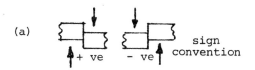

(a)   sign convention

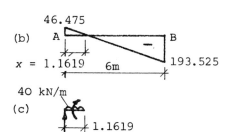

Fig. 2.11

From the similar triangles on the shear force diagram, Fig. 2.11b, the position of the zero shear is

$$\frac{46.475}{x} = \frac{193.525}{(6 - x)}$$

$$x = \frac{46.475}{(193.525 + 46.475)} \times 6 = 1.1619\text{m}$$

the bending moment at X is

$M_x + 46.4750 \times 1.1619 - 40 \times (1.1619)^2/2$

$M_x = - 26.9993$ kNm

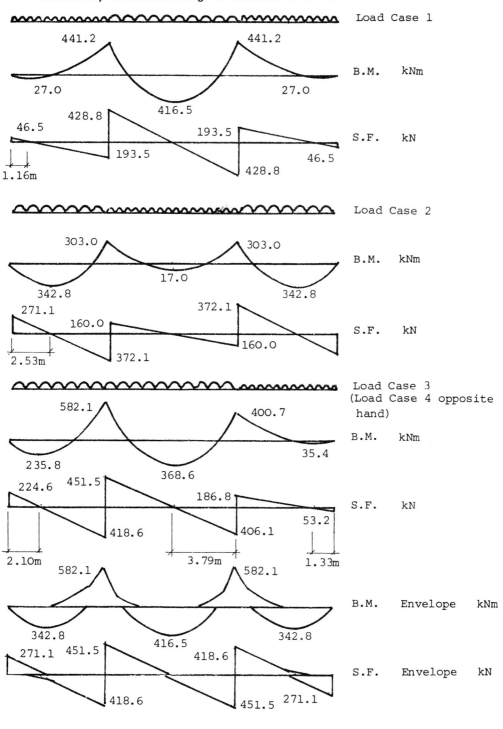

Load Case 1

B.M.   kNm

S.F.   kN

Load Case 2

B.M.   kNm

S.F.   kN

Load Case 3
(Load Case 4 opposite
hand)

B.M.   kNm

S.F.   kN

B.M.   Envelope   kNm

S.F.   Envelope   kN

Fig. 2.12

These calculations are repeated for all other loading conditions. The bending moment and shear force diagrams **are** drawn for each case and combined to form the envelopes as shown in Fig. 2.12.

QUESTION 2.3

Complete example 2.1, i.e. do the calculations for the remaining three load cases and draw the bending moment and shear force envelopes.

(Answer. *The full Bending Moment and Shear Force diagrams are given in Fig. 2.12)*

APPROXIMATE METHOD (cl.3.3.4(CP110))

For continuous beams of three or more spans which do not differ by more than 15% of the longest, the ultimate bending moments and shear forces may be obtained from Table 4 (CP110). The characteristic imposed load must not exceed the characteristic dead load, and no redistribution of moments is allowed (see Chapter 4 for redistribution).

Table 4. Ultimate bending moments and shear forces

	At outer support	Near middle of end span	At first interior support	At middle of interior spans	At interior supports
Moment	0	$\dfrac{Fl}{11}$	$\dfrac{-Fl}{9}$	$\dfrac{Fl}{14}$	$\dfrac{-Fl}{10}$
Shear	0.45F	—	0.6F	—	0.55F

In Table 4, l is the effective span and F is the total ultimate load ($1.4G_k + 1.6Q_k$). No redistribution of the moments found from Table 4 should be made.

This is an alternative to the previous method. The use of this table will reduce the labour involved in computation but it may not be used where there are large span differences. The values of bending moments and shear forces will generally be conservative and hence overestimate the steel reinforcement required. The use of Table 4 (CP110) is restricted to beams carrying uniformly distributed loads.

The disadvantage of using Table 4 is that bending moment and shear force envelopes can not be readily drawn thus making bar curtailment difficult. However empirical rules for curtailment are given in cl.3.11.7.2 (CP110) which are presented in 9K.

QUESTION 2.4

Using Table 4 (CP110) calculate the values of bending moment and shear force for a beam with four spans of 8m. The loading is g_k = 40 kN/m and q_k = 32 kN/m.

(Answer: *Bending Moments* *623.7 kNm, -762.3 kNm, 490.1 kNm, -686.1 kNm*
Shear Forces *385.9 kN, -514.6 kN, +514.6 kN, -471.7 kN)*

2.E. ONE FREE JOINT SUBFRAME (BEAM AND COLUMN STRUCTURE) (cl.3.5.2(CP110))

The use of the simply supported continuous beam as a subframe as described in 2D ignores the columns so that some method must be used to find the bending moments in the columns. The single free joint is used and its variations are shown in Fig. 2.13.

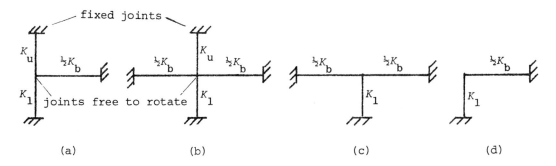

Fig. 2.13

Because the single joint system is a gross simplification of the structure some correction to the analysis must be introduced. This is done by taking half the actual beam stiffness in each case thus increasing the bending moment in the columns. This subframe may also be used to find the hogging moment at the end support in a continuous beam. The axial force in the columns may be found from the continuous beam analysis or by taking half the maximum load on all the adjacent spans.

LOADS

In each case the load system adopted should give the greatest unbalance at the joint as shown in Fig. 2.14.

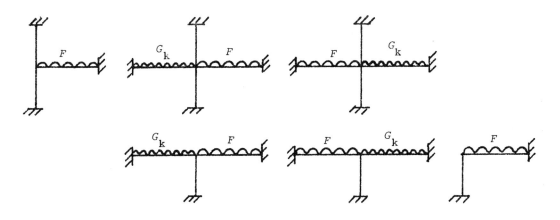

Fig. 2.14

The column bending moment found may then be combined with the maximum axial load for design.   This leads to slight overdesign because maximum bending moment and maximum axial force do not usually occur under the same loading case.   The error is acceptable because it is usually on the safe side and does not lead to a great loss of economy.   The alternative is to calculate the axial forces for the load case giving the greatest bending moment and the bending moment for the case giving the greatest axial force, the design can then be done for each in turn and the largest one used.

EXAMPLE 2.2

Fig. 2.15 shows a one joint subframe for a four storey building and it is required to determine the axial force and bending moment in column AC at joint C for the ultimate limit state.

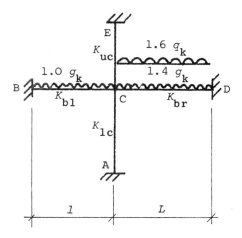

Fig. 2.15

Making the following assumptions:

(a) all floors including the roof carry the same load and that all the floors are fully loaded with the collapse load.

(b) the load carried by column ACE is half the load carried by all beams framing into it

(c) the floor at level BCD is fully loaded with its collapse load in the long span CD and carries only dead load in the short span BC.   This arrangement gives the maximum bending moment in the column and is illustrated in Fig. 2.15.

The maximum out of balance moment of the fixed end moment at joint C if rotation is prevented is given by

$$M_F = (1.4\ g_k + 1.6\ q_k)\frac{L}{12} - \frac{g_k\ l}{12}$$

Then, using the simple moment distribution procedures suggested in cl.3.5.2(CP110) the bending moment in column AC at C is

$$M_{CA} = M_F \frac{K_{1c}}{K_{uc} + K_{1c} + \tfrac{1}{2}K_{bl} + \tfrac{1}{2}K_{br}}$$

where $K = \dfrac{EI}{L}$ the stiffness of the beam or column.

The end moment in the beam BC at C is

$$M_c = M_F \frac{\tfrac{1}{2}K_{bl}}{K_{uc} + K_{1c} + \tfrac{1}{2}K_{bl} + \tfrac{1}{2}K_{br}}$$

The maximum axial force in the column AC is given by

$$N = \frac{4}{2} (1.4\ g_k + 1.6q_k)\ (L + 1)$$

Note: In the above the axial force has been calculated using the full
load on all floors.   Because this is unlikely to happen it is
usual to allow a reduction in the imposed loads when several floors
are carried by a single column or a large area of floor is carried
by a single beam see CP3 Chapter V and Chapter 12 - Columns.

QUESTION 2.5

Fig. 2.16 shows part of an elevation
of a multi-storey building and
the loading per unit length for each
floor.   Determine the axial load N
and the greatest bending moment at B
for the ultimate limit state.   The
column is a short braced column.
CP3 Ch V loading allows 20%
reduction in axial imposed load on a
column for 3 floors.   Partial
safety factor for dead load = 1.4
Partial safety factor for imposed
load = 1.6

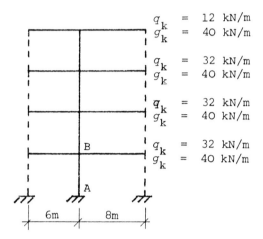

$$q_k = 12\ \text{kN/m}$$
$$g_k = 40\ \text{kN/m}$$

$$q_k = 32\ \text{kN/m}$$
$$g_k = 40\ \text{kN/m}$$

$$q_k = 32\ \text{kN/m}$$
$$g_k = 40\ \text{kN/m}$$

$$q_k = 32\ \text{kN/m}$$
$$g_k = 40\ \text{kN/m}$$

Fig. 2.16

Relative beam and column stiffnesses
are:

8m beam = .6 x 10^6 mm^3

6m beam = .8 x 10^6

columns = .5 x 10^6

Ignore self weight of column.

(Answer: $N = 2563\ KN$; $M_B = 132.9\ KNm$)

2.F.   TWO FREE JOINT SUBFRAME (cl.3.2.2.1(CP110))

A larger subframe of a structure may be chosen for analysis which involves
more calculations.   This is illustrated in Fig. 2.17.

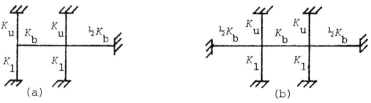

Fig. 2.17

Essentially two joints are free to rotate in the one plane of the structure. Notice once again the outer beam stiffnesses are halved.

The greatest bending moments are obtained at the ultimate limit state, considering only the vertical loading, when:

(i) The centre span is loaded with F and the side spans with G_k or

(ii) (iii) and (iv) any two of the three beams are loaded with F and the other beam with G_k.

The two free joint subframe is again easily solved using a hand method of computation, e.g. "moment distribution".   Because there are two free joints the carry over between the free joints may make the calculations lengthy to reach the required degree of accuracy.   If the structure and loading is symmetrical about a centre beam (loading case (1)) the centre beam stiffness is halved and there is no carry over between the free joints.

QUESTION 2.6

Using the two free joint subframe calculate the maximum shear forces and bending moments at the joint A and B and the maximum and minimum bending moments in spans AB and BC for the structure shown in Fig. 2.18.

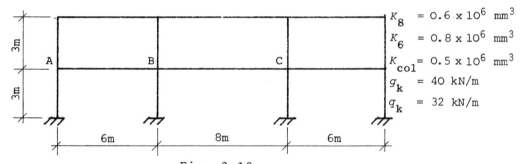

$$K_8 = 0.6 \times 10^6 \text{ mm}^3$$
$$K_6 = 0.8 \times 10^6 \text{ mm}^3$$
$$K_{col} = 0.5 \times 10^6 \text{ mm}^3$$
$$g_k = 40 \text{ kN/m}$$
$$q_k = 32 \text{ kN/m}$$

Fig. 2.18

(*Answer: In the beams at the supports*

$$V_A = 331.9 \text{ kN} \quad V_{BA} = 369.4 \text{ kN} \quad V_{BC} = 437.2 \text{ kN}$$

$$M_A = 342.2 \text{ kNm} \quad M_{BA} = 448.2 \text{ kNm} \quad M_{BC} = 554.5 \text{ kNm}$$

In the beams near the centre of span

$$M_{AB \text{ max}} = 218.1 \text{ kNm} \quad M_{AB \text{ min}} = 40.1 \text{ kNm}$$

$$M_{BC \text{ max}} = 350.4 \text{ kNm} \quad M_{BC \text{ min}} = 91.2 \text{ kNm}$$

In the columns

$$M_A = 97.8 \text{ kNm} \quad M_B = 107.6 \text{ kNm}$$

The first subframe is of the same general form as that shown in Fig. 2.17a which gives the forces and bending moments shown in Fig. 2.19.   The second subframe is of the same general form as that shown in Fig. 2.19b which gives the forces and bending moment shown in Fig. 2.20.   The third subframe is of opposite hand to the first subframe and is not shown.)

Bending Moment kNm

Shear Force kN

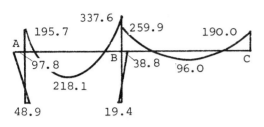
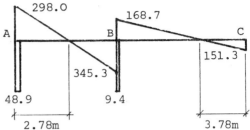

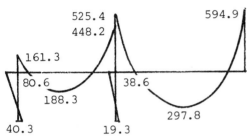
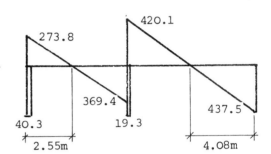

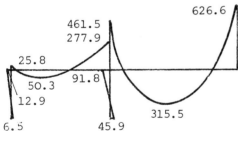
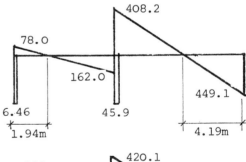

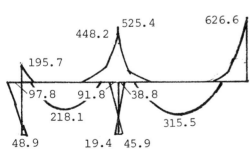
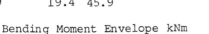
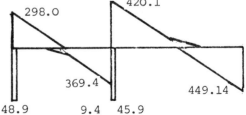

Bending Moment Envelope kNm

Shear Force Envelope kN

Fig. 2.19

Bending Moment kNm

Shear Force kN

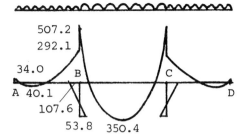

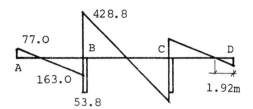

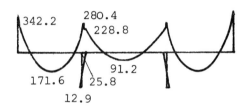

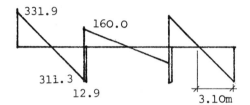

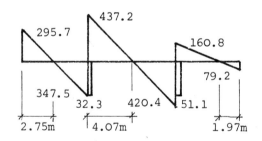

Bending Moment Envelope kNm

Shear Force Envelope kN

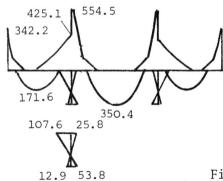

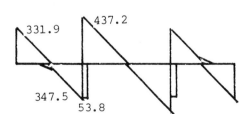

Fig. 2.20

2.G. ONE FLOOR LEVEL SUBFRAME (cl.3.2.2.1(CP110))

This subframe includes the continuous beam at one level together with all
the columns joining it, both above and below as shown in Fig. 2.21.   The
columns are assumed to be fixed at their extremities.   The full stiffness
is used for all members.

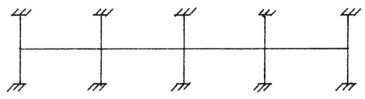

Fig. 2.21

The analysis of this subframe is not significantly more difficult than the
continuous beam in section D.   The loading cases are exactly the same as
for the continuous beam and there is the advantage that the column forces
and moments will be found from the same set of analyses.

QUESTION 2.7

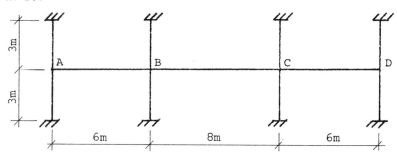

Fig. 2.22

Analyse the frame shown in Fig. 2.22 given that:

g_k = 40 kN/m q_k = 32 kN/m

$K_{8m\ beam}$ = 0.6 x 10^6 mm^3

$K_{6m\ beam}$ = 0.8 x 10^6 mm^3

K_{column} = 0.5 x 10^6 mm^3

(Answer: The full set of Bending Moment and Shear Force diagrams is
given in Fig. 2.23.)

Bending Moment   kNm

Shear Force kN

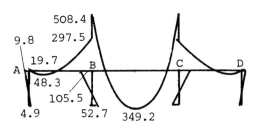

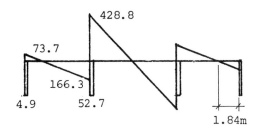

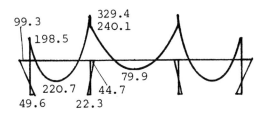

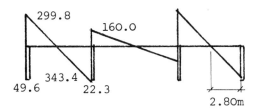

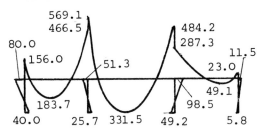

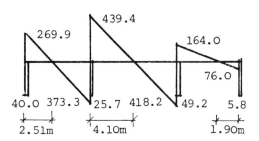

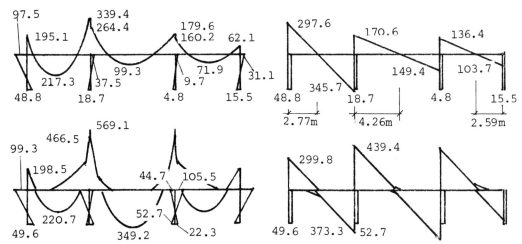

Bending Moment Envelope kNm   Fig. 2.23   Shear Force Envelope kN

3 Frame Analysis for Horizontal and Vertical Loads

3.A. INTRODUCTION

The introduction and section A of Chapter 2 also apply to this chapter, although now the effects of horizontal forces will be considered, that is load combinations (2) and (3) (cl.2.3.3.1(CP110)).

3.B. LATERAL STABILITY

The ability of a structure to resist lateral forces will depend on the shape of the frame, or the type of construction, or the strength of the components or a combination of all three.

FRAME SHAPE AND OVERALL STABILITY

The structures shown in Fig. 3.1a, a water tower, and in Fig. 3.1b, a single bay structure with cantilevers, appear to be of completely different types, but both are relatively high compared with the width.   In both cases the resultant R of the vertical and horizontal forces may pass outside the foundation (or nearly so) and overturning would be possible.

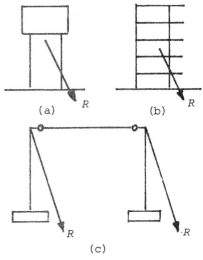
(a)   (b)

(c)

Fig. 3.1

The type of structure shown in Fig. 3.1c may be met in some circumstances. Tall columns are connected by a roof structure which merely connects the tops of the columns.   In this case the resultant R of the vertical and horizontal forces on each column may fall outside the column base and failure may be by overturning.   This sort of construction may be used in factories.

The structure shown in Fig. 3.2a is of normal multi-storey construction, its height is not large compared with its width and overturning is not likely.   There is usually no need to check overall stability for this type of structure.

BRACED AND UNBRACED FRAMES

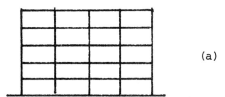

(a)

The structure in Fig. 3.2a broadly represents both braced and unbraced frames. An open frame as shown is an unbraced frame which will deform in the manner shown in Fig. 3.2b. The ability of the unbraced frame to resist lateral forces will depend on the flexural strength and stiffness of the columns and beams.

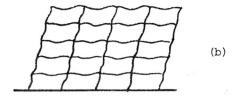

(b)

The structure shown in Fig. 3.2c is very similar to that in Fig. 3.2b except that bracing is provided for the full height of one bay.

In this case the braced bay will act like a vertical girder to resist all lateral forces. The beams and columns will in general be designed for the forces calculated as in Chapter 2. In only a few cases, usually tall buildings, will it be necessary to consider the axial forces induced in the columns by lateral forces acting on the braced bay. Bracing may not appear as actual members but may be effected by infilling panels of concrete or brickwork. Lightweight infilling and glazing should be ignored because its strength is low or negligible.

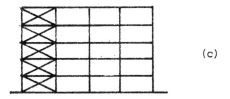

(c)

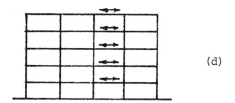

(d)

Often a frame may have the appearance of an unbraced frame. If two or more frames in a row are braced and the floors are continuous through unbraced

Fig. 3.2

frames, the floors may provide effective support as shown in Fig. 3.2d by transferring the horizontal forces back to the braced frames. The braced frames must be designed to carry all the horizontal forces on the structure.

QUESTION 3.1

For each of the structures shown in Fig. 3.3 state whether the frame should be treated as braced or unbraced and whether a check on overturning should be made.

(Answers: *(a)*   *braced, check overturning*

           (b)   *unbraced,*   "   "

           (c)   *unbraced in ground floor, braced above.*
               No check on overturning.)

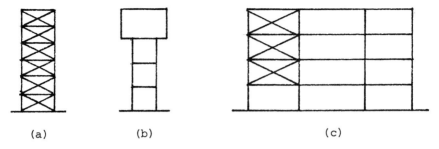

Fig. 3.3

3.C. OVERTURNING (cl.2.3.3.1(CP110))

If a structure is tall compared with its breadth, overturning is most
likely to occur under the action of dead load and wind.   This is load
combination (2) (cl.2.3.3.1(CP110)) which is $0.9G_k + 1.4W_k$.   It should be
noted that the partial safety factor of 0.9 is applied to the
characteristic dead load because it is possible for all sections to be
slightly undersize.   Occasionally a structure will be met in which the
load combination $1.4G_k + 1.4W_k$ or load combination (3),
$1.2G_k + 1.2Q_k + 1.2W_k$ is critical for overturning.   Load combination (3)
is more likely to be critical in unbraced frames where the flexural
strength of the columns will be critical.

QUESTION 3.2.

Check each of the structures shown in Fig. 3.4 for overturning, giving the
eccentricity of the resultant of the forces on the structure and state
whether the structure is considered safe or unsafe.

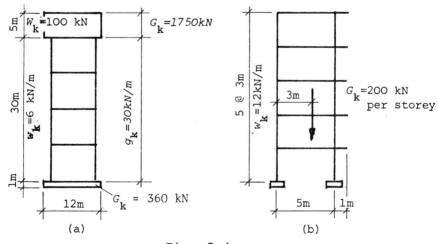

Fig. 3.4

(Answer: (a)   eccentricity = 3.22m - safe

(b)   eccentricity = 2.60m - unsafe)

3.D. UNBRACED FRAMES (cl.3.2.2.(CP110))

Member forces should be calculated for load combination (1) (cl.2.3.3.1
(CP110)) and for load combination (3).   The member forces which are most
critical should be used in design.   Load combination (3) is
$1.2G_k \pm 1.2Q_k + 1.2W_k$.   These forces may be simultaneously applied if
using a full frame analysis, usually by computer, because of the large
number of redundants.   There is no need to consider loaded and unloaded
spans, all spans may be fully loaded.

If hand computation is to be used vertical loads must be applied separately
from the horizontal loads, and the following simplifications shown in
Fig. 3.5 are the only ones permitted (cl.3.2.2.1(CP110)).   Fig. 3.5a
shows the subframe permitted for vertical loads and Fig. 3.5b shows the
system of pinned joints which may be assumed to be inserted in the
structure to make the analysis.   The pins are assumed at the mid-height of
the columns and the mid span of the beams.

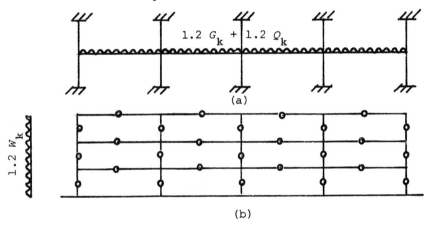

Fig. 3.5

The basic method of introducing pinned joints into the frame leads to two
alternative methods of analysis.   In the first, which is illustrated in
example 3.1 each level of the frame is divided into a series of three pinned
portals and the shear force at that level is shared between the portals in
the proportion of their spans.   The solution of each portal is then a
simple matter.   The forces and moments in the inner columns are obtained
by adding, algebraically, the forces obtained from each separate portal.
The second method, illustrated in Example 3.2, is to assume that all the
columns are made of a homogeneous material and that the axial stress in the
columns at any level is proportional to the distance from the centroid of
the cross section of all the columns at that level.   If the relationship
between the cross sectional areas of the columns is known, the axial force
in each column can be determined and the horizontal shears and bending
moments can be obtained using the principals of statics.

In both methods the uniformly distributed wind loads must be collected together into a concentrated load horizontally applied at the floor levels.

EXAMPLE 3.1

For the unbraced structure shown in Fig. 3.6 sketch the bending moment diagrams using the method of dividing the horizontal shear on the frame between the bays in the proportion of their spans.

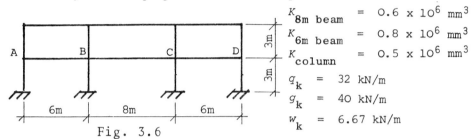

$$K_{8m\ beam} = 0.6 \times 10^6\ mm^3$$
$$K_{6m\ beam} = 0.8 \times 10^6\ mm^3$$
$$K_{column} = 0.5 \times 10^6\ mm^3$$
$$q_k = 32\ kN/m$$
$$g_k = 40\ kN/m$$
$$w_k = 6.67\ kN/m$$

Fig. 3.6

The uniformly distributed loads actually applied as shown in Fig. 3.7a are treated as point loads at each floor level as shown in Fig. 3.7b.

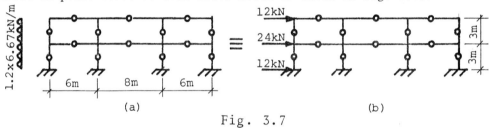

(a)   (b)

Fig. 3.7

Horizontal force at roof level = $1.2 \times 6.67 \times \dfrac{3}{2}$ = 12 kN

Horizontal force at first floor level = $1.2 \times 6.67 \times 3$ = 24 kN

The roof beams and the top half of the upper storey columns can now be separated from the rest of the structure as shown in Fig. 3.8 with the 12 kN force applied at beam level.

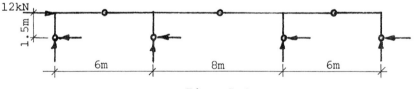

Fig. 3.8

To simplify analysis the three bay frame is split into three separate portals and the horizontal force of 12 kN is divided between the portals in the proportion of their spans as shown in Fig. 3.9.

For a 6m span

$$\text{Horizontal force} = \frac{12 \times 6}{6 + 8 + 6} = 3.6\ kN$$

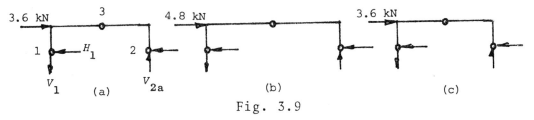

Fig. 3.9

Each separate portal has three pins and is therefore statically determinate.   Consider the frame in Fig. 3.9(a)

Taking moments about joint number 2, clockwise positive

$$6V_1 + 1.5 \times 3.6 = 0; \quad \text{therefore } V_1 = 0.9; \quad \text{and } V_{2a} = 0.9 \text{ kN}$$

Taking moments about joint number 3, for the left hand portion of the portal frame

$$\frac{6}{2} \times V_1 + 1.5H_1 = 0; \quad \text{therefore } H_1 = 2V_1 = 1.8 \text{ kN}$$

The same method applied to the portal frames in Figs. 3.9b & c gives the results shown in Fig. 3.10.

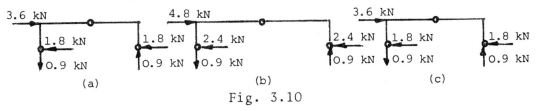

Fig. 3.10

The three separate portals are now recombined and the forces acting on the three bay frame are shown in Fig.3.11a and the bending moment diagram obtained therefrom is shown in Fig. 3.11b.

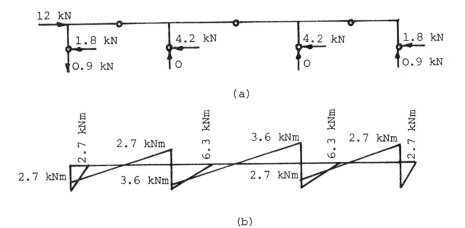

Fig. 3.11

The next lower floor level can now be analysed in a similar way.   The forces acting on the part of the frame at first floor level are shown in Fig. 3.12.

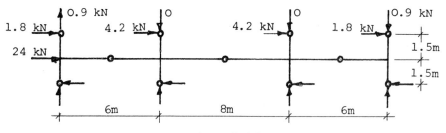

Fig. 3.12

Again the analysis is simplified by assuming that the horizontal force of 24 kN is divided between the separate H frames in the proportion of their spans.   The forces applied to each frame are shown in Fig. 3.13 together with the reactive forces calculated in a similar way to those for the roof structure.

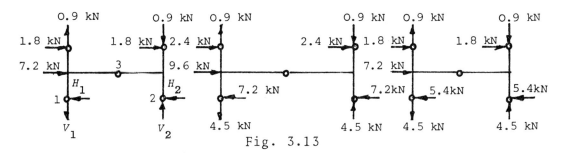

Fig. 3.13

The calculation for the 6m span portal follows.

Taking moments about joint number 2

$$3 \times 1.8 \times 2 + 1.5 \times 7.2 + 6.0 \times 0.9 - 6.0 \times V_1 = 0$$

Therefore V_1 = 4.5 downwards and V_2 = 4.5 upwards

Taking moments about joint number 3 for the left hand part of the frame

$$1.5 \times 1.8 + \frac{6}{2} \times 0.9 + 1.5 \times H_1 - \frac{6}{2} \times 4.5 = 0$$

Therefore H_1 = 5.4 and H_2 = 5.4

The bending moment diagram and the shear force diagram for the recombined frame are shown in Fig. 3.14a and 3.14b.

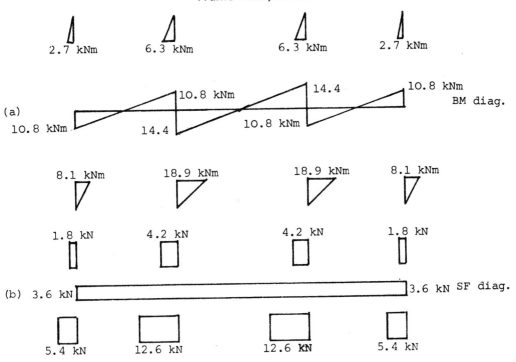

Fig. 3.14

If the bending moments due to the vertical loads $1.2 \, G_k + 1.2 \, Q_k$ are now calculated, using the method of section 2G, and added to the values given in Fig. 3.14 the bending moment diagram is as shown in Fig. 3.15.

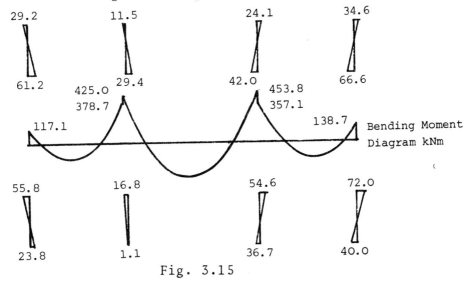

Fig. 3.15

Comparison of the bending moments in Fig. 3.15 with the bending moment
envelope values of Fig. 2.23 shows that the effect of wind loads on this
structure is negligible since the values produced are in all cases lower
than the values when load combination (1) is applied.   It must be realised
that this is NOT always the case.   In the foregoing example a structure of
only two storeys has been considered whereas in a higher structure the
effect of the horizontal forces would be greater, firstly because the wind
pressures on buildings increase with the height of the building, and
secondly, and far more importantly the shear force on the ground floor
columns is the sum of all the shear forces on the columns above.

QUESTION 3.3

The total characteristic wind
forces applied to the two bay
frame shown in Fig. 3.16 are
equivalent to 10 kN per metre
height of the structure.
Using the method of example 3.1
calculate the bending moments
due to wind forces only and
sketch the bending moment
diagram.

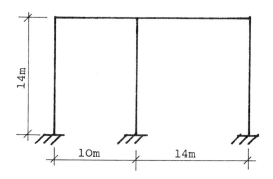

Fig. 3.16

Note: The method used in
example 3.1 would not normally
be applied to a single storey
structure of only two bays since
a proper solution is relatively
simple.   This question should, therefore, be treated purely as a simple
exercise in applying the method.

(Answer: given in Fig. 3.17)

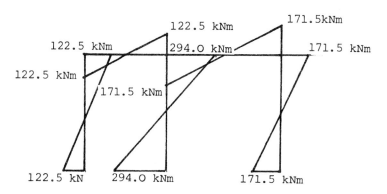

Fig. 3.17

EXAMPLE 3.2

Draw the bending moment diagram for the wind loads applied to the unbraced frame shown in Fig. 3.6 using the method of proportional axial stresses.

The stress due to axial forces produced by the horizontal loads on the structure is assumed to be proportional to the distance from the centroid of all the columns. If the columns are all of the same cross section the axial force in the columns will be proportional to their distance from the centroid of the group.

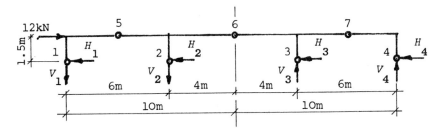

Fig. 3.18

The applied forces at roof level are exactly the same as those shown in Fig. 3.8 but the vertical reactions at the pins shown in Fig. 3.18 have the relationship given below:

$$\frac{V_1}{10} = \frac{V_2}{4} = \frac{V_3}{4} = \frac{V_4}{10}$$

Therefore $V_1 = 2.5 \, V_2 = V_4; \quad V_3 = V_2$

Taking moments about pin 4 for the whole structure as shown in Fig. 3.18

$$12 \times 1.5 - 20 \, V_1 - 14 \, V_2 + 6 \, V_3 = 0$$

$$18 - 20 \, (2.5 \, V_2) - 14 \, V_2 + 6 \, V_2 = 0$$

$$18 = (50 + 14 - 6) \, V_2$$

Therefore $V_2 = \dfrac{18}{58}$

Therefore $V_1 = 2.5 \left(\dfrac{18}{58}\right) = \dfrac{45}{58}$

Taking moments about pin 5 for forces to the left of pin 5

$$3 \, V_1 = 1.5 \, H_1$$

therefore $H_1 = 2 \, V_1 = \dfrac{90}{58}$

Taking moments about pin 6 for forces to the left of pin 6

$$1.5H_1 + 1.5H_2 - 10V_1 - 4V_2 = 0$$

$$\frac{450}{58} + \frac{72}{58} - \frac{135}{58} = 1.5\ H_2$$

$$H_2 = \frac{387}{87}$$

In the same way

$$H_3 = \frac{387}{87} \qquad ; \qquad H_4 = \frac{90}{58}$$

The lower level is dealt with in a similar way and the arrangement of the frame now under consideration is shown in Fig. 3.19.

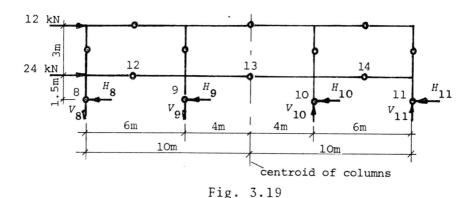

Fig. 3.19

$$V_8 = 2.5\ V_9 = V_{11} ; \quad V_{10} = V_9 \qquad \text{as before.}$$

Taking moments about pin 11 for the whole structure as shown in Fig. 3.19.

$$24 \times 1.5 + 12 \times 4.5 - 20\ V_8 - 14\ V_9 + 6\ V_{10} = 0$$

$$36 + 54 = (20 \times 2.5 + 8)\ V_9$$

$$V_9 = \frac{90}{58}$$

$$V_8 = 2.5 \times \frac{90}{58} = \frac{225}{58}$$

Taking moments about pin 12 for the segment of the frame shown in Fig. 3.20

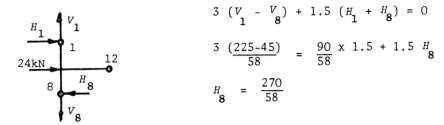

$$3 \ (V_1 - V_8) + 1.5 \ (H_1 + H_8) = 0$$

$$\frac{3 \ (225-45)}{58} = \frac{90 \times 1.5 + 1.5 \ H_8}{58}$$

$$H_8 = \frac{270}{58}$$

Fig. 3.20

Taking moments about pin 13 for the segment of the frame shown in Fig. 3.21

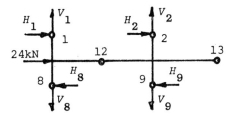

Fig. 3.21

$$10 \ (V_1 - V_8) + 4 \ (V_2 - V_9) + 1.5 \ (H_1 + H_2 + H_8 + H_9) = 0$$

$$1.5 H_9 = \frac{10(225-45)}{58} + \frac{4(90-18)}{58} - 1.5 \left(\frac{90}{58} + \frac{387}{87} + \frac{270}{58} \right)$$

$$H_9 = \frac{1161}{87}$$

Similarly $H_{10} = \dfrac{1161}{87}$

$$H_{11} = \frac{270}{58}$$

The complete bending moment diagram for wind loads is shown in Fig. 3.22. Comparison of Fig. 3.14a and 3.11b show differences in the bending moments obtained by the two methods.   If a full elastic analysis, probably using a computer program, were done, there would be yet a third set of results.   This state of affairs seems very unsatisfactory, but, providing the principals of statics are not violated no great harm will be done.   The reason is that before failure of a structure occurs a certain amount of redistribution of bending moments takes place.

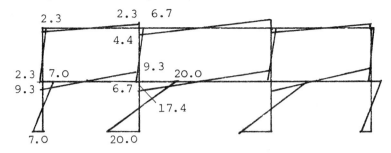

Bending Moment kNm

Fig. 3.22

3.E   TYING FORCES   (cl.3.1.2.2(CP110))

As a result of the partial collapse of a block of flats due to a gas explosion it is now considered essential for all buildings to contain sufficient ties and strengthening elements to ensure that in such an accident the building does not collapse.   The horizontal ties required should be placed at each floor and roof level and there are separate requirements for peripheral and internal ties.   Additional reinforcement should be provided to ensure that external columns and walls are tied in if the peripheral and internal ties are not adequate.   For buildings of five storeys or more there is a requirement that the minimum column or wall reinforcement is made effectively continuous as a tie from foundation to roof level which appears to indicate that, where minimum column reinforcement is used, tension laps should be provided.

In cast in situ structures the normal reinforcement can be expected to provide adequate tying although the requirements for continuity and the anchorage of the internal ties to the peripheral ties calls for some attention in detailing.   The designer of precast concrete structures must ensure that the code requirements for tying are fully satisfied.

4 Redistribution of Moments

4.A THEORY OF COLLAPSE OF BEAMS

It was stated in Chapter 2 that a reliable method of ultimate strength analysis was not yet available so that elastic analysis which is not too unreasonable for loads up to working load is used as a basis for design. For loads significantly greater than working load the elastic analysis may not apply because of the lack of linearity of the stress-strain curves for the materials and the cracks which develop in the concrete. Consequently for the ultimate limit state (i.e. collapse is imminent) redistribution of the bending moments obtained from elastic analysis is permitted.   The assumption is that when the bending moment at a section reaches M_u, failure does not occur, but that a limited hinge-like rotation takes place without increase of bending moment at that section.

The moment/curvature or $M-\phi$ relationship is assumed to be as shown in Fig. 4.1.

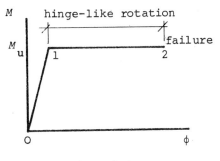

Fig. 4.1

The way in which the $M-\phi$ curve shown in Fig. 4.1 affects the behaviour of a beam under increasing load can be conveniently explained by reference to a beam of span L with both ends rigidly built in as shown in Fig. 4.2a.   For a uniformly distributed load βF applied to the beam, the bending moment diagram will be as shown in Fig. 4.2b whilst all sections remain on the line 0-1 of Fig. 4.1 i.e. whilst all sections remain elastic.   If the beam is of uniform strength throughout its length and βF is increasing a stage will be reached where the sections near the support will reach point 1 on the curve of Fig. 4.1 and the bending moment cannot increase.   The load at this point is $\beta_y F$ and the bending moment at the supports is $M_u = \dfrac{\beta_y FL}{12}$.   The bending moment at the centre of the span

is $\dfrac{M_u}{2} = \dfrac{\beta_y FL}{24}$

Increasing the load above $\beta_y F$
causes greater deflections and
greater bending moment at the
centre of the span without any
increase of the support moment.
At the supports the beam
curvature continues to increase
along the line 1-2 indicated in
Fig. 4.1.   Eventually under
the collapse load F the bending
moment at the centre of the
span reaches M_u.

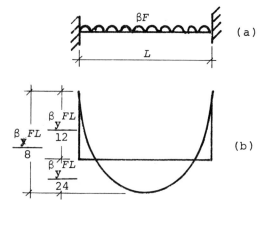

At this load the beam now
behaves like a three hinged
bar with friction controlled
joints as shown in Fig. 4.2d
and deflections will rapidly
increase without further
increase in load.   For the beam
of uniform strength

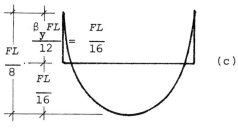

$$M_u = \frac{FL}{16}$$

i.e. the total range of
bending moments within the beam

is $\frac{FL}{8}$ as shown in Fig. 4.2c.

Fig. 4.2

The foregoing assumes that the
beam is of uniform strength and
that the length of the line 1-2
in Fig. 4.1 is virtually without
limit.   These assumptions are
not always true for reinforced concrete.   The assumption that the beam is
of uniform strength can be made true for particular beams but it. does not
invalidate the general theory if the beam is not of uniform strength.   The
second assumption, about the rotational capacity of the beam cross section,
is much less likely to be true.   Steel is a ductile material and is well
able to give the necessary amount of rotational capacity but concrete is
brittle and fails by cracking.   The combination of the two materials leads
to an intermediate position where the rotational capacity will depend on
which of the two materials is relatively the most highly stressed.   If a
reinforced concrete beam contains only a small quantity of reinforcement,
the steel will reach its limiting yield stress earlier in the loading
history of the beam and consequently a relatively large amount of rotation
can be permitted, but if the quantity of reinforcement is large, only small
amounts of rotation can be permitted.   For this reason the full mechanism
as shown in Fig. 4.2d may not be obtained in all cases, and a limit is
placed on the amount of redistribution.   For the case considered the

bending moment at the supports obtained by an elastic analysis for the collapse load is $\frac{FL}{12}$.   This is greater than the maximum bending moment of $\frac{FL}{16}$ in the beam at failure which is shown in Fig. 4.2c.   The apparent reduction in bending moment is therefore

$$\frac{FL}{12} - \frac{FL}{16} = \frac{FL}{48}$$

and expressed as a percentage is

$$\frac{\frac{FL}{48}}{\frac{FL}{12}} \times 100 = 25 \text{ per cent}$$

which is an allowable amount.   The maximum reduction permitted is 30%. The design of the cross section is obviously important since the section must be able to give the rotational capacity required.   Section design is covered in this chapter but it relies on the work of Chapters 6, 7 and 8.

4.B. REDISTRIBUTION

The maximum amount of redistribution permitted is 30% which is usually applied as a reduction of bending moment at the supports with a corresponding increase in bending moment in the centre of the span. As will be seen later there are occasions when it is advantageous for the bending moment at the centre of the span to be reduced and the bending moment at the supports increased.   For the time being an example of redistribution in which the bending moments at the supports are reduced is shown in Fig. 4.3.   The process of redistribution can be seen without considering the behaviour of the beam under increasing load.

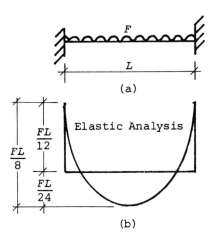

Fig. 4.3a shows a built in beam of span L loaded with a uniformly distributed ultimate load F.   The bending moment diagram obtained using an elastic analysis is shown in Fig. 4.3b.   For 10% redistribution the support bending moments are reduced by 10% as shown in Fig. 3.4c, leading to more equal bending moments at the supports and at centre span.   The total range of bending moments is still $FL/8$ which is the same as the maximum bending moment for a simply supported beam carrying the same load.   This is called the free bending moment.

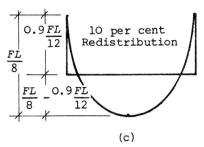

Fig. 4.3

QUESTION 4.1

For the beam with rigidly built in ends
shown in Fig. 4.4a

$$M = \frac{Fab^2}{L^2}$$

Sketch the elastic bending moment
diagram for the beam shown in Fig. 4.4b
and the bending moment diagram after 30%
redistribution.

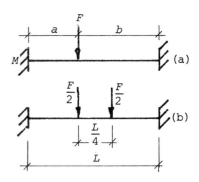

Fig. 4.4

(Answer: the bending moment diagrams are given in Fig. 4.5)

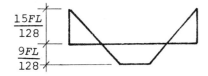

Fig.4.5

4.C POINTS OF CONTRAFLEXURE (cl.3.2.2.3)

When the elastic bending moments are reduced the points of contraflexure in
the member change position as shown in Fig. 4.6.

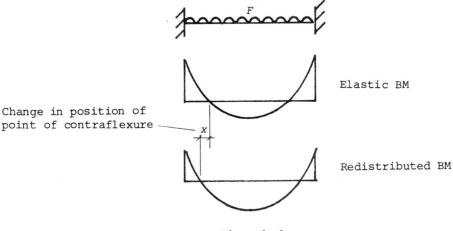

Fig. 4.6

In the bending moment diagram after redistribution has taken place there is
a sagging moment in length x, but this assumes that a hinge-like condition
exists at the supports.   In order for this hinge to develop the moment of
resistance of the sections near the supports must be no greater than the

the minimum values used for design. In practice, however, the strengths of the materials are so variable that a much greater moment of resistance is probably available but not reliably so. This leads to a bending moment diagram similar to the one obtained by using the design ultimate loads and elastic analysis. It is obvious therefore that there could be a hogging bending moment in the length x. If reinforcement is not provided for this large cracks could occur leading to premature failure.

Both conditions must be allowed for and in order to do this it is stated in CP110 that the moment of resistance of any section must not be less than 70% of the maximum bending moment calculated for that section by using the design ultimate loads and elastic analysis (cl.3.2.2.3(CP110)). The way in which this works is illustrated in Example 4.1. The example is not typical because in practical situations several load cases must be considered but it is included to illustrate the principle.

EXAMPLE 4.1

In the beam shown in Fig. 4.7a the ends are rigidly built in and the design ultimate load is 24 kN/m. Using this loading and elastic analysis the end support moment is

$$\frac{\omega L^2}{12} = \frac{24 \times 5^2}{12} = 50 \text{ kNm}$$

the bending moment at the centre of the span is

$$\frac{\omega L^2}{24} = \frac{24 \times 5^2}{24} = 25 \text{ kNm}$$

and the distance from the support to the point of contraflexure is 1.055 m as shown in Fig. 4.7b.

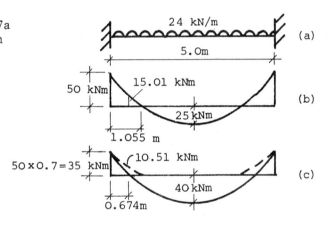

Fig. 4.7

The sections are to be designed for bending moments etc after 30% redistribution and the bending moments and span moments become 35 kNm and 40 kNm respectively as shown in Fig. 4.7c. The bending moment diagram at this stage is that shown by solid lines in Fig. 4.7c. The distance x to the point of contraflexure is obtained thus

$$\text{BM at point of contraflexure} = 0 = 35 - 24 \times 2.5\, x + \frac{24x^2}{2}$$

Therefore $x = 0.674$ m

At this point the bending moment in Fig. 4.7b is

$$50 - 24 \times 2.5 \times 0.674 + \frac{24 \times 0.674^2}{2} = 15.01 \text{ kNm}$$

and considering the solid line in Fig. 4.7c the reduction in bending moment is 100% which is NOT permitted. The bending moment to be used in design should be not less than

$$0.7 \times 15.01 = 10.51 \text{ kNm.}$$

The broken lines in Fig. 4.7c represent 70% of all the corresponding values in Fig. 4.7b and in this case the values shown by the broken lines must be used for design.

QUESTION 4.2

Sketch the bending moment envelope after redistribution (30 per cent maximum reduction) for the beam shown in Fig. 4.8.

(*Answer:*   *shown in Fig. 4.9*)

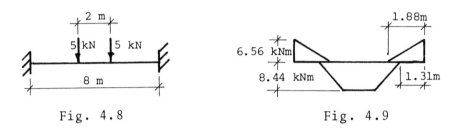

Fig. 4.8   Fig. 4.9

4.D. REDISTRIBUTION FOR MULTI-SPAN BEAMS

The examples considered so far in this chapter have been for single span beams, where alternative loading conditions do not introduce further complications.   The process is explained in Example 4.2 by reference to a two span continuous beam in Fig. 4.10 with load cases (1), (2) and (3)

EXAMPLE 4.2

The continuous beam considered has two spans each of 8 m.   The characteristic dead load g_k = 20 kN/m and the characteristic imposed load q_k = 20 kN/m

The total load on an unloaded span is

$$G_k = 20 \times 8 = 160 \text{ kN}$$

and on a fully loaded span is

$$F = 1.4 G_k + 1.6 Q_k$$

$$F = 1.4 \times 8 \times 20 + 1.6 \times 8 \times 20$$

$$= 480 \text{ kN}$$

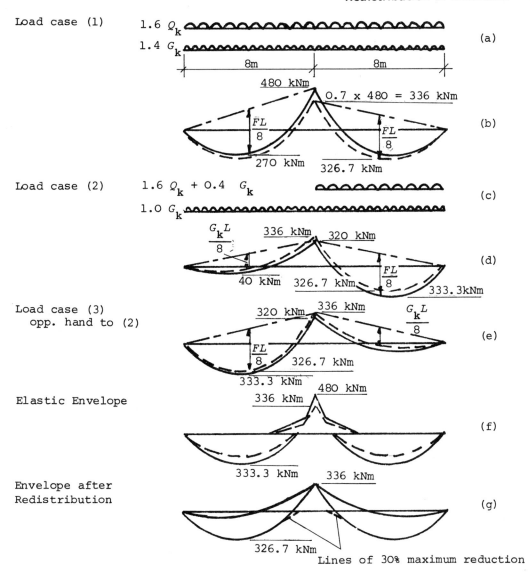

Load case (1)

1.6 Q_k

1.4 G_k

8m   8m

(a)

480 kNm

0.7 x 480 = 336 kNm

$\frac{FL}{8}$

$\frac{FL}{8}$

(b)

270 kNm   326.7 kNm

Load case (2)   1.6 Q_k + 0.4 G_k

1.0 G_k

(c)

$\frac{G_k L}{8}$ 336 kNm   320 kNm

(d)

40 kNm   326.7 kNm $\frac{FL}{8}$

333.3kNm

Load case (3)
  opp. hand to (2)

320 kNm   336 kNm $\frac{G_k L}{8}$

(e)

$\frac{FL}{8}$ 326.7 kNm

333.3 kNm   480 kNm

Elastic Envelope

336 kNm

(f)

333.3 kNm   336 kNm

Envelope after
Redistribution

(g)

326.7 kNm

Lines of 30% maximum reduction

Fig. 4.10

The load cases to be considered are

Load case 1 - both spans fully loaded as shown in Fig. 4.10a.   The elastic
    bending moment diagram for this is shown in Fig. 4.10b by solid lines.

Load case 2 - the left hand span carrying dead load only and the right hand
    span carrying full load as shown in Fig. 4.10c with the corresponding
    bending moment diagram shown in Fig. 4.10d.

Load case 3 - is the opposite way round to load case 2 i.e. maximum load on
    the left hand span and minimum load on the right hand span.   This load
    case is not shown but its bending moment diagram is shown in Fig. 4.10e.

The three bending moment diagrams, shown in Fig. 4.10b, d and e, are then superimposed and the outline or envelope is shown by solid lines in Fig. 4.10f.   Since these bending moments cannot be reduced by more than 30% the broken line on Fig. 4.10f gives the envelope values reduced by 30%.

The effect of redistribution is shown in Fig. 4.10g and the diagram is arrived at in the following way:

The bending moment at the centre support for load case 1 is 480 kNm.   If it is reduced by 30% the new value is 336 kNm which is the maximum value for bending moment at the centre support in Fig. 4.10g.   In order to maintain static equilibrium for load case 1 the sagging bending moments in the span must be increased and the new bending moment diagram for load case 1 is shown by broken lines in Fig. 4.10b and the **new** bending moment in the span is 326.7 kNm.   Note that the central depth of the new parabola is still $FL/8$.   Comparison of this new bending moment diagram with that for load case 2 as shown at Fig. 4.10d shows that for load case 2 the maximum bending moment in the fully loaded span is 333.3 kNm and at the support is 320 kNm.   The bending moment at the centre of the fully loaded span can also be reduced by a maximum of 30% but a much smaller reduction will be used, i.e. the reduction will be from 333.3 kNm to 326.7 kNm.   Again static equilibrium must be maintained so that the bending moment at the support must be increased to 336 kNm and the bending moment diagram for the unloaded span is also changed as shown by the broken lines in Fig. 4.10d. The same result is shown for load case 3 in Fig. 4.10e.   If the broken lines shown in Fig. 4.10 b, d and e are superimposed they will give the solid line shown in Fig. 4.10g.

A check must now be made to see if more than 30% reduction has been made at any point.   This is done by superimposing Fig. 4.10f on Fig. 4.10g and if the broken lines of Fig. 4.10f give values in excess of those in Fig. 4.10g the higher value must be used.   This does occur for two short lengths and these are shown in Fig. 4.10g.

4.E. A QUICKER METHOD OF REDISTRIBUTION

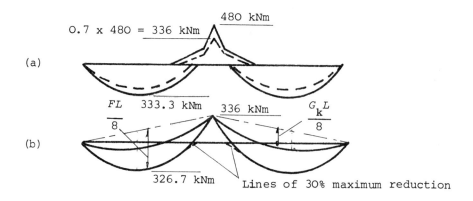

Fig. 4.11

Fig. 4.11a is the elastic envelope for the beam of Example 4.2. The maximum support moments shown can be reduced by 30% to 336 kNm at the centre support and zero at the end supports. If the beam had more than two spans the support moments would all change. The straight chain dot line shown in Fig. 4.11b connects the points representing the reduced support moment. On these lines the curves are drawn which represent the free bending moments due to the maximum load $\frac{FL}{8}$ and the minimum load $\frac{G_k L}{8}$. The envelope after redistribution is now almost complete without having to consider the individual load cases, it is only necessary to consider the maximum and minimum loads on the span.

The diagram thus obtained must still be compared with the broken (70%) lines of Fig. 4.11a and where 70% of the elastic value is the greater that value must be used as before.

QUESTION 4.3

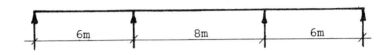

Fig. 4.12

If g_k = 40 kN/m and q_k = 32 kN/m draw the design bending moment envelope for the beam shown in Fig. 4.12 after 30% redistribution. Note: the elastic envelope for this beam has already been drawn, see question 2.3 Chapter 2.

(Answer: See Fig. 4.13)

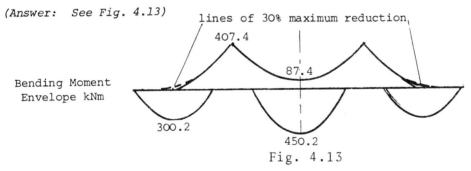

Fig. 4.13

4.F. THE DESIGN OF SECTIONS AFTER REDISTRIBUTION

Note. It is essential that readers have studied chapters 6, 7 and 8 which deal with the design of sections before attempting to read the following.

When redistribution of moments is carried out it is assumed that a considerable degree of plastic rotation at constant moment can be allowed without the premature failure of the section. It must be ensured in the design that this rotation is available.

The amount of rotation available at a plastic hinge is controlled by the strains in the concrete in compression. For a given strain a greater degree of rotation will be obtained for smaller values of neutral axis depth, expressed as $\frac{x}{d}$ than for larger values. The neutral axis depth is usually small for small quantities of tension reinforcement but if it is necessary to carry a large bending moment on a small section the value of $\frac{x}{d}$ can be reduced by increasing the quantity of compression steel. The amount of hinge rotation needed increases as the reduction in bending moment increases.

Accordingly to ensure that sufficient rotational capacity is available a limit is placed on the value of $\frac{x}{d}$ which depends on the percentage reduction of moment. The following formula is extracted from CP110

$$x \not> (0.6 - \beta_{red}) \, d \qquad\qquad \text{(cl.3.2.2.3 (4)(CP110))}$$

where $\beta_{red} = \dfrac{\text{percentage reduction}}{100}$

To enable this control to be readily exercised lines giving values of $\frac{x}{d}$ are included in the design charts which form parts 2 and 3 of CP110.

EXAMPLE 4.3.

Calculate the areas of reinforcement needed for a beam of 700 mm effective depth and 400 mm breadth if it is to carry a design ultimate bending moment of 1050 kNm after 30% redistribution. Assume $f_{cu} = 25 \text{ N/mm}^2$; $f_y = 425 \text{ N/mm}^2$ and $\dfrac{d'}{d} = 0.10$.

For 30% redistribution $\qquad \dfrac{x}{d} < 0.6 - 0.3 = 0.3$

$$\frac{M}{bd^2} = \frac{1050 \times 10^6}{400 \times 700^2} \doteq 5.35 \ \text{N/mm}^2$$

A line is drawn horizontally on the beam design chart on page 101 for $\dfrac{M}{bd^2} = 5.35$.

Where it cuts the dotted line for $\dfrac{x}{d} = 0.3$

$$\frac{100 \, A_s}{bd} = 1.65$$

and

$$\frac{100 \, A'_s}{bd} = 1.0$$

Therefore $\qquad A_s = \dfrac{1.7 \times 700 \times 400}{100} = 4620 \text{ mm}^2$

use 6 bars 32 mm dia.

and
$$A'_s = \frac{1.0 \times 700 \times 400}{100} = 2800 \text{ mm}^2$$

use 4 bars 32 mm dia.

QUESTION 4.4

A beam of 500 mm effective depth and 300 mm breadth is to carry a bending moment of 300 kNm after a reduction of 30% from elastic analysis. Determine the longitudinal reinforcement required if f_{cu} = 25 N/mm^2 and f_y = 425 N/mm^2.   Take d' = 50 mm.

(Answer: $\dfrac{100 \ A_s}{bd}$ = 1.25, 4-25; $\dfrac{100 \ A'_s}{bd}$ = 0.5, 4-16)

5 Serviceability Limit States and Reinforcement Details

5.A. SERVICEABILITY LIMIT STATES

(a) INTRODUCTION

The serviceability limit states of deflection and cracking frequently
control many important dimensions particularly in reinforced concrete beams.
Similarly the requirements for fire resistance also influence the dimensions
of members.   Therefore, although fire resistance is not strictly a
serviceability limit state it is included in this chapter as also are other
controlling factors on the size of beams and spacing of reinforcement.   The
principal controls upon section dimensions which are not covered in this
chapter are those of strength.   Strength is considered at the ultimate
limit state which is dealt with in later chapters.   Vibration is a
serviceability limit state which is important in some structures but it is
considered too difficult for inclusion in an elementary book such as this.

The leading dimensions of a structure (i.e. span, height etc) are determined
by the requirements of the user and by aesthetic considerations.   They are
rarely under the control of the structural engineer although he can often
influence them where constructional difficulty and consequent extra cost is
to be avoided.

(b) DEFLECTION

Excessive deflections may produce cracks in non-load-bearing elements and
finishes, discomfort to the users of the structure and adversely affect the
appearance of the structure.   The designer must, therefore, ensure that
deflections are not excessive.   The result of this will frequently control
the depth of section and the methods used are discussed in detail in 5.D.
Deflection.

(c) CRACKING

Excessive cracking is unsightly and leads to corrosion of the reinforcement
and deterioration of the structure.   Its control is exercised almost
entirely by limitations on the spacing of the reinforcement and the amount
of concrete cover to the steel.   Cracking is therefore dealt with in 5.C.
Arrangement of reinforcement.

(d) DURABILITY

The structure must be durable, it must not fail because of attacks on it by the weather and other environmental factors.   Durability is achieved by controls on the strength of the concrete and the thickness of the cover to the reinforcement.   It is discussed in detail in 5.C. Arrangement of reinforcement.

(e) FIRE RESISTANCE

Adequate fire resistance is necessary in buildings to allow escape of the occupants and reasonable safety for fire fighters engaged in bringing the fire under control.   Fire resistance is obtained by ensuring that cross sections are of a minimum thickness and that the cover to the reinforcement is sufficient.   Fire resistance is therefore covered partly in 5.C. Arrangement of reinforcement and partly in 5.E. Fire resistance.

5.B. SECTION DIMENSIONS

(a) OVERALL DIMENSIONS

Once the span of a beam or the height of a column is fixed the remaining dimensions including the reinforcement will usually be fixed by:

  (i)   the amount of steel and concrete required to resist the forces induced by the application of dead and imposed loads.

  (ii)   the need to satisfy the serviceability limit states and to provide adequate fire resistance.

(iii)   the need to allow for the connection of other members.

Sometimes one or both overall cross section dimensions will be controlled by aesthetic considerations or by the economic advantages of re-use of shuttering.

(b) REINFORCEMENT

The quantity, strength and arrangement of reinforcement required is determined by :

  (i)   the axial force, shear force, bending and twisting moments applied to the member.

  (ii)   the size of the member.

(iii)   the cover required for durability and fire protection.

  (iv)   the space needed between the bars to allow placing and compaction of the concrete.

  (v)   the limitation of space between the bars to ensure that excessive cracking does not occur.

(vi)   the need to ensure that deflections are not excessive.

(vii)   the minimum necessary for safety, corrosion resistance and fire resistance.

(viii) the maximum for both economy and effectiveness.

(c) FIRE RESISTANCE (section 10 (CP110))

The required fire resistance of a building is usually specified in hours. This concept of a period of fire resistance is based on the time necessary for the occupants of the building to escape and for the fire fighters to control the blaze.   The smaller the area in which the fire can be contained the smaller the escape and fire fighting times will need to be, although any materials stored in the building will affect these times.   It is therefore advantageous to divide buildings into small portions by fire resisting walls and floors connected by fire resisting self closing doors which not only prevent spread of flame but also spread of smoke which hinders escape and fire fighting.

The period for which fire resistance is needed is determined by the volume of the enclosed section thus for a larger volume a greater period of fire resistance is needed than for a lesser volume.   These considerations are covered in the Building Regulations, CP110 is merely concerned with the fire resistance of the reinforced concrete elements of construction.

The fire resistance of reinforced concrete depends to a large extent on the control of the temperature of the reinforcement and hence on the **degree** of insulation provided.   The insulation provided to the reinforcement is obtained by concrete cover or a mixture of concrete cover, plaster and other finishes.   The thickness of section also enters into the calculation.   Beams should have a minimum width, floors a minimum thickness and columns a minimum lateral dimension.   The figures for beams, floors and columns are given in Tables 54, 56 and 59 (CP110). The cover to give the required degree of insulation is also given in these tables.   Cover is more specifically dealt with in 5.C(b).

All the figures given in these tables can be modified for different surface finishes or ceiling treatments.   Further information is given in CP110 which should be referred to if needed.

QUESTION 5.1

What is the minimum beam width and the minimum thickness of solid floor slab for a building in which four hours fire resistance is required? Siliceous aggregate concrete without plaster or other finishes may be assumed.

(Answers: 280 mm;   150 mm)

Table 54. Fire resistance of reinforced concrete beams

Description	Dimension of concrete to give a fire resistance in hours					
	4	3	2	1½	1	½
	mm	mm	mm	mm	mm	mm
(1) Siliceous aggregate concrete:						
a. average concrete cover to main reinforcement	65*	55*	45*	35	25	15
b. beam width	280	240	180	140	110	80
(2) As (1) with cement or gypsum plaster 15 mm thick on light mesh reinforcement:						
a. average concrete cover to main reinforcement	50*	40	30	20	15	15
b. beam width	250	210	170	110	85	70
(3) As (1) with vermiculite/gypsum plaster† or sprayed asbestos‡ 15 mm thick:						
a. average concrete cover to main reinforcement	25	15	15	15	15	15
b. beam width	170	145	125	85	60	60
(4) Lightweight aggregate concrete:						
a. average concrete cover to main reinforcement	50	45	35	30	20	15
b. beam width	250	200	160	130	100	80

* Supplementary reinforcement, to hold the concrete cover in position, may be necessary. Reference should be made to **10.2**.
† Vermiculite/gypsum plàster should have a mix ratio in the range of 1½–2 : 1 by volume.
‡ Sprayed asbestos should conform to BS 3590.

Table 59. Fire resistance of concrete columns (all faces exposed)

Type of construction	Dimension of concrete to give fire resistance in hours					
	4	3	2	1½	1	½
	mm	mm	mm	mm	mm	mm
(1) Siliceous aggregate concrete:						
a. without additional protection	450	400	300	250	200	150
b. with cement or gypsum plaster 15 mm thick on light mesh reinforcement	300	275	225	150	150	150
c. with vermiculite/gypsum plaster* or sprayed asbestos† 15 mm thick	275	225	200	150	120	120
(2) Limestone aggregate concrete or siliceous aggregate concrete with supplementary reinforcement in concrete cover	300	275	225	200	190	150
(3) Lightweight aggregate concrete	300	275	225	200	150	150

* Vermiculite/gypsum plaster should have a mix ratio in the range of 1½–2 : 1 by volume.
† Sprayed asbestos should conform to BS 3590.

Table 56. Fire resistance of reinforced concrete floors (siliceous or calcareous aggregate)

Elementary Structural Design in Concrete to CP 110 60

Floor construction		Minimum dimension to give fire resistance in hours					
		4	3	2	1½	1	½
		mm	mm	mm	mm	mm	mm
(1) Solid slab	Average cover to reinforcement	25	25	20	20	15	15
	Depth, overall†	150	150	125	125	100	100
(2) Cored slabs in which the cores are circular or are higher than wide. Not less than 50 % of the gross cross section of the floor should be solid material	Average cover to reinforcement	25	25	20	20	15	15
	Thickness under cores	50	40	40	30	25	20
	Depth, overall†	190	175	160	140	110	100
(3) Hollow box section with one or more longitudinal cavities which are wider than high	Average cover to reinforcement	25	25	20	20	15	15
	Thickness of bottom flange	50	40	40	30	25	20
	Depth, overall†	230	205	180	155	130	105
(4) Ribbed floor with hollow infill blocks of clay, or inverted T-section beams with hollow infill blocks of concrete or clay. A floor in which less than 50 % of the gross cross section is solid material must be provided with a 15 mm plaster coating on soffit	Average cover to reinforcement	25	25	20	20	15	15
	Width of rib, or beam, at soffit	125	100	90	80	70	50
	Depth, overall†	190	175	160	140	110	100
(5) Upright T-sections	Average bottom cover to reinforcement	65*	55*	45*	35	25	15
	Side cover to reinforcement	65*	55*	45*	35	25	15
	Least width of downstanding leg	150	140	115	90	75	60
	Thickness of flange†	150	150	125	125	100	90
(6) Inverted channel sections with radius at intersection of soffits with top of leg not exceeding depth of section	Average bottom cover to reinforcement	65*	55*	45*	35	25	15
	Side cover to reinforcement	40*	30*	25*	20	15	10
	Least width of each downstanding leg	75	70	60	45	40	30
	Thickness at crown†	150	150	125	125	100	90
(7) Inverted channel sections or U-sections with radius at intersection of soffits with top of leg exceeding depth of section	Average bottom cover to reinforcement	65*	55*	45*	35	25	15
	Side cover to reinforcement	40*	30*	25*	20	15	10
	Least width of each downstanding leg	70	60	50	40	35	25
	Thickness at crown†	150	150	100	100	75	65

* Supplementary reinforcement, to hold the concrete cover in position, may be necessary. Reference should be made to 10.3.
† Non-combustible screeds and finishes may be included in these dimensions.

5.C. ARRANGEMENT OF REINFORCEMENT

(a) MINIMUM DISTANCE BETWEEN BARS (cl.3.11.8.1(CP110))

During concreting the aggregate must be allowed to move between bars to
obtain adequate compaction and bond.   For this reason cl.3.11.8.1(CP110)
generally indicates bar spacings slightly greater than the aggregate size.

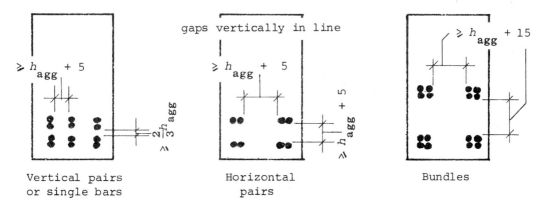

| Vertical pairs or single bars | Horizontal pairs | Bundles |

Fig. 5.1

When bar sizes are large the dissipation of shear stress round each bar
becomes a controlling factor in which case the space between the bars should
be not less than the bar size.   A further consideration is the use of
immersion type (poker) vibrators for compaction of the concrete, these are
commonly 40 mm in diameter or more so that the space between top bars should
be at least 50 mm.   These considerations are shown diagrammatically in
Fig. 5.1.   It can be seen that the use of bundled bars can help to reduce
congestion providing that bond stress is not a problem (see Chapters 9 and 10).

QUESTION 5.2

If for a reinforced concrete beam the aggregate size is 15 mm determine the
minimum horizontal and vertical distance between

(a) individual bars

(b) horizontal pairs

(c) bundles of 4 bars

(Answers: (a) 20, 10   (b) 20, 20   (c) 30, 30)

(b) CONCRETE COVER TO THE REINFORCEMENT (cl.3.11.2(CP110))

Cover to the steel reinforcement is necessary to ensure the bond of the
steel with the concrete so that both steel and concrete are effective in
resisting the applied forces.   Cover is also necessary to prevent corrosion
of the steel reinforcement and to resist damage by fire.   The amount of
cover needed also depends on the durability of the concrete i.e. its
resistance to degradation under the attack of the atmosphere and the elements
which compose its environment.   The durability of concrete is dependent on

many factors, most of which are improved by increasing its strength. Therefore, the nominal cover thicknesses given in Table 19 (CP110) are related to the conditions of exposure and the concrete strength. The nominal cover thicknesses given should be regarded as a minimum to ensure proper bond and corrosion resistance for ALL bars. The cover is, therefore, calculated from the steel nearest to the concrete surface which is usually shear steel in the form of stirrups or links in beams.

The nominal cover should always be at least equal to the size of the bar and in case of bundles of three or more bars should be equal to the size of a single bar of equivalent area.

Table 19. Nominal cover to reinforcement

	Nominal cover				
Condition of exposure	Concrete grade				
	20	25	30	40	50 and over
	mm	mm	mm	mm	mm
Mild: e.g. completely protected against weather, or aggressive conditions, except for brief period of exposure to normal weather conditions during construction	25	20	15	15	15
Moderate: e.g. sheltered from severe rain and against freezing whilst saturated with water. Buried concrete and concrete continuously under water	—	40	30	25	20
Severe: e.g. exposed to driving rain, alternate wetting and drying and to freezing whilst wet. Subject to heavy condensation or corrosive fumes	—	50	40	30	25
Very severe: e.g. exposed to sea water or moorland water and with abrasion	—	—	—	60	50
Subject to salt used for de-icing	—	—	50*	40*	25

* Only applicable if the concrete has entrained air (see **6.3.6**).

The cover to main reinforcement in beams should also be considered from the point of view of placing the concrete. The aggregate must be able to pass between the shutter and the main side bars, see 5.C(a) and example 5.1.

The fire resistance (see 5.Bc for a more complete discussion) of reinforced concrete construction is dependent upon the cover to the main tension reinforcement, the type of aggregate and the minimum thickness of the section. The cover for the different types of aggregate and periods of fire resistance for beams, slabs and columns is given in Tables 54, 56 and 59(CP110). It should be noted that the amount of concrete cover can be reduced if additional protection is provided by plaster or other suitable insulating material applied to the surface of the concrete. Where the thickness of the concrete cover is greater than 40 mm it may be necessary depending on the type of aggregate used, to provide supplementary reinforcement within the thickness of the cover. The purpose of the supplementary reinforcement is to prevent spalling of the concrete due to heating and consequent reduction of fire resistance.

EXAMPLE 5.1

Figure 5.2 shows the arrangement of bars
in the bottom of a reinforced concrete
beam.   The exposure is mild and the
required fire resistance is 2 hours.
The siliceous aggregate has a maximum
size of 20 mm and the characteristic
strength of the concrete is 20 N/mm^2.
Determine the minimum value of the
cover c.

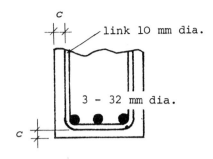

link 10 mm dia.

3 - 32 mm dia.

Fig. 5.2

Durability - Reference to Table 19 (CP110)
   shows that for concrete grade 20 and
   mild exposure the required nominal
   cover is 25 mm to all steel therefore
   for durability c = 25 mm.

Fire resistance - Reference to Table 54 (CP110) shows that for siliceous
   aggregate concrete the required average cover to main reinforcement is
   45 mm.

   Therefore for fire resistance c = 45 - 10 mm link dia

   $$= 35 \text{ mm}$$

Concreting - it seems practical to provide at least the same distance
   between the bars and the shutter as between one bar and the next, giving
   a cover of 20 + 5 = 25 mm.   Since the link bars are parallel to the
   direction of movement of the concrete the 25 mm space need only be
   applied to main bars.
   Therefore for concreting c = 25 - 10 ≒ 15 mm

Finally - Three possible values of c have been obtained i.e. 25 mm, 35 mm,
   15 mm.   The largest value, i.e. 35 mm, obtained for fire resistance
   must be used.

   Therefore c = 35 mm

   Additionally the cover to the main reinforcement is 45 mm which is greater
   than 40 mm, therefore additional reinforcement must be provided within
   the thickness of the cover to prevent early spalling of the concrete.
   Such reinforcement should not be more than 20 mm from the face of the
   concrete and should consist of a wire fabric or equivalent, weighing
   not less than 0.5 kg/m^2 A suitable fabric would have 2 mm diameter
   wires at not more than 100 mm pitch.

QUESTION 5.3

(a) What is the required cover for moderate exposure for grade 25 concrete?

(b) What is the required cover for siliceous aggregate concrete in a
    reinforced concrete beam for 4 hours fire resistance?

(Answers: (a) 40 mm   (b) 65 mm)

(c) MAXIMUM COVER AND MAXIMUM DISTANCE BETWEEN BARS (cl.3.11.8.2(CP110))

The maximum cover and maximum distance between bars is restricted in order
to control cracking.   The crack width is related to the stress in the
reinforcing bars and the distance from the bar or the neutral axis.

On the tension side of a reinforced concrete beam for small loads the steel
and concrete acting compositely will carry tensile stresses.   At the
limiting tensile stress for concrete , cracks will occur and the tensile
force in the concrete adjacent to the crack will be transferred to the
reinforcement.   The concrete which was formerly carrying tensile stress
will now shorten, tending to return to its original unstressed length.
The concrete immediately adjacent to the reinforcement is still firmly
attached to it and cannot shorten whereas the concrete further away from
the steel is able to shorten more.   The concrete at the neutral axis has
zero stress and is therefore not cracked.   Cracks developing from the
surface will tend to be wedge shaped and those between reinforcing bars will

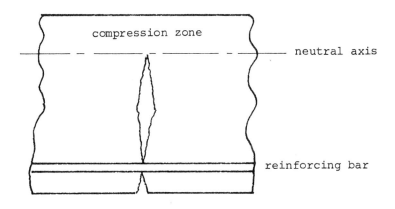

Fig. 5.3

tend to be diamond shaped as shown in Fig. 5.3.   The width of the crack
will also depend on the difference between the steel stress when the concrete
first cracks and the stress at the service load.   The difference will be
greater for high tensile steel and where reductions of bending moment have
been made during redistribution (see Chapter 4).   The shrinkage and creep
characteristics of the concrete will also affect the width of the cracks.

Crack widths should not exceed 0.3 mm in width for normal environments and
should be less for aggressive environments (see cl.2.2.3.2(CP110)).   A method
for the calculation of crack widths is given in Appendix A (CP110) but for
most structures in normal environments the rules given in cl.3.11.8.2(CP110)
may be used.   The values given in Table 24 are based on calculations using
the methods in Appendix A (CP110).   Nevertheless, if difficulty is found
in satisfying the bar spacing and cover rules of cl.3.11.8.2(CP110)
calculations will often show that cracks widths are not likely to be
excessive.   Calculations are more likely to show satisfactory results
because of the generalisations made, which must be on the safe side, in the

preparation of Table 24 (CP110).   Difficulty in satisfying the bar
spacing requirements of cl.3.11.8.2(CP110) are most likely to be found
when checking for cracking at the corners of beams which are designed for
4 hours fire resistance.   The minimum cover for fire resistance then
conflicts with the maximum for crack control.

It should be noted that the maximum spacing of secondary reinforcement
in slabs is five times the effective depth to ensure proper dispersion
of concentrated loads.

3.11.8.2 *Maximum distance between bars in tension.* Unless the calculation of crack widths (see Appendix A)
shows that a greater spacing is acceptable, the following rules should be applied to beams in normal internal
or external conditions of exposure.

(1) In the application of these rules any bar with a diameter less than 0.45 times the diameter of the
maximum bar size in the section should be ignored except when considering those in the side faces of
beams. Bars placed in the side face of beams to control cracking should be of a size not less than $\sqrt{s_b b/f_y}$,
where s_b is the spacing of the bars and b the breadth of the section at the point considered.

(2) The clear horizontal distance between adjacent bars, or groups, near the tension face of a beam
should not be greater than the value given in Table 24 depending on the amount of redistribution carried
out in analysis and the characteristic strength of the reinforcement.

Table 24. Clear distance between bars

f_y	% redistribution to or from section considered										
	−30	−25	−20	−15	−10	0	+10	+15	+20	+25	+30
N/mm²	mm	mm	mm	mm	mm	mm	mm	mm	mm	mm	mm
250	215	230	245	260	275	300	300	300	300	300	300
410	130	140	150	155	165	185	205	215	220	230	240
425	125	135	145	155	160	180	200	210	215	225	235
460	115	125	130	140	150	165	180	190	200	205	215
500	105	115	120	130	135	150	165	175	180	190	195

(3) The clear distance from the corner of a beam to the surface of the nearest longitudinal bar should
not be greater than half the clear distance given in Table 24.

(4) When the overall depth of a beam exceeds 750 mm, longitudinal bars should be provided over a
distance of 2/3 of the overall depth from the tension face. This reinforcement should be positioned near the
side faces and be spaced at not more than 250 mm; it may be used in calculating the resistance moment
of the section.

The above rules are not applicable to members subjected to particularly aggressive environments unless
in the calculation of the resistance moment f_y has been limited to 300 N/mm².

The above rules for beams also apply to slabs except that, in normal internal or external conditions of
exposure:

(1) when a slab is not more than 200 mm thick, or 250 mm thick if the characteristic strength of reinforcement used in design is not more than 425 N/mm², no check is required but the clear distance between bars
should not exceed three times the effective depth of the slab;

(2) when the amount of tension reinforcement in a slab, expressed as a percentage of the gross cross-
sectional area, is less than 0.5 % the clear distance between bars may be twice that given by Table 24;

(3) when the amount of tension reinforcement in the slab is between 0.5 % and 1.0 % the clear distance
between bars may be equal to the appropriate figure from Table 24 divided by that percentage.

When using Table 24 for slabs, if the amount of redistribution is not known, e.g. when using Table 13,
a value may be assumed of −15 % for support moments and zero for span moments.

QUESTION 5.4

Check that the bar spacing and cover is satisfactory for the beam sections shown in Fig. 5.4.

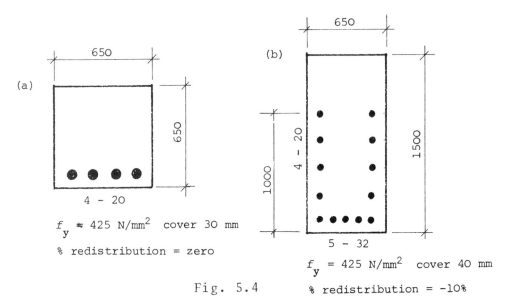

(a)

650

650

4 - 20

$f_y \approx 425$ N/mm^2 cover 30 mm

% redistribution = zero

(b)

650

1500

1000

4 - 20

5 - 32

$f_y = 425$ N/mm^2 cover 40 mm

% redistribution = -10%

Fig. 5.4

(d) EFFECTIVE DEPTH

The effective depth d of a reinforced concrete beam is the distance from the compression surface of a concrete section to the centroid of the cross sectional area of the tensile steel as shown in Fig. 5.5. The effective depth is used for calculating deflections, and for determining the moment of resistance at the ultimate limit state.   The use of effective depth is a simplification which reduces the complexity of calculations particularly where several layers of bars are used.

line of centroid of steel area

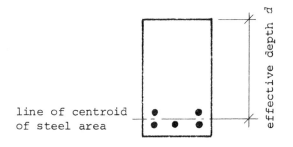

effective depth d

Fig. 5.5

QUESTION 5.5

Caculate the effective depth of the beams shown in Fig. 5.6.   All contain 20mm size aggregate.

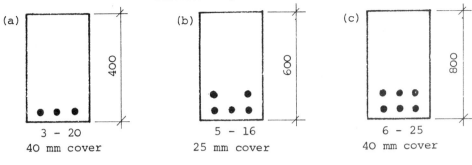

Fig. 5.6

(Answers: (a) 350   (b) 555   (c) 728 mm.)

(e) USE OF BAR AREA TABLES

All reinforcing bars, whether of square, round or other sections, produced in Great Britain have a nominal size such that the cross-sectional area of the bar is the area of a circle equal in diameter to the nominal size.

In designing reinforcement calculations usually end with an area of steel e.g. 2100 mm^2 for a beam or 780 mm^2 per metre width for a slab.   This area of steel must be converted to an actual number of bars of a certain size in the case of a beam, or in the case of the slab a size of bar at a certain pitch.   To enable this conversion to be made easily tables, similar to the ones used in practice, are given on page 68.   The upper table is used for beams and gives the cross-sectional area of groups of bars, and the lower table gives the cross-sectional area of bars per metre width for pitches between 60 mm and 300 mm.   The pitch of the bars is defined as the distance between the centrelines of adjacent bars measured at right angles to the bars.

When using the tables it may be advantageous to start on the horizontal line for four bars when determining the actual reinforcement for a beam, and on the vertical line for 12 mm bars when determining the reinforcement for a slab.   The following examples show how the tables are used.   The lowest line of the upper table gives the circumference of a single bar which is used when checking bond stresses (see Chapters 9 and 10).

EXAMPLE 5.2

A calculation shows that a 2100 mm^2 of reinforcement is needed for a beam, determine suitable bar sizes.

As suggested above enter the upper bar area table at the line for 4 bars indicated by an arrow in the left hand margin and read across until an area is indicated which is similar to the 2100 mm^2 required.   It can be seen that in the column headed by a bar size of 25 mm an area of 1964 mm^2 is given and in the column headed by a bar size of 32 mm an area of 3217 mm^2 is given. The value of 1964 mm^2 is obviously too small whilst the value of 3217 mm^2 is roughly 50% greater than needed.   Further examination of the table shows

CROSS SECTIONAL AREAS OF GROUPS OF BARS mm²										
bar size mm		6	8	10	12	16	20	25	32	40
number of bars	1	28	50	79	113	201	314	491	804	1256
	2	57	101	157	226	402	628	982	1608	2513
	3	85	151	236	339	603	942	1473	**2413**	3770
	4	113	201	314	452	804	1257	1964	3217	5026
	5	141	251	393	565	1005	1571	**2455**	4021	6283
	6	170	302	471	679	1206	1885	2945	4825	7540
	7	198	352	550	792	1407	2199	3436	5630	8796
	8	226	402	628	905	1608	2533	3927	6434	10050
	9	254	452	707	1018	1809	2827	4418	7238	11310
	10	283	503	785	1131	2011	3142	4909	8042	12570
circum-ference		18,9	25,1	31,4	37,7	50,3	62.8	78,5	100,5	125,7

CROSS SECTIONAL AREAS OF BARS PER METRE WIDTH mm²								
bar size mm		6	8	10	12	16	20	25
pitch of bars	60	471	837	1309	1884	3350	5234	8181
	80	353	628	982	1414	2512	3926	6136
	100	283	503	785	1131	2011	3141	4909
	120	236	419	654	942	1674	2617	4091
	140	202	359	561	**808**	1435	2244	3506
	150	189	335	524	754	1338	2094	3273
	160	177	314	491	707	1256	1964	3068
	180	157	279	436	627	1115	1746	2727
	200	141	251	393	565	1005	1572	2454
	250	113	201	314	452	804	1257	1964
	300	95	168	262	377	669	1047	1636

that increasing the number of 25 mm bars to five gives an area of 2455 mm^2 and reducing the number of 32 mm bars to three gives an area of 2413 mm^2, both are marked by a heavy box.   Either of these results would be satisfactory depending on other considerations like the bar spacing rules already given or other parts of the design discussed in later chapters. It should be noted that although a suggestion is made that the bar area table be entered at the line for four bars beams may in fact contain two bars only or more, up to a maximum which depends on the size of the beam and may be twelve or sixteen.   In general round about four bars are suitable for most building works but six or eight in two rows may be used on occasion.

EXAMPLE 5.3

A calculation shows that a slab needed 780 mm^2 of steel per metre width of slab, determine the size and pitch of suitable reinforcement.

Following the suggestion that, for slabs, the lower bar area table is entered at the column for the 12 mm bar size, indicated by an arrow above the table, it is found that a pitch of 140 mm gives an area of 808 mm^2 per metre width and a pitch of 150 mm gives an area of 754 mm^2 per metre width.   The pitch of 140 mm should be used.   If other considerations indicate that a different bar size is used then 10 mm bars can be used at 100 mm pitch giving an area of 785 mm^2 or 16 mm bars can be used at 250 mm pitch.   Either of these two arrangements may be used but the 10 mm bars cost more and the wide spacing of the 16 mm bars may be greater than that allowed to control cracking.   The bar area used must always be greater than the area indicated by the design requirements.

(f) MINIMUM AREA OF MAIN TENSILE REINFORCEMENT (cl.3.11.4.1(CP110))

The minimum area of main longitudinal reinforcement is given in cl.3.11.4.1 (CP110).   This figure is provided empirically to prevent excessive local curvature in a member, and to provide some resistance to shear forces.   It also ensures a minimum resistance to forces applied during construction which have not been anticipated in the design calculations.

3.11.4.1 *Minimum area of main reinforcement.* The area of tension reinforcement in a beam or slab should not be less than 0.15 % $b_t d$ when using high yield reinforcement, or 0.25 % $b_t d$ when mild steel reinforcement is used, where b_t is the breadth of the section and d is the effective depth. For a box, T- or I-section, b_t should be taken as the average breadth of the concrete below the upper flange.

It should also be appreciated that a beam should not contain less than two bars as tension reinforcement.   A rectangular column should contain not less than four, and a circular column not less than six.   Separate reinforcing bars should be not less than 6 mm diameter, nor greater than 40 mm diameter for normal construction.

The use of 3.11.4.1(CP110) is illustrated in Example 5.4.

Example 5.4

A Tee beam has an effective depth of 600 mm and a rib breadth of 300 mm, calculate the minimum area of high yield reinforcement and determine the number and size of bars.

$$A_s = \frac{0.15 \times 300 \times 600}{100} = 270 \text{ mm}^2$$

(2-16 mm bars)

(g) MINIMUM AREA OF SECONDARY REINFORCEMENT IN SLABS (cl.3.11.4.2(CP110))

In slabs it is not only necessary to specify a minimum quantity of main, reinforcement but also a minimum quantity of secondary or distribution reinforcement as given in cl.3.11.4.2(CP110).   This is necessary to ensure that concentrated loads are distributed across a reasonable width of slab and it also has the additional advantage of controlling shrinkage cracks. The quantity of reinforcement is specified as a percentage of the gross cross-sectional area, i.e. the overall slab thickness h is used not the effective depth.   The calculation is illustrated in Example 5.5.

3.11.4.2 *Minimum area of secondary reinforcement.* In a solid concrete suspended slab, the amount of reinforcement provided at right angles to the main reinforcement, expressed as a percentage of the gross cross-section, should not be less than 0.12 % of high yield reinforcement or, alternatively, not less than 0.15 % of mild steel reinforcement. In either case, the distance between bars should not exceed five times the effective depth of the slab.

Example 5.5

A slab has an overall thickness of 200 mm, determine the quantity of secondary reinforcement needed assuming high yield steel.

$$A_s = \frac{0.12 \times 1000 \times 200}{100} = 240 \text{ mm}^2/ \text{ metre width}$$

10 mm at 300 mm pitch

Maximum pitch is $5d$ approximately 5 x 170 = 850 mm

QUESTION 5.6

Determine the minimum main and secondary reinforcement for a slab of 150 mm overall depth assuming mild steel and an effective depth of 120 mm.

(Answer: Main steel, 300 mm^2/m, 10 mm at 300 mm pitch;
           Secondary steel, 225 mm^2/m, 8 mm at 200 mm pitch)

(h) MINIMUM AREA OF LINKS (cl.3.11.4.3(CP110))

3.11.4.3 *Minimum area of links.* When in a beam or column part or all of the main reinforcement is required to resist compression, links or ties at least one quarter the size of the largest compression bar should be provided at a maximum spacing of twelve times the size of the smallest compression bar. Links should be so arranged that every corner and alternate bar or group in an outer layer of reinforcement is supported by a link passing round the bar and having an included angle of not more than 135°. All other bars or groups within a compression zone should be within 150 mm of a restrained bar. For circular columns, where the longitudinal reinforcement is located round the periphery of a circle, adequate lateral support is provided by a circular tie passing round the bars or groups.

Links are provided in beams to resist the shear forces.   If the shear is small then the shear force will be resisted by the compression zone, the dowel action of the steel and the aggregate interlock.   This will be considered in more detail later.   The member however may be subjected to unforseen tensile forces in construction or in service which tend to reduce the shear resistance of the member.   For members of major structural importance therefore it is preferable to provide the minimum area of links in beams such that:

for high yield links $\dfrac{A_{sv}}{s_v} = 0.0012b_t$

for mild steel links $\dfrac{A_{sv}}{s_v} = 0.002b_t$

where A_{sv} is the cross-sectional area of the two legs of a link,
    b_t is the breadth of the beam at the level of the tension reinforcement,
    s_v is the spacing of the links.

Links are also provided in columns to prevent premature buckling failure of the longitudinal bars.   The size and spacing is determined empirically and to be effective must be a minimum size to prevent lateral movement of the longitudinal bar.   Links provide similar control on buckling for compression bars in beams. The rules are given in cl.3.11.4.3(CP110) above.

The smallest practical bar diameter for a link is 6 mm and the largest to be bent in the form of a closed link is dependant on section size.   Links should preferably be spaced not closer than 75 mm centres to allow for concreting, and when resisting shear the spacing must not exceed 0.75 d. A maximum spacing in practice not often exceeded is 300 mm.

QUESTION 5.7

(a) Determine the minimum size and the maximum spacing of mild steel links for a column of cross section 400 mm square containing four high yield steel longitudinal bars of 25 mm diameter plus four high yield steel bars of 12 mm diameter.

(b) Determine the minimum size of high yield steel links to resist the shear in a beam 300 mm wide with an effective depth of 600 mm.

(*Answers: (a)   8 mm dia. 140 mm pitch (b), 8 mm dia 280 mm pitch.*)

(i) MAXIMUM AREA OF REINFORCEMENT (cl.3.11.5(CP110))

A maximum area of reinforcement is specified to allow the concrete to be properly placed and compacted round the reinforcement.   Also if excessive reinforcement is used the member does not behave plastically at failure and therefore gives less warning of imminent collapse.

3.11.5 Maximum areas of reinforcement in members. In a beam, neither the area of tension reinforcement nor the area of compression reinforcement should exceed 4 % of the gross cross-sectional area of the concrete.

In a column, the percentage of longitudinal reinforcement should not exceed 6 in vertically cast columns and 8 in horizontally cast columns, except that at laps in both types of column the percentage may be 10.

In a wall, the area of vertical reinforcement should not exceed 4 % of the gross cross-sectional area of the concrete.

QUESTION 5.8

Determine the maximum area of tensile steel for a beam 300 mm wide x 500 mm deep.

(Answer: 6,000 mm²)

5.D. DEFLECTION (cl.3.3.8(CP110))

Excessive deflections may produce cracks in non-load-bearing elements and finishes, discomfort to the users of the structure and affect its appearance.

If a member behaves in a linear elastic manner the deflection is of the form $\frac{KWL^3}{EI}$.   The stress-strain relationship for concrete is, however, non-linear and therefore Youngs modulus *(E)* varies with the stress.   The second moment of area *(I)* is for a composite cross section of steel and concrete which may or may not be cracked.   Since *E* and *I* cannot be determined with any great accuracy for a reinforced concrete member, CP110 adopts a simple approach based on limiting *span/effective depth* ratios given in Tables 8 and 9 (CP110).

This is not illogical since deflection is related to *span/depth* ratio as follows.

For a beam the deflection is given by:

$$a = \frac{K_1 WL^3}{EI} \qquad \cdots\cdots\cdots (1)$$

and for a rectangular cross section the bending moment

$$M = K WL = \frac{fI}{h/2} \qquad \cdots\cdots\cdots (2)$$

combining equations (1) and (2)

$$\frac{a}{L} = K_3 \left(\frac{L}{h}\right)$$

(note: d may be substituted for h providing the constant K_3 is modified).

Values of the *span/effective depth* ratios shown in Tables 8 and 9 (CP110) are modified by factors for tension and compression reinforcement, shown in Tables 10 and 11 (CP110).   The effective depth of the beam may be written as

$$minimum\ effective\ depth = \frac{Span}{(factor\ table\ 8\ or\ 9)\ (fact\ tab\ 10)\ (fact\ tab\ 11)}$$

The addition of compressive steel is seen in Table 11 to reduce the effective depth of the beam.   This is because it increases the stiffness and reduces the effects of creep and shrinkage.   The addition of tension steel however, necessitates an increase in the effective depth of the beam.   The reason is because an increase in the area of tension steel increases the depth of the compressive zone and the effects of shrinkage.   This produces greater curvature and greater creep deflection.   Also from Table 10 it is seen that an increase in tensile stress in the steel requires a greater effective depth of beam as would be expected.

The use of Table 8 will restrict the deflection to approximately span/250. Table 8 may be used for the calculations relating to beams of greater than 10 m span if this deflection is acceptable, but it is more usual for such beams to have the deflection restricted to a smaller value than span/250 which will be done by using Table 9.

It should be noted that for cantilevers where the span exceeds 10 m special deflection calculations are required.   The methods to be used are given in Appendix A (CP110).

QUESTION 5.9

Using Equation 13 (CP110) to determine the service stress in the steel f_s, and assuming $\beta_b = 1$.

(a) Determine the effective depth of a continuous beam of 10 m span which contains 1% tension reinforcement (f_y = 410 N/mm^2) and 0.5% compression reinforcement.   The quantities of reinforcement provided are exactly those indicated by the calculation.

(b) Determine the effective depth of a simply supported beam of 12 m span which is provided with 1.51% tension reinforcement (f_y = 460 N/mm^2) and no compression bars.   The area of tension reinforcement obtained by calculation is 1.25%.

(*Answers:*   (a) f_s = 238 N/mm^2, d = 337 mm
            (b) f_s = 220 N/mm^2, d = 625 mm)

Table 8. Basic span/effective depth ratios for rectangular beams

Support conditions	Ratio
Cantilever	7
Simply supported	20
Continuous	26

Table 8 should only be used for spans greater than 10 m if the engineer is satisfied that a deflection of span/250 is acceptable. When it is necessary further to restrict the deflection, to avoid damage to finishes or partitions, Table 9 should be used for spans exceeding 10 m.

Table 9. Special span/effective depth ratios for rectangular beams

Span	Cantilever	Simply supported	Continuous
m			
10		20	26
12	Value to be	18	23
14	justified by	16	21
16	calculation	14	18
18		12	16
20		10	13

Deflection is influenced by the amount of tension reinforcement and its stress and therefore the span/ effective depth ratios should be modified according to the area of reinforcement provided and its service stress at the centre of the span (or at the support in the case of a cantilever). Values of span/effective depth ratio obtained from Table 8 or 9 should therefore be multiplied by the appropriate factor obtained from Table 10.

Table 10. Modification factor for tension reinforcement

Service stress (f_s)	$\frac{100A_s}{bd}$							
	0.25	0.50	0.75	1.00	1.50	2.00	2.50	$\geqslant 3.0$
N/mm^2								
145 ($f_y = 250$)	2.0	1.98	1.62	1.44	1.24	1.13	1.06	1.01
150	2.0	1.91	1.58	1.41	1.22	1.11	1.04	0.99
200	2.0	1.46	1.26	1.15	1.02	0.94	0.89	0.85
238 ($f_y = 410$)	1.60	1.23	1.09	1.00	0.90	0.84	0.80	0.77
246 ($f_y = 425$)	1.55	1.20	1.06	0.98	0.88	0.83	0.79	0.76
250	1.52	1.18	1.05	0.97	0.87	0.82	0.78	0.75
267 ($f_y = 460$)	1.41	1.11	0.99	0.92	0.84	0.78	0.75	0.72
290 ($f_y = 500$)	1.27	1.03	0.92	0.86	0.79	0.74	0.71	0.68
300	1.22	0.99	0.90	0.84	0.77	0.72	0.69	0.67

The service stress may be estimated from the equation

$$f_s = 0.58 \frac{f_y A_{s.req}}{A_{s.prov}} \times \frac{1}{\beta_b} \tag{13}$$

where f_s is the estimated service stress in the tension reinforcement,

f_y is the characteristic strength of the reinforcement,

$A_{s.req}$ is the area of tension reinforcement required at mid-span to resist the moment due to ultimate loads (at support for a cantilever),

$A_{s.prov}$ is the area of tension reinforcement provided at mid-span (at support for a cantilever),

β_b is the ratio of the resistance moment provided at mid-span to the mid-span moment taken from the maximum moments diagram before redistribution.

If the percentage of redistribution is not known but the design ultimate moment at mid-span is obviously the same or greater than the elastic ultimate moment, the stress f_s in Table 10 may be taken as $0.58f_y$.

Compression reinforcement also influences deflection and the value of the span/effective depth ratio obtained from Table 8 or 9, modified by the factor obtained from Table 10 may be multiplied by a further factor obtained from Table 11.

Table 11. Modification factor for compression reinforcement

$\dfrac{100A'_s}{bd}$	Factor
0.25	1.07
0.50	1.14
0.75	1.20
1.0	1.25
1.5	1.33
2.0	1.40
$\geqslant 3.0$	1.50

Intermediate values may be interpolated.

The area of compression reinforcement A'_s used in Table 11 may include all bars in the compression zone even those not effectively tied with links.

Permissible span/effective depth ratios obtained from Tables 8 to 11 take account of normal creep and shrinkage deflection. If it is expected that creep or shrinkage of the concrete may be particularly high (e.g. if the free shrinkage strain is expected to be greater than 0.000 75 or the creep coefficient greater than 4) or if other abnormally adverse conditions are expected, the permissible span/effective depth ratio should be suitably reduced. A reduction of more than 15 % is unlikely to be required.

5.F. SLENDER BEAMS (cl.3.3.1.3(CP110))

Slender beams are beams in which the breadth of the compression face is small by comparison with the depth.   The compression side of a beam may be likened to a slender strut which fails by buckling.   In the case of a beam however the tension side is stable and the compression side cannot move in the plane of the beam (usually vertical) but can only move laterally (usually horizontally).   The tension side remains in sensibly the same place. Slender beams therefore have a tendency to fail by lateral deflection and by rotation.   To prevent this type of failure the clear distance between effective lateral restraints must be limited to

$$60b_c \quad \text{or} \quad \frac{250b_c^{\,2}}{d}$$

whichever is the lesser.

The limits for cantilevers are $25b_c$ and $\dfrac{100b_c^{\,2}}{d}$

This provides a first estimate of the width of a beam.

QUESTION 5.10

Do the following beams comply with the code requirements?

(a) the cross section shown in Fig. 5.7(a) is that of a beam which has a span of 10m and effective lateral restraint at both supports.

(b) the cross section shown in Fig. 5.7(b) is that of a cantilever which has a projection of 2.5m.   Lateral restraint is provided at the root of the cantilever only.

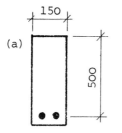

(a)

150

500

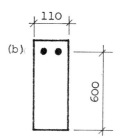

(b)

110

600

Fig. 5.7

(Answers: (a) no, (b) no.)

6 Singly Reinforced Concrete Beams

6.A. CONCRETE BEAMS

Beams may be made of any material providing it has strength to resist the
tensile, compressive and shear stresses induced in it by the loads on the
beam.   In most cases cost is important, and low material cost can help to
keep building costs down.   In this respect concrete is a good material in
that it can be cast in almost any shape desired for relatively low cost
with good durability.   It is reasonably strong in compression, its main
disadvantage being its low tensile strength which is about one tenth of the
compressive strength.   Plain concrete beams are therefore limited in
carrying capacity by the low tensile strength, and massive sections are
needed for relatively small loads.

Steel is much stronger than concrete both in tension and in compression but
is much more expensive and difficult to work.   The tensile weakness of
concrete can therefore be overcome by the provision of steel reinforcement
round which the concrete is cast to make a reinforced concrete beam.

6.B. REINFORCED CONCRETE BEAMS (cl.3.3.5.1(CP110))

In its simplest form the reinforced concrete beam consists of a concrete
beam which contains two or more reinforcing bars as shown in Fig. 6.1.

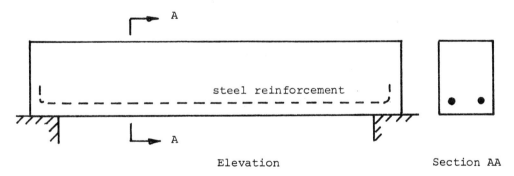

Elevation   Section AA

Fig. 6.1

The reinforcing bars are placed near the bottom of the beam where they are
most effective in resisting the tensile stresses due to bending.   The
reinforced concrete beam can therefore be considered as a composite beam

(a beam built up of two or more materials).   The elastic analysis of such beams is adequately dealt with in many text books on elementary stress analysis.   Reinforced concrete beams are not analysed using the usual elastic composite beam theory for two main reasons.   First, the concrete in tension usually cracks so that it is normal to assume that the tensile strength of the concrete is zero.   Second, although elastic theory has been used in the past for strength calculations for reinforced concrete, it is now considered more satisfactory to use ultimate strength theories.

CP110 therefore restricts the strength calculations for reinforced concrete to the ultimate limit state and the methods used enable the ultimate strength of sections to be determined.   The bending moments, shears etc. for which sections must be designed are calculated by the methods outlined in Chapters 1-4 inclusive.   In the design of a rectangular beam section the span and ultimate load for which it must be designed are already known. The section dimensions, namely breadth, depth and cross sectional area of steel reinforcement, have to be determined.   The usual process consists of making a trial analysis for sections in which the breadth and depth are fixed and the steel area is to be determined.   If the resulting section is not satisfactory a further trial must be made.   The rules given in Chapter 5 will help determine whether the section is satisfactory and will also help to determine the initial depth and breadth to be used in trial calculations.   For a given bending moment there is no unique section which will satisfy the requirements, there are many possible combinations of breadth, depth and steel area.   The overall dimensions will be influenced by many factors including the strength of the materials. The characteristic strengths of the materials used in reinforced concrete are usually:-
concrete   20, 25 and 30 N/mm^2.
steel   250, 410, 425 and 460 N/mm^2.

CP110 gives formulae and graphs which assist in the design of sections. The rest of this chapter explains the derivation of these and gives simple examples of their use.

6.C. DEPTH OF THE COMPRESSION ZONE

Consider a beam subjected to pure bending (i.e. no shear forces acting on it).   The applied bending moment at collapse is equal to the resisting moment on the section provided by the internal stresses.   This is called the ultimate moment of resistance M_u.   In order to derive formulae for the determination of M_u it is necessary to consider the distribution of normal stresses on the section at collapse.

As in the simple theory of bending, plane sections are assumed to remain plane.   A neutral axis therefore exists above which all the section is in compression and strain is proportional to distance from the neutral axis.

Below the neutral axis the concrete is assumed to be cracked and all the tensile stresses to be carried by the steel.   It is also assumed that the stresses in all the bars are equal. The resultant tensile force therefore acts at the centroid of the cross sectional area of the group of bars. The depth from the compression face to this resultant is called the effective d as shown in Fig. 6.2.

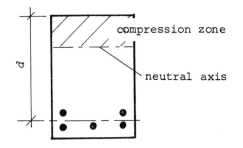

Fig. 6.2

Experiments show that, at failure, the stresses in a singly reinforced section (tensile steel only) are approximately as shown in the stress diagram of Fig. 6.3c.   Note that only two thirds of the design strength of the concrete is reached.   This is because the mechanism of failure of the concrete in a beam is not the same as that in a cube.   It is desirable that the steel yields before failure of the concrete in the compression zone so that brittle failure is avoided.   In this case the beam is said to be under-reinforced.   Two methods of analysis of sections are permitted by CP110.   The easiest of these uses a simplified form of stress diagram as shown in Fig. 6.3d.

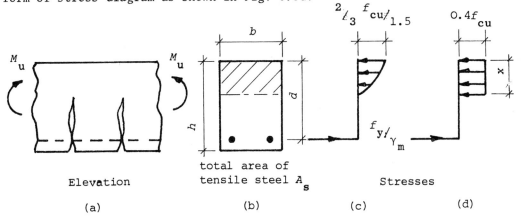

Elevation

(a)

total area of tensile steel A_s

(b)

Stresses

(c)

(d)

Fig. 6.3

The depth of the compression zone may be obtained by considering the equilibrium of the normal forces i.e. the sum of the longitudinal forces in the beam must be zero.   Thus, referring to the stress diagram of Fig. 6.3d which has a rectangular stress block,

resultant of compressive stresses = resultant of tensile stresses

$$0.4 \ f_{cu} \ b.x = \frac{f_y}{\gamma_m} \ A_s$$

$$x = \frac{(0.87 f_y) \ A_s}{0.4 \ f_{cu} \ b} \qquad \dots\dots\dots 6.1$$

QUESTION 6.1

Determine the value of the depth x of the compression zone for the section shown in Fig. 6.4 if f_{cu} = 30 N/mm^2 f_y = 250 N/mm^2 and the concrete cover is 50 mm.

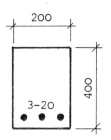

Fig. 6.4

(Answer: x = 85.5 mm)

6.D. THE LEVER ARM (cl.3.3.5.3(CP110))

From considerations of equilibrium of forces on a section of a beam the tensile and compressive forces are equal and opposite, but they are not concurrent.   They therefore form a couple.   The distance between these two forces is called the lever arm z.   The tensile force acts at the centroid of the steel and the compressive force acts at the centre of the concrete in compression.

$$\text{Lever arm} = z = d - \frac{x}{2} \qquad \text{(for rectangular stress block).}$$

Substituting for x from equation 6.1

$$z = d - \frac{(0.87\ f_y)A_s}{2(0.4\ f_{cu}\ b)}$$

$$\text{approximately} \quad z = \left[1 - \frac{1.1\ f_y\ A_s}{f_{cu}\ b\ d}\right] d \qquad \dots\dots\dots\ 6.2$$

Equation 6.2 corresponds to Equation 5(CP110).

QUESTION 6.2

Determine the lever arm for the beams shown in Fig. 6.5.

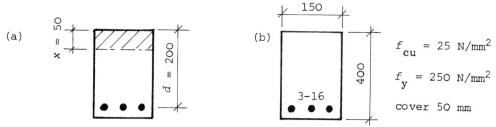

(a)

(b)

f_{cu} = 25 N/mm^2

f_y = 250 N/mm^2

cover 50 mm

Fig. 6.5

(Answers: (a) 175 mm;   (b) 298 mm)

6.E. THE MOMENT OF RESISTANCE AT THE ULTIMATE LIMIT STATE

The moment of resistance of the section at the ultimate limit state must be equal to or greater than the ultimate applied bending moment.

The ultimate moment of resistance M_u is equal to the couple formed by the tensile force and the compressive force

$$M_u = z \cdot \text{compressive force} = z \cdot \text{tensile force}$$

$$\text{Therefore } M_u = 0.4 \, f_{cu} bx \left(d - \frac{x}{2} \right) \qquad \ldots\ldots\ldots \text{ 6.3}$$

$$\text{and } M_u = (0.87 f_y) A_s \, z \qquad \ldots\ldots\ldots \text{ 6.4}$$

Equation 6.4 corresponds to Equation 1 (CP110).

Note: If Equation 6.4 is used for the design of reinforcement the value of z should not exceed 0.95d as stipulated in CP110.

QUESTION 6.3

Obtain M_u for the beam shown in Fig. 6.6 expressing your answer in kNm.

Obtain the answer by two methods using

(a) the strength of the concrete

(b) the   "   "   " steel

$f_{cu} = 25 \text{ N/mm}^2 \; f_y = 250 \text{ N/mm}^2$

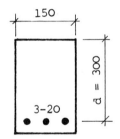

(Answer: (a) 47.5 kNm (b) 47.3 kNm
The two answers should be the same but the
factor 1.1 in Equation 6.2 is an approxi-
mation, hence the difference.)

Fig. 6.6

6.F. MAXIMUM DEPTH OF THE COMPRESSION ZONE (cl.3.3.5.1(CP110))

So that the tension steel will reach its yield stress before the concrete fails in compression and brittle failure avoided, some limitation must be placed on the percentage of tension steel in the beam.   As tension steel is added to a beam the ratio of x/d increases as shown in Fig. 6.7.   It has been found from experiment and it can be shown by a more complicated theoretical approach, based on strain compatibility, that the steel does not reach yield when x/d is greater than 0.5 (approx).

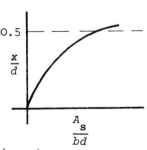

Fig. 6.7

QUESTION 6.4

If $\frac{x}{d} \leqslant 0.5$, calculate the maximum area of steel that may be used in the beam section shown in Fig. 6.8 if $f_{cu} = 25$ N/mm² and $f_y = 425$ N/mm². Give your answer in mm² and as a percentage ρ.

$$\rho = \frac{100 \ A_s}{bd}$$

(Hint: Equate compressive force to the tensile force)

(Answer: $A_s = 609$ mm², $\rho = 1.35\%$)

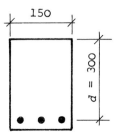

Fig. 6.8

6. G. MAXIMUM MOMENT OF RESISTANCE (cl. 3.3.5.3 (CP110))

If the steel is to yield before concrete failure, for any section, the maximum value of x is $\frac{d}{2}$. If this is substituted in

$$M_u = 0.4 \ f_{cu} \ bx \left(d - \frac{x}{2} \right) \qquad \cdots \cdots \cdots \cdots 6.3$$

this produces the maximum possible value

$$M_u = 0.4 \ f_{cu} \cdot \frac{bd}{2} \left(d - \frac{d}{4} \right) = 0.4 \ f_{cu} \cdot \frac{3}{8} \ bd^2$$

$$M_u = 0.15 \ f_{cu} \ bd^2 \qquad \cdots \cdots \cdots \cdots 6.5$$

Use of this formula which is Equation 2 (CP110) ensures that a singly reinforced beam will not fail by crushing of the concrete.   In order for the beam to resist a bending moment equal to M_u found above sufficient steel must be provided.

Substituting $\qquad\qquad x = \frac{d}{2}$ in Equation 6.4

$$M_u = A_s \ \frac{f_y}{1.15} \cdot \left(d - \frac{d}{4} \right)$$

$$M_u = (0.87 \ f_y) \ A_s \ \frac{3.d}{4} \qquad \cdots \cdots \cdots \cdots 6.6$$

which is a special case of Equation 6.4 with $z = \frac{3d}{4}$

This is the smallest allowable value for z.   If z is unknown this value may be conservatively assumed for design purposes.

QUESTION 6.5

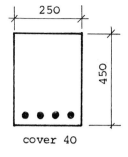

Determine:

(a) the maximum bending moment that can be carried by the singly reinforced beam cross section shown in Fig. 6.9,

(b) the number of 20 mm diameter bars required for the bending moment.

cover 40

Fig. 6.9

f_{cu} = 20 N/mm^2 and f_y = 425 N/mm^2

(Answers: (a) 120 kNm   (b) A_s = 1082 mm^2 4-20 = 1257 mm^2)

6.H. DESIGN GRAPHS (cl.3.3.5.2(CP110))

The simplified approach using a rectangular compression block for the concrete has been presented to give an idea of the principles involved and to derive the simple formulae given in CP110.   It is suggested in CP110 that rectangular singly reinforced beams be designed on the basis of the moment of resistance being given by the lesser of the two values of M_u obtained from equations 6.4 and 6.5.   Equation 6.5 gives no trouble but equation 6.4 involves the lever arm z, from equation 6.2.   The lever arm is dependent upon the area of steel A_s which is unknown.   It is possible to substitute equation 6.2 into equation 6.4 and obtain a quadratic equation for A_s.   Solution of this equation for each design would involve much unnecessary work and design graphs would be advantageous.

Once the decision to use graphs has been made many of the disadvantages of the assumptions made in deriving the simplified formulae can be removed. The need for the limitation of the depth of the compression zone is reduced (it is still maintained at 0.5 d for singly reinforced beams) because proper allowance can be made for the tension steel not reaching its yield stress in heavily reinforced sections.   Additionally the 10% restriction on redistribution can be removed.   If redistribution is considered, however, the depth of the compression zone must be restricted to provide the necessary rotational characteristics but such control can be built into the graphs.

The design graphs given in CP110 parts 2 and 3 are based on the following assumptions

(1) beam (or column) failure will not occur until the concrete strain reaches 0.0035.

(2) The strain in the steel and concrete is proportional to the distance from the neutral axis.

(3) The stress distribution in the concrete in compression is given by the curve of Fig. 1 (CP110) with γ_m = 1.5.

(4) The stress in the steel is determined from the trilinear stress-strain diagram of Fig. 2 (CP110) with γ_m = 1.15,

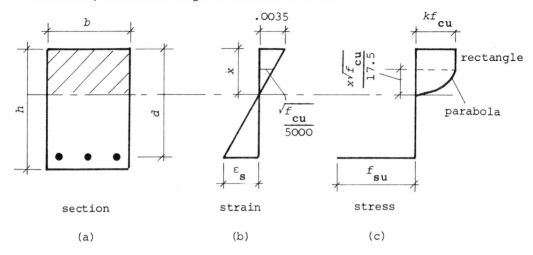

Fig. 6.10

Assumptions 1, 2 and 3 are illustrated in the strain and stress diagrams of Fig. 6.10 b and c.   In the stress diagram Fig. 6.10c the steel stress is given as f_{su}, the value of f_{su} is dependent on the depth of the compression zone x.   The maximum strain in the concrete, Fig. 6.10b, is always 0.0035 and if x/d is small the strain ε_s in the steel is large and reference to Fig. 2(CP110) will show that it corresponds to values of strain between points 2 and 3 of the curve.

Therefore $f_{su} = f_y/\gamma_m$

As the area of tension steel is increased, the value of x/d increases and strain ε_s in the steel is reduced (the maximum concrete strain is still 0.0035).   Eventually the value of ε_s will correspond to values between points 2 and 1 of the stress-strain curve and finally to points between 1 and 0.   For these values

$$f_{su} < f_y/\gamma_m$$

and loss of economy may result.

The above assumptions are used to derive expressions relating $\frac{M}{bd^2}$, $\frac{x}{d}$ and $\frac{100 A_s}{bd}$ which are then used to draw the design graphs given in Parts 2 and 3 of CP110.   The expressions are derived by the same methods used earlier in the chapter for the simple approximate formulae.   The algebra involved is, unfortunately, more complicated because of the parabolic stress-strain relationship for concrete and the trilinear stress-strain relationship for steel.

The design graph from CP110, for singly reinforced beams using steel for which $f_y = 425$ N/mm^2 is given on page 85.   It has four lines on it each one being for a different concrete strength.   It will be noticed that the line for $f_{cu} = 25$ N/mm^2 has a kink at about the value of

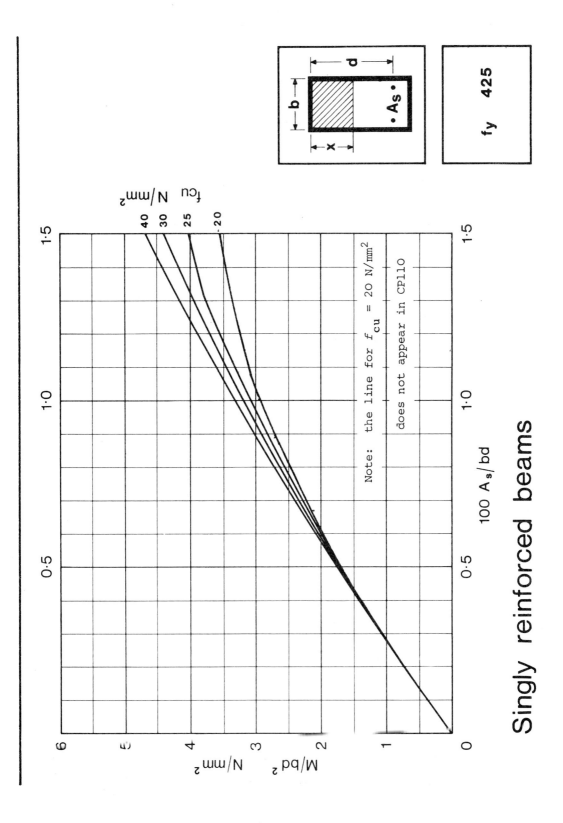

Note: the line for $f_{cu} = 20 \text{ N/mm}^2$

does not appear in CP110

f_y 425

f_{cu} N/mm²

40 30 25 20

M/bd^2 N/mm²

$100\ A_s/bd$

Singly reinforced beams

$\frac{M}{bd^2}$ = 3.8, for values of $\frac{M}{bd^2}$ < 3.8 the steel stress is equal to $\frac{f_y}{1.15}$ and for values of $\frac{M}{bd^2}$ > 3.8 the steel stress is less than $\frac{f_y}{1.15}$.

EXAMPLE 6.1

A beam of the cross section shown in Fig. 6.9 is to carry a bending moment of 80 kNm at the ultimate limit state.   Assuming that f_{cu} = 25 N/mm^2 and f_y = 425 N/mm^2 determine the area of reinforcement needed (a) using Equations 6.5 and 6.6 (b) using the design graph from CP110.

(a) Assuming bars of 20 mm dia.

$$d = 450 - 40 - 10 = 400 \text{ mm}$$

Using Equation 6.5

$$M_u = 0.15 \times 25 \times 250 \times 400^2 \times 10^{-6} \text{ kNm}$$

$$= 150 \text{ kNm}$$

Beam will not fail by crushing of concrete

Rearranging Equation 6.6

$$A_s = \frac{M_u}{(0.87 f_y)} \frac{4}{3d}$$

$$= \frac{80 \times 10^6 \times 4}{0.87 \times 425 \times 3 \times 400} = 721 \text{ mm}^2$$

$$3 - 20 \text{ mm dia} = 942 \text{ mm}^2$$
$$\text{or} \quad 4 - 16 \text{ mm dia} = 804 \text{ mm}^2$$

(b) $$\frac{M}{bd^2} = \frac{80 \times 10^6}{250 \times 400^2} = 2.0$$

From the design graph

$$\frac{100 A_s}{bd} = 0.61$$

Therefore $$A_s = \frac{0.61 \times 250 \times 400}{100}$$

$$= 610 \text{ mm}^2$$

$$2 - 20 \text{ mm dia} = 628 \text{ mm}^2$$

Note: the use of the design graph gives greater economy.

QUESTION 6.6

The bending moment to be applied to a rectangular cross section at the ultimate limit state is 300 kNm.   If b = 300 mm, h = 600 mm, cover = 40 mm f_{cu} = 25   and f_y = 425 N/mm^2, determine the number and size of reinforcing bars (a) using the approximate equations 6.5 and 6.6 (b) using the design graph.

(Answer: (a) A_s = 1976 mm^2, 5 bars 25 mm

(b) A_s = 1790 mm^2, 4 bars 25 mm dia)

7 Flanged Beams

7.A. INTRODUCTION

Most beams form part of a floor system and the reinforced concrete floor slab provides a flange for the rectangular section of the beams.   The flange or slab acts as a wide compression zone for the beam thus increasing the carrying capacity for a given rib width.

Internal beams become 'T' beams, and the beams round the outside of the building, and round staircases or lift shaft openings are 'L' beams.

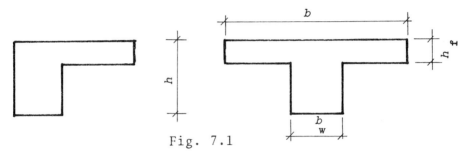

Fig. 7.1

'T' and 'L' beams are specified by the following dimensions as shown in Fig. 7.1

h =   overall depth

b_w =   breadth of rib (or web)

b =   effective width

h_f =   overall depth of slab (or flange)

This chapter shows how 'T' and 'L' beams may be designed by methods similar to those used for rectangular singly reinforced concrete beams.

7.B. EFFECTIVE WIDTH OF FLANGE (cl.3.3.1.2(CP110))

The self weight and imposed load for 'T' and 'L' beams are determined from the actual width of the flange which is usually taken as half the distance between adjacent beams on each side of the rib.

The effective width of the flange is used for strength calculations as given in cl.3.3.1.2(CP110).   This is to allow for the fact that the compressive stress in the flange is higher above the rib than at some distance from the rib.   The effective width concept allows the use of full concrete stresses over the full effective width as shown in Fig. 7.2.

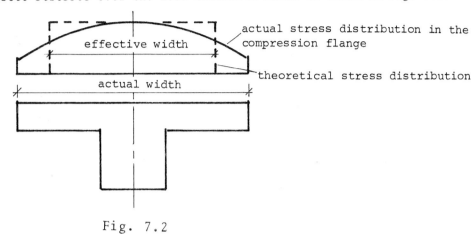

Fig. 7.2

3.3.1.2 Effective width of flanged beam. In the absence of any more accurate determination, the effective flange width for a T-beam should not exceed the lesser of:

the width of the web plus one-fifth of the distance between the points of zero moment, or the actual width of the flange

and for an L-beam, the effective flange should not exceed the lesser of:

the width of the web plus one-tenth of the distance between points of zero moment, or the actual width of the flange.

For a continuous beam the distance between the points of zero moment may be taken as 0.7 times the effective span.

QUESTION 7.1

Determine the effective width of the beams shown in Fig. 7.3.

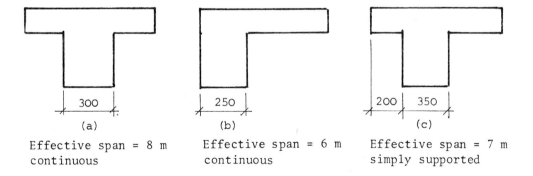

(a)   (b)   (c)

Effective span = 8 m   Effective span = 6 m   Effective span = 7 m
continuous   continuous   simply supported

Fig   7.3

(Answers: (a) 1420 mm (b) 670 mm (c) 1250 mm)

7.C. MOMENT OF RESISTANCE AT THE ULTIMATE LIMIT STATE

A 'T' or 'L' beam may be considered to have a rectangular cross section provided the depth of the compression zone x lies within the depth of the flange h_f, as shown in Fig. 7.4.   This is generally the case in practice.

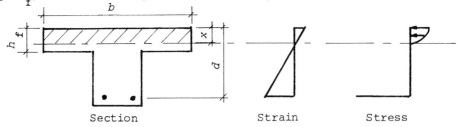

Section   Strain   Stress

Fig. 7.4

The advantage of the 'T' beam is that part of the concrete is omitted in the tension zone where it would be cracked anyway.   The self weight is therefore reduced.   The graphs for the design of a rectangular cross section may therefore be used by calculating $\dfrac{M}{bd^2}$ and determining $100\ A_s/bd$ from the graph.

QUESTION 7.2

Determine the area of tensile steel required for the beam shown in Fig. 7.5a. Use the design graph on page 85.

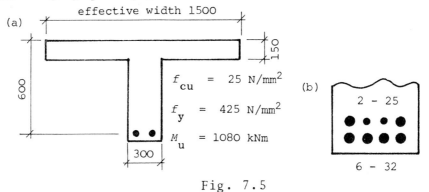

f_{cu} = 25 N/mm^2

f_y = 425 N/mm^2

M_u = 1080 kNm

Fig. 7.5

(Answers: A_s = 5490 mm^2, 6-32 mm and 2-25 mm arranged as shown in Fig.7.5b)

7.D. DEPTH OF THE COMPRESSION ZONE

If the design graphs are used the depth of the compression zone x must be less than the depth of the flange h_f.   The graphs for singly reinforced beams do not give values of x/d but reference to page 101 will show that the graphs for doubly reinforced beams have a line for zero compression steel and also have lines for approximate values of x/d.   These are very close together and are difficult to use.   A reasonable approximate value may be obtained by equating the compressive force to the tensile force.

$$0.4\ f_{cu} \cdot b\ x\ =\ A_s\ \frac{f_y}{1.15}$$

$$\text{hence} \qquad x\ =\ \frac{A_s\ (0.87\ f_y)}{b\ (0.4\ f_{cu})} \qquad \cdots\cdots\cdots\ 7.1$$

The graphs use parabolic stress distribution whereas the above assumes rectangular distribution in the compression zone.

QUESTION 7.3

Determine the depth of the compression zone for the beam of Question 7.2 based on the theoretical area of steel 5490 mm^2.

(Answer: $x = 135$ mm $< h_f$ therefore satisfactory)

7.E. MAXIMUM MOMENT OF RESISTANCE (cl.3.3.5.3(CP110))

The maximum moment of resistance of a 'T' or 'L' beam with thick flanges, so that $h_f > d/2$, occurs when $x = d/2$ and is calculated exactly as for a singly reinforced rectangular beam; this case is rare.   For flanged beams of more normal proportions the maximum moment of resistance is obtained when x equals $d/2$ and the neutral axis falls within the rib.   There is usually little error if it is assumed that the maximum moment of resistance occurs when $x = h$.   This assumption is conservative and reduces the calculations.

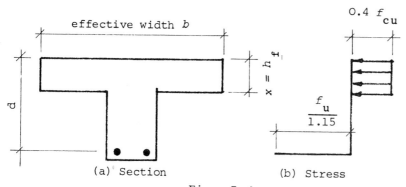

(a) Section   (b) Stress

Fig. 7.6

Taking moments of forces about the tensile steel for the simple rectangular stress block of Fig. 7.6(b).

$$M_u\ =\ 0.4\ f_{cu}\ b\ h_f\ (d -\ {}^{h_f}/2) \qquad \cdots\cdots\cdots\ 7.2$$

Equation 7.2 is the same as Equation 7 (CP110).

The area of tensile steel needed to resist M_u may be obtained by equating the compressive and tensile forces.

$$0.4 \, f_{cu} \, b \, h_f = \frac{A_s \, f_y}{1.15}$$

$$\text{Therefore } A_s = \frac{0.4 \, f_{cu} \, b \, h_f}{0.87 \, f_y} \qquad \dots\dots\dots \; 7.3$$

QUESTION 7.4

Determine the maximum moment of
resistance and the area of steel
required for the 'L' beam shown in
Fig. 7.7.

Take f_{cu} = 30 N/mm^2 and

f_y = 425 N/mm^2

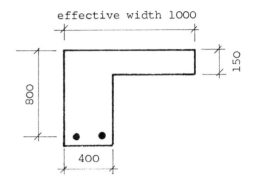

Fig. 7.7

(Answers: 1305 KNm; A_s = 4868 mm^2
*This is the area of steel required
for the maximum moment of
resistance of the section.)*

7.F. ALTERNATIVE SIMPLE METHOD OF DESIGN OF FLANGED BEAMS

Equation 7.2 derived in 7.E, is the same as Equation 7 (CP110).
Referring to Fig. 7.6 and taking moments about the centre of thickness of
the flange

$$M_u = \frac{f_y}{1.15} \cdot A_s \left(d - \frac{h_f}{2} \right) \qquad \dots\dots\dots \; 7.4$$

which is the same as equation 6 (CP110) and rewriting

$$A_s = \frac{M_u}{0.87 \, f_y \left(d - \frac{h_f}{2} \right)} \qquad \dots\dots\dots \; 7.5$$

The equations 7.2 and 7.5 can now be used for the design of "T" and "L"
beams.   Equation 7.2 is used to ensure that failure will not occur due to
crushing of the concrete and equation 7.5 can be used to determine the area
of tension steel.   The use of this method is simple but is less economical
than using graphs.

QUESTION 7.5

Using Equation 7.5 determine the area of tensile steel required for the
beam in Question 7.2.

(Answer: A_s = 5563 mm^2 *compared with 5490 mm^2 using graphs)*

7.G TRANSVERSE REINFORCEMENT IN FLANGES (cl.3.11.4.2(CP110))

Transverse reinforcement should be added to the flanges of 'T' or 'L' beams to resist the applied forces. For a single beam the flanges act as cantilevers as shown in Fig. 7.8(a), whereas multiple 'T' beam flanges may be considered to act as a continuous slab as shown in Fig. 7.8(b).

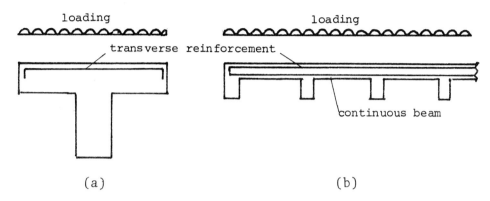

Fig. 7.8

The code requires that the amount of reinforcement on the top surface across the full effective width of the flange should be greater than 0.3% of the longitudinal cross sectional area of the flange. This is to resist the shear stresses produced by the variation in compressive stresses across the width of the flange as mentioned in 7.B.

7.H. DEFLECTION OF FLANGED BEAMS (cl.3.3.8.2(CP110))

A flanged beam is less stiff than a rectangular beam of the same overall dimensions. To ensure that the deflection remains within allowable limits the span/effective depth ratio is multiplied by a factor, obtained from Fig. 7.9, which depends on the ratio of web width to effective flange width.

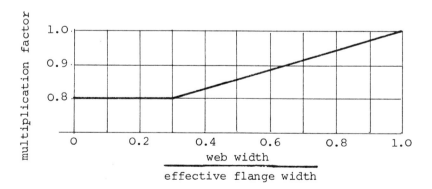

Fig. 7.9

8 Doubly Reinforced Beams

8.A. INTRODUCTION

A doubly reinforced concrete member is reinforced in both the compression
and tension zones of the concrete.   The section of the member is usually
rectangular but it may be a 'T' or 'L' section.

A doubly reinforced member is used :

(a) Where construction depth is restricted and a singly reinforced concrete
member would not provide the necessary moment of resistance.

(b) Where the bending moment reverses as at the supports of a continuous
'T' beam.

8.B. MAXIMUM MOMENT OF RESISTANCE OF A SINGLY REINFORCED SECTION

A singly reinforced concrete beam has a limited moment of resistance
depending on the depth of the compression zone.   The maximum depth of the
compression zone is $d/2$.

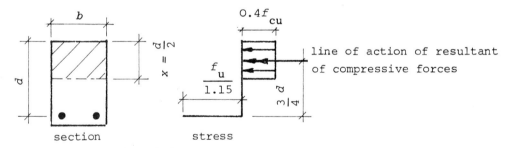

Fig. 8.1

Considering the singly reinforced rectangular section shown in Fig. 8.1
and taking moments about the tensile steel, the maximum moment of resistance
is

$$M_{us} = 0.4 f_{cu} b \frac{d}{2} \frac{3}{4} d = 0.15 f_{cu} bd^2 \quad \ldots \ldots \ 8.1(6.5)$$

For a 'T' or 'L' beam the ultimate concrete stress $0.4 f_{cu}$, acts on the
area of the slab and the maximum depth of the compression zone is h_f

$$M_{us} = 0.4 f_{cu} b.h_f \left(d - h_{f/2} \right) \quad \ldots \ldots \ 8.2(7.2)$$

QUESTION 8.1

Determine the maximum moment of resistance for the sections shown in Fig. 8.2 based on failure of the concrete in the compression zone.

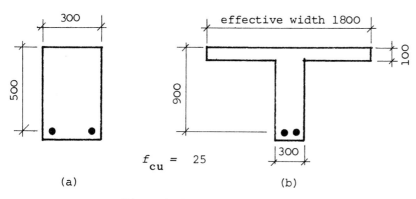

$f_{cu} = 25$

(a)

(b)

Fig. 8.2

(Answers: (a) 281 kNm (b) 1530 kNm)

8.C. MAXIMUM AREA OF STEEL FOR A SINGLY REINFORCED SECTION

In the following the simple method is used unless otherwise stated. When the compression zone depth is $d/2$ then the moment of resistance is at a maximum for a singly reinforced concrete beam. The required tensile steel to provide this moment of resistance may be obtained by taking moments about the line of action of the compression force as shown in Fig. 8.1.

$$M_{us} = A_{ss} \frac{f_y}{1.15} \left(d - \frac{d}{4} \right) \qquad \ldots \ldots 8.3(6.6)$$

Or by equating horizontal forces;

$$\text{compressive force} = \text{tensile force}$$

$$b \, \frac{d}{2} \, 0.4 \, f_{cu} = A_{ss} \frac{f_y}{1.15} \qquad \ldots \ldots 8.4$$

(for a 'T' or 'L' beam $\frac{d}{2}$ is replaced by h_f)

QUESTION 8.2

Determine the area of tensile steel required for the sections shown in Fig. 8.2, to develop the maximum moment of resistance as a singly reinforced section.

Assume $f_y = 410 \text{ N/mm}^2$.

(Answers: (a) 2104 (b) 5049 mm^2)

8.D. AREA OF COMPRESSION STEEL (cl.3.3.5(CP110))

If a section is required to carry a bending moment in excess of that which it can support as singly reinforced concrete beam then compression steel must be added.   Additional tension steel will also be needed.

The stress in the compression steel is calculated from the strain at the level of the compression steel, see Fig. 8.3c, and the stress-strain diagram of Fig. 2 (CP110).   Fig.2 (CP110) shows that the limiting stress in the compression steel is reached at a strain of 0.002 and that the stress is

$$f_{sl} = \frac{f_y}{\gamma_m + \frac{f_y}{2000}}$$

putting γ_m = 1.15

$$f_{sl} = \frac{2000\, f_y}{2300 + f_y}$$

for f_y = 250

$$f_{sl} = \frac{2000\, f_y}{2300 + 250} = 0.78\, f_y$$

and f_y = 425

$$f_{sl} = \frac{2000\, f_y}{2300 + 425} = 0.73\, f_y$$

For the simple formulae a value of 0.72 f_y has been adopted in CP110 which gives a safe result for most steels which are readily available.   This stress can only be used if the strain at the level of the compression steel is not less than 0.002 from Fig. 8.3c

$$\frac{x - d'}{x} = \frac{\varepsilon'_s}{0.0035}$$

Therefore $\frac{d - 2d'}{d} = \frac{0.002}{0.0035}$

Therefore $\frac{d'}{d} = \frac{3}{14} = 0.21$

Therefore only if d' is greater than $0.21d$ will the strain in the compression steel be less than 0.002.   Such a low strain will only occur in very shallow beams which should not be doubly reinforced anyway.   Low strains can occur in beams where redistribution has been used but more sophisticated methods discussed later should be used for those

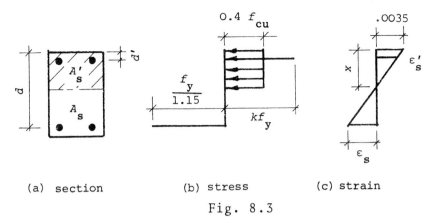

(a) section   (b) stress   (c) strain

Fig. 8.3

Considering the compression steel only and taking moments about the centroid of the tension steel, the moment of resistance due to the compression steel is

$$M_{ud} = k \, f_y \, A'_s \, (d - d')$$

$$M_{ud} = 0.72 \, f_y \, . \, A'_s \, (d - d') \qquad \ldots\ldots\ldots 8.5$$

The stress in the compression steel is restricted to a lower value than in the tensile steel because of the tendency for bars in compression to buckle. Nevertheless, the tendency of the compression bars to buckle must be reduced to a reasonable level by links enclosing them. The links should have a diameter not less than one quarter of the diameter of the largest compression bar and be spaced at a pitch not more than twelve times the size of the smallest compression bar (cl.3.11.4.3). The arrangement of such links is further discussed in Chapter 12 - Columns.

QUESTION 8.3

Determine the additional moment of resistance provided by the compression steel in the beams shown in Fig. 8.4.

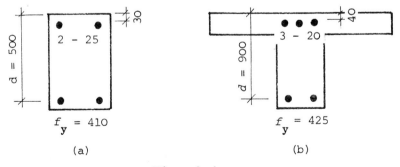

(a)   (b)

Fig. 8.4

(Answer: (a) 132.6 kNm   (b) 245 kNm.)

8.E. ADDITIONAL AREA OF TENSILE STEEL

If compression steel is added to a singly reinforced concrete beam then
additional tensile steel must be added to balance it.

$$M_{ud} = A_{sd} \cdot \frac{f_y}{1.15} \cdot (d - d') \qquad \cdots\cdots\cdots \text{ 8.6}$$

Alternatively from equating horizontal forces:

$$\text{additional compressive force} = \text{additional tensile force}$$

$$A'_s (0.72 f_y) = A_{sd} \frac{f_y}{1.15} \qquad \cdots\cdots\cdots \text{ 8.7}$$

QUESTION 8.4

Determine the theoretical extra area of tensile steel required for the
beams of Question 8.3.

(Answer: (a) 813   (b) 780 mm²)

8.F. MOMENT OF RESISTANCE OF DOUBLY REINFORCED BEAMS
    (cl.3.3.5.3(CP110))

Doubly reinforced beams as considered up to now are treated as two separate
beams each carrying their share of the total bending moment.   This is shown
diagrammatically in Fig. 8.5.   The singly reinforced cross section is shown

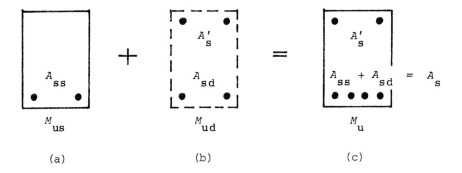

(a)   (b)   (c)

Fig. 8.5

in Fig. 8.5a with its steel area A_{ss} giving its moment of resistance M_{us}.
In Fig. 8.5b is shown the additional compression and tension reinforcements
with areas A'_s and A_{sd} giving a moment of resistance M_{ud}.   These two are
added together to give the final doubly reinforced section shown in Fig. 8.5c
with its steel areas A'_s and A_s giving a total moment of resistance M_u.
The two parts shown in Figs. 8.5a and b are not entirely independent since
the strains in both steel and concrete must comply with the linear strain
distribution diagram as shown in Fig. 8.3c.

Equations 8.1 and 8.5 can now be combined to give

$$M_u = 0.15 f_{cu} bd^2 + (0.72f_y) A'_s (d - d') \qquad \ldots\ldots\ldots 8.8$$

Similarly equations 8.3 and 8.6 combine to give

$$M_u = (0.87f_y) A_{ss} \frac{3}{4}\frac{d}{} + (0.72f_y)A'_s (d - d') \qquad \ldots\ldots\ldots 8.9$$

And combining equations 8.4 and 8.7 gives

$$A_{ss} \frac{f_y}{1.15} + A_{sd} \frac{f_y}{1.15} = 0.4 f_{cu} b \frac{d}{2} + (0.72f_y)A'_s$$

$$(0.87f_y)A_s = 0.4 f_{cu} b \frac{d}{2} + (0.72f_y)A'_s \qquad \ldots\ldots\ldots 8.10$$

Equations 8.8 and 8.10 correspond to equations 3 and 4 of CP110.

The above equations are developed for rectangular beams, where the maximum depth of the compression zone is $d/2$. For 'T' and 'L' beams the maximum depth of the compression zone is h_f and the corresponding equations are:

$$M_u = bh_f\, 0.4\, f_{cu} \left(d - \frac{h_f}{2}\right) + \left(0.72f_y\right) A'_s (d-d') \qquad \ldots\ldots 8.11$$

$$M_u = (0.87f_y) A_{ss} \left(d - \frac{h_f}{2}\right) + (0.87f_y) A_{sd} (d-d') \qquad \ldots\ldots 8.12$$

$$(0.87f_y)A_s = 0.4f_{cu} b h_f + (0.72f_y)A'_s \qquad \ldots\ldots 8.13$$

The simple method for the design of doubly reinforced beams can now be written as a series of steps:

(i) find the applied bending moment M.

(ii) for the section size (which should be already fixed) find the maximum moment M_{us} which it can carry as a singly reinforced beam and the area of tension steel A_{ss} needed for M_{us}.

(iii) calculate the areas A'_s and A_{sd} of compression and tension steel needed based on the moment $M_{ud} = M - M_{us}$.

(iv) find the actual bar sizes to be used for A'_s and $A_s = A_{ss} + A_{sd}$.

(v) obtain minimum links to prevent buckling of the compression steel.

QUESTION 8.5

For all problems f_y = 410

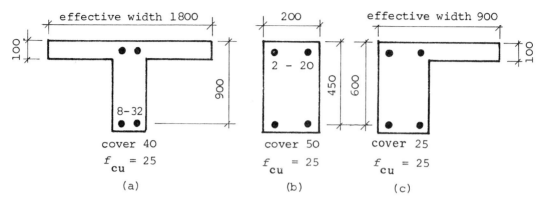

Fig. 8.6

(a) For the beam cross section shown in Fig. 8.6a determine the minimum area A'_s of compression steel needed to make the tension steel fully effective and determine the moment of resistance of the beam.

(b) For the beam cross section shown in Fig. 8.6b determine the area of tension steel needed to make the beam fully effective.   What then would be its moment of resistance.

(c) Determine the areas of compression and tension steel needed for the cross section shown in Fig. 8.6c if it is to carry a bending moment of 800 kNm.

(Answer: (a) A'_s = 1677 mm^2, d' = 50 mm, M_u = 1951 kNm

(b) A_s = 1781 mm^2, M_u = 224 kNm

(c) d' = 35 mm, A'_s = 1829 mm^2, A_s = 4037 mm^2)

8.G   DESIGN GRAPHS

The design graphs may also be used to determine the areas of tension and compression reinforcement.   The values obtained will be more accurate than from the simple method since the parabolic stress distribution in the concrete has been used, and the limiting stress in the compression reinforcement is

$$\frac{f_y}{1.15 + f_y/2000}.$$

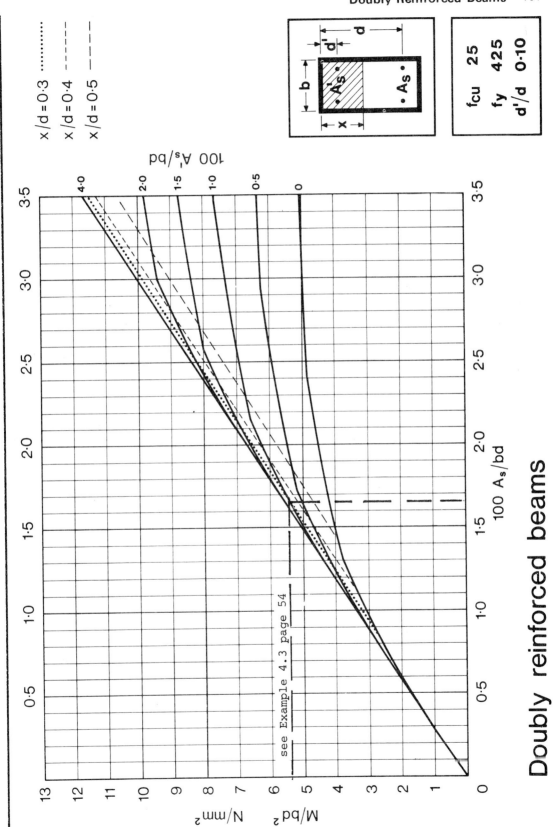

fcu 25
fy 425
d'/d 0·10

x/d = 0·3 ·········
x/d = 0·4 — — — —
x/d = 0·5 — — —

100 A'_s/bd

M/bd² N/mm²

100 A_s/bd

see Example 4.3 page 54

Doubly reinforced beams

To use the graphs it is necessary to:

(1) Estimate b and d to determine M/bd^2.

(2) Choose f_{cu}, f_y and d'/d and find the correct graphs from CP110 Part II.

(3) Read the total area of tension steel $100A_s/bd$ from the graph, which depends on choice of $100A'_s/bd$, several alternative sets of tension and compression steel are often possible.   Generally economy is the best guide but there may be other considerations.

(4) For a 'T' or 'L' beam check that $x \leqslant h_f$.

QUESTION 8.6

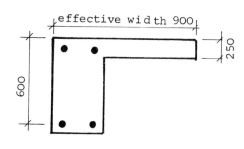

Fig. 8.7

Determine the area of steel required in tension and compression for the beam section shown in Fig. 8.7   Also check the depth of the compression zone.
M_u = 1500 kNm and it may be assumed that f_{cu} = 25 N/mm², f_y = 425 N/mm² and $\frac{d'}{d}$ = 0.1.
In using the design graph it may be assumed that $\dfrac{100A'_s}{bd}$ = 0.5.

(*Answer:* A_s = 8100, A'_s = 2700, x = 240 mm approx)

8.H   DEPTH OF THE COMPRESSION ZONE

The value of the depth of the compression zone (x) from the design graphs may not be of the required accuracy.   A better value may be obtained by equating the compressive force to the tensile force.

$$b.x \ \ 0.4 \ f_{cu} + A'_s \ (0.72) \ f_y = A_s \ \frac{f_y}{1.15}$$

This value is still approximate since it assumes a rectangular stress block in the compression zone.   Ideally the block should be parabolic.

QUESTION 8.7

Check the depth of the compression zone (x) for the beam of question 8.6.

(*Answer:*   241 mm)

9 Curtailment of Reinforcement

9.A. INTRODUCTION

A reinforcing bar is terminated for one or more of the following reasons:

(1) to fit the member,

(2) to economise on steel. It is normal for bending moments to vary along the length of the member. Bars are designed for the maximum bending moment but it is often possible to reduce the number of bars at a convenient section where the bending moment is less.

(3) to make construction easier,

(4) because bars are made in stock lengths e.g. approx 6 m for 8 mm diameter and 12 m for 32 mm diameter, it is sometimes found that the available length is too short and the bar must be extended. (Note it is possible to have extra length bars rolled but this is not economic unless a large quantity is needed).

A bar may be terminated as a straight, or 90° bend, or a 180° bend as shown in Fig. 9.1.

straight   'L' shaped 90° bend   hook 180° bend
                        (or bob)

Fig. 9.1

The greater the change in direction at the end of the bar the more effective the anchorage, but it also increases the cost for bending. The surface condition of the bar is also important. The rougher the surface the better the bond between the concrete and the steel. Bars which are rough due to rusting must be used with caution because (a) of the reduction in cross sectional area and (b) the surface rust may not be firmly attached.

9.B. ANCHORAGE OF A STRAIGHT BAR (cl.3.11.6.2(CP110)

The withdrawal of a bar from concrete at the ultimate limit state is prevented by shearing stresses (or bond stresses) between the surface of the steel and the adjacent concrete. The bond stresses indicated in Fig. 9.2 are assumed to be uniform along the anchorage length of the bar.

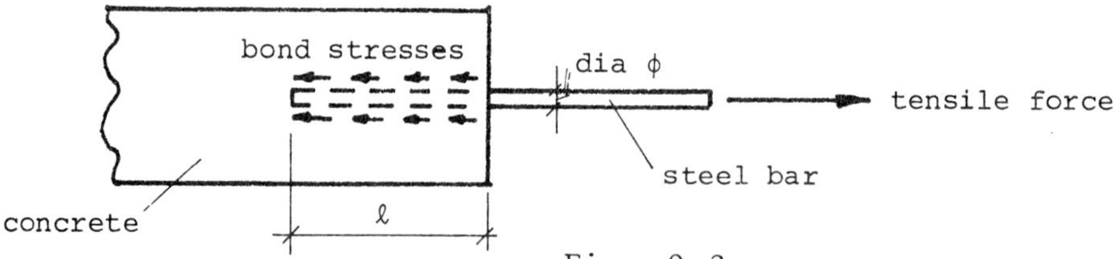

bond stresses

dia ϕ

tensile force

steel bar

concrete

ℓ

Fig. 9.2

From considering the equilibrium of forces at the ultimate limit state

$$\text{tensile force} = \text{bond force}$$

$$\frac{\pi(\phi)^2}{4} \cdot f_u = \pi \cdot \phi \cdot f_{bs} \cdot \ell \qquad \dots\dots\dots 9.1$$

where f_{bs} is the anchorage bond stress which varies with the surface condition of the bar, strength of the concrete, and whether the bar is in tension or compression.   Values of f_{bs} are given in Table 22 (CP110).   It is useful to obtain the anchorage bond length needed for a fully stressed bar by rearranging Equation 9.1 and putting

$$f_u = 0.87f_y$$

$$\ell = \frac{(0.87f_y)\phi}{4\ f_{bs}} \qquad \dots\dots\dots 9.2$$

Table 22. Ultimate anchorage bond stresses

Bar type	Concrete grade			
	20	25	30	40 or more
	N/mm^2	N/mm^2	N/mm^2	N/mm^2
Plain bar in tension	1.2	1.4	1.5	1.9
Plain bar in compression	1.5	1.7	1.9	2.3
Deformed bar in tension	1.7	1.9	2.2	2.6
Deformed bar in compression	2.1	2.4	2.7	3.2

When considering bond stresses there are three classifications of bars, plain, Type 1 deformed bar and Type 2 deformed bar.   The bond stresses for deformed bars given in Table 22 (CP110) apply to the Type 1 bar.   The stresses given for deformed bars may be increased by 30% if Type 2 deformed bars are used.   The commonest types of deformed bars in use are the square twisted bar and the ribbed bar shown in Figs 9.3a and b respectively.

It will be noted that the bond stresses given in Table 22 (CP110) are higher for bars in compression than for those in tension.   There are two main reasons for this.

(a) When a bar is in tension it tends to reduce in diameter hence there is a reduction in the frictional component of the bond stress.   Conversely, when a bar is compressed its diameter tends to increase with a consequent increase in the frictional component of the bond stresses.

Type 1

square twisted bar

(a)

Type 2

ribbed bar

(b)

Fig. 9.3

(b) Bars in compression are often arranged in such a way that the bearing provided by the end of the bar helps in transferring the load in the bar to the concrete.   This is particularly true in column splices.

The bar perimeter should always be taken as 3.14 times the bar size no matter whether the bar is round or square twisted.   Square twisted bars are manufactured in the same nominal sizes as round bars and their actual dimensions are adjusted so that the cross sectional area is the same as for round bars, size for size.

Table 9.1 gives full anchorage bond lengths for characteristic strengths of steel and concrete.   The bond length for a bar in tension is based on a stress of $0.87f_y$.   The bond length for a bar in compression is based on a stress of $(2000f_y)/(2300 + f_y)$.

Table 9.1 - Full Anchorage Bond Lengths in Bar Diameters

Bar type	f_y	concrete grade		
	N/mm^2	20	25	30
Plain bar in tension	250	45.3	38.8	36.2
" " " compression	250	32.7	28.8	25.8
Type 1 Deformed bar in tension	425	54.4	48.7	42.0
" " " " " compression	425	37.1	32.5	28.9
Type 2 Deformed bar in tension	425	41.8	37.4	32.3
" " " " " compression	425	28.6	25.0	22.2

QUESTION 9.1

Determine from Equation 9.2 the anchorage length required for a plain straight bar in tension at the ultimate limit state, if the diameter is 16 mm, f_y = 250 N/mm^2, f_{cu} = 20 N/mm^2.

(Answer: 725 mm)

9.C. BUNDLED BARS (cl.3.11.6.3(CP110))

It is permitted to use groups of bars in contact so as to reduce the space
needed in a section for the reinforcement.   The surface area in contact
with the concrete is obviously reduced with a consequent reduction in the
effectiveness of the bond.   Table 23 (CP110) gives reduction factors by
which the actual perimeter of a group of bars must be multiplied.

Table 23. Reduction factor for effective perimeter of a group of bars

No. of bars in a group	Reduction factor
2	0.8
3	0.6
4	0.4

9.D. JOINTS IN BARS (cl.3.11.6.5 and cl.3.11.6.6(CP110))

Where force is to be transferred from one bar to another in the same line of
action, as may happen when a stock length bar is to be extended, the force
may be transmitted by a lapped joint or a mechanical joint or a welded joint.
The connection should preferably occur away from points of high stress and
where several parallel bars are to be joined the joints should be staggered.

(a) Lapped joints - in a lapped joint the ends of the two bars are placed
    side by side as shown in Fig. 9.4(a).   The force in one bar is

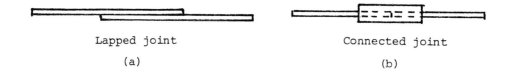

Lapped joint   Connected joint

(a)   (b)

Fig. 9.4

transferred by bond stresses to the surrounding concrete and hence by bond
to the other bar.   The lap length is the same as that given by Equation
9.2 except that for deformed bars in tension the length of the lap should
be 25% greater than that given by Equation 9.2.   In no case, however,
should the lap length be less than 25 times the bar size plus 150 mm for
tension reinforcement and for compression reinforcement it should be not
less than 20 times the bar size plus 150 mm.

(b) Mechanical joints - For bars in tension or compression the joint may be
    made with proprietary connectors where the force is transmitted through
    the connector.   For bars in compression a simple sleeve type locating
    device may be used provided the butting bars have the ends sawn
    square to ensure that a full contact surface is obtained.

(c) Welded joints - Welded joints are either butt welded with the bars in
line or else the bars are placed side by side and connected by fillet
welds as shown in Fig. 9.5.

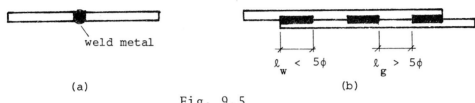

weld metal

$\ell_w < 5\phi$ $\ell_g > 5\phi$

(a)   (b)

Fig. 9.5

The strength of butt welded joints in compression may be taken as 100% of
the strength of the parent metal, but the strength of butt welds in tension
should be taken as 80% of the strength of the parent metal.   However, if
the welding is carried out under strict supervision and not more than 20%
of the bars at any cross section are welded then 100% strength may be
assumed.   In all cases the welds must have been demonstrated to have 100%
of the strength of the parent metal by means of tests.

Lap welds as shown in Fig. 9.5(b) are permitted but should be used with
care.   They are intended for use where prefabricated cages of reinforcement
or mesh are placed in the shutter and welded together in place.
Alternatively, they may be used for the connection of precast elements.
These are specialised applications and although some information is given
in CP110 it is insufficient for design and the specialist literature must
be consulted or tests made.

QUESTION 9.2

A 25mm deformed bar is to be lapped with a 16mm Type 1 deformed
bar.   The joint is to transmit tension at the ultimate limit state.
Determine the lap length required for steel of characteristic strength of
410 N/mm^2 and a characteristic concrete strength of 25 N/mm^2.

(Answer: 938 mm)

9.E. ANCHORAGE BY HOOKS AND BENDS (cl.3.11.6.7(CP110))

Where there is not sufficient length available to provide anchorage by
means of a single straight bar, anchorage may be provided by means of hooks
or in the case of high yield steel by the use of deformed bars.   High yield
steel is usually produced in the form of high yield steel bars therefore
despite the improvement in bond stress the anchorage lengths needed can
be longer than for mild steel round bars.   Deformed bars, therefore, may
also need hooks to give adequate anchorage.

The dimensions of hooks are controlled by the size of the member in which
they are to be placed and by the minimum radius permitted in bending the

bars.   Part of the steel specification includes a ductility test which is
performed by bending the bar round a former the size of which depends on
the type of steel.   The bar must not crack in the test.   The minimum
radius of bend to be used when making hooks should be not less than twice
the test bend radius guaranteed by the manufacturer of the reinforcement.
In general this leads to hooks of the minimum dimensions shown by solid
lines in Fig. 9.6(a) and (b) for mild steel and Fig. 9.6(c) and (d) for
high yield steel.

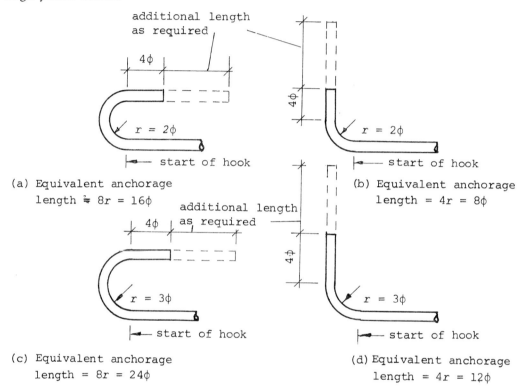

(a) Equivalent anchorage
    length $\doteqdot$ 8r = 16ϕ

(b) Equivalent anchorage
    length = 4r = 8ϕ

(c) Equivalent anchorage
    length = 8r = 24ϕ

(d) Equivalent anchorage
    length = 4r = 12ϕ

Fig. 9.6

For anchorage purposes a hook or bend may be treated as an equivalent
length of straight bar.   These equivalent lengths are given for the
standard bends in Fig. 9.6.   The use of greater bend radii than those
shown in Fig. 9.6 is permitted in which case the equivalent anchorage
lengths are still 8r and 4r with a maximum of 24ϕ.   The effective anchorage
length of the hook commences at the start of the bend.

Hooks will frequently not give sufficient anchorage and additional
anchorage length must be provided either before the start of the hook or
beyond the straight tail of the hook as shown by broken lines in Fig. 9.6.
The use of extensions beyond the straight tail of a hook must be carefully
considered.   Hooks fall in one of two ways

(a) by drawing the hook out through its hole in the concrete, the hook is therefore progressively bent and straightened.

(b) by splitting of the concrete due to the pressure on the inside face of the hook.   This form of failure is obviously more likely to occur when extended tails are used due to the higher tension in the bar at the commencement of the hook.

Hooks cannot be used to anchor compression bars.   Hooks must not be used to shorten the length of laps.

EXAMPLE 9.1

A 20 mm ribbed bar is to be anchored by means of a 90° bend of 60 mm radius and an extended tail in grade 25 concrete.   If the stress in the bar is 350 N/mm² at the commencement of the bend, determine the dimensions of the hook and show them on a sketch.

$$\text{Anchorage length needed} \quad = \quad \frac{f_u \phi}{4 f_{bs}}$$

$$= \quad \frac{350 \phi}{4 \times 1.9 \times 1.3} \quad = \quad 35.4 \phi$$

Note: the 1.3 is to give the 30% increase allowed above the stresses given in Table 22 for ribbed bars.

$$\text{Anchorage due to bend} \quad = \quad 4r \ = \quad 12\phi$$

$$\text{Therefore straight extension needed} = \quad (35.3 - 12)\phi$$

$$= \quad 24\phi \text{ approximately}$$

See Fig. 9.7 for sketch of hooked bar.

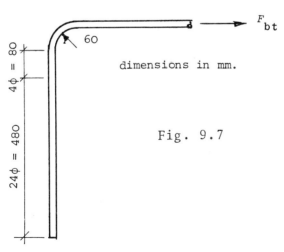

dimensions in mm.

Fig. 9.7

QUESTION 9.3

What is the maximum tensile stress which can be anchored by a 180° bend of radius 2ϕ in a mild steel plain bar?   The concrete strength is 20 N/mm².

(Answer: 76.8 N/mm²)

9.F. BEARING STRESSES INSIDE BENDS (cl.3.11.6.8(CP110))

A bar for which a hook or bend is used to provide additional anchorage is likely to produce high bearing stresses in the concrete on the inside of the bend.   The standard hooks and bends shown in Fig. 9.6 will not in general give cause for concern, but where the bar is extended more than 4ϕ beyond the end of the bend such extension being shown by broken lines in Fig. 9.6 or as shown in Fig. 9.7 the bearing stresses on the concrete may be excessive and should be checked using cl.3.11.6.8(CP110).

3.11.6.8 *Bearing stress inside bends.* The bearing stress inside a bend in a bar which does not extend or is not assumed to be stressed beyond a point four times the bar size past the end of the bend need not be checked. The bearing stress inside a bend in any other bar should be calculated from the equation:

$$\text{bearing stress} = \frac{F_{bt}}{r\phi}$$

where F_{bt} is the tensile force due to ultimate loads in a bar or group of bars,
  r is the internal radius of the bend,
  ϕ is the size of the bar or, in a bundle, the size of a bar of equivalent area.

This stress should not exceed $\dfrac{1.5f_{cu}}{1+2\phi/a_b}$, where a_b for a particular bar or group of bars in contact should be taken as the centre to centre distance between bars or groups of bars perpendicular to the plane of the bend; for a bar or group of bars adjacent to the face of the member, a_b should be taken as the cover plus ϕ as defined above.

The allowable stresses have been plotted and are given in Fig. 9.8.

QUESTION 9.4

(a) Determine the bearing stress for a 20 mm diameter bar stressed to 50 N/mm², bent 180° to a radius of 2 bar diameters.

(Answer: 19.6 N/mm²)

(b) Determine the allowable bearing stress if f_{cu} = 30 N/mm², and the centre to centre distance between bars is 40 mm. Assume 20 mm dia bar stressed to 50 N/mm²

(Answer: 22.5 N/mm²)

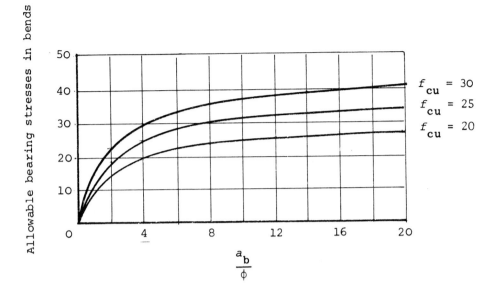

Fig. 9.8

9.G. ANCHORAGE AT ENDS OF MEMBERS (cl 3.11.7.1(CP110))

(a) Simply supported ends

At a simply supported end of a member each tension bar should be anchored by one of the following methods which are:-

(i) Related to the ₵ of the support as shown in Fig. 9.9.

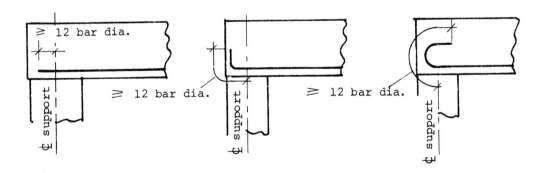

Fig. 9.9

(ii) Related to the face of the support as shown in Fig. 9.10.

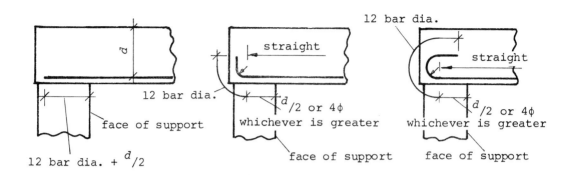

Fig. 9.10

QUESTION 9.5

Determine the minimum length from the face of the support to the end of the beam which contains 20 mm diameter tension bars and 40 mm cover to the steel. The ₵ of the support is 150 mm from the front face, and the effective depth of the beam is 350 mm.   Assume mild steel bars.

(Answer: 90° or 180° bend, radius 2 bar diameter, 250 mm)

(b) Ends continuous with a column

There is no specific guidance given in CP110 for the condition where a beam stops at a column and is rigidly jointed to it but the anchorage system described in 9.E and Example 9.1 may be used.   The anchorage should not commence before the centre line of the column.

9..H. THEORETICAL CUT OFF IN BENDING (cl.3.11.7(CP110))

Economy can be improved if reinforcement is cut off when it is no longer needed to resist tensile forces due to bending.   The theoretical curtailment point occurs where the moment of resistance of the CONTINUING bars equals the theoretically applied bending moment.   In Fig. 9.11 an example is shown where 4 bars are needed to resist the maximum bending moment in a beam, further along the beam the bending moment has reduced to half the maximum.   At this point two only of the bars are theoretically needed so that 2 can be cut off.

The procedure just described is rather facile because the reduction from four bars to two will also cause an increase in lever arm so that two bars in a section can resist slightly more than half the bending moment resisted by four bars.   Sometimes the smaller number of bars will also be more highly stressed than the greater number at the position of maximum bending moment   This is illustrated in Example 9.2.

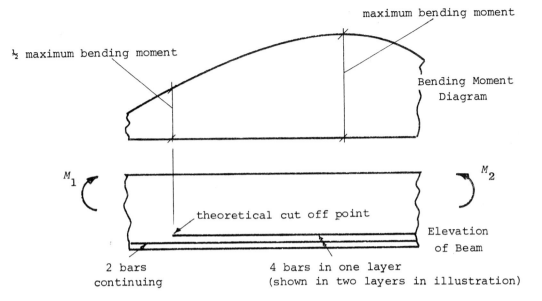

Fig. 9.11

EXAMPLE 9.2

A cantilever beam has a breadth of 300 mm and an effective depth of 700 mm, it projects 5 m from its support and carries a total uniformly distributed load of 28 kN/m.   The tension reinforcement in the top is 4 - 25 mm bars for which f_y = 425 N/mm^2 and the concrete strength is 25 N/mm^2.

Find the position for theoretical cut off for two of the bars.

The Bending Moment diagram is shown in Fig. 9.12.

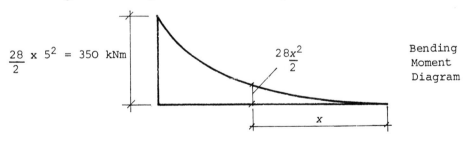

Fig. 9.12

At Cut Off there will be two 25 mm bars

$$\frac{100 \; A_s}{bd} = \frac{100 \times 982}{300 \times 700} = 0.47$$

Referring to the graph for singly reinforced beams (page 85) $f_y = 425$, $f_{cu} = 25$ find $\frac{100\ A_s}{bd} = 0.47$ on the horizontal axis, project up to the line for $f_{cu} = 25$ and then across to the vertical axis to get a value of

$$\frac{M}{bd^2} = 1.60$$

Therefore the moment of resistance of the section with two 25 mm bars is

$$1.60 \times 300 \times 700^2 \times 10^{-6} = 235.2 \text{ kNm}$$

If x is the distance from the free end of the cantilever at which this is equal to the applied bending moment

$$28\ \frac{x^2}{2} = 235.2$$

$$x = \sqrt{235.2 \times \frac{2}{28}} = 4.10 \text{ m}$$

Hence, theoretically, two bars only are needed for the end 4.10 m of the cantilever as shown in Fig. 9.13.   However, if bars are cut off at this point large cracks will occur see 9.I and 9.J.

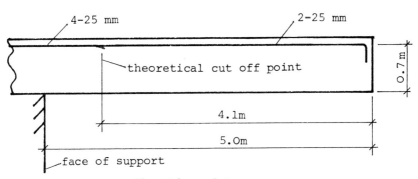

Fig.   9.13

QUESTION 9.6

A reinforced concrete beam is simply supported on a span of 6m.   It carries a central concentrated load of 54 kN.   The beam is 200 mm wide, the effective depth is 300 mm and it contains 4-20 mm bars.   If $f_y = 425$ N/mm^2 and $f_{cu} = 25$ N/mm^2 determine the theoretical position at which only two bars are needed and the moment of resistance of the section containing two bars.

(Answer: 2.1 m from the support, $M_u = 37.2$ kNm for two bars.)

9.I. EXTENSION BEYOND THEORETICAL CUT OFF (cl.3.11.7.1(CP110))

A bar must extend beyond the point at which it is theoretically no longer required for the following reasons

   (a) to allow for inaccuracies in loading and analysis.

   (b) to allow for inaccuracies in placing bars.

   (c) large cracks may appear at the curtailment section.   These reduce resistance to shear forces and introduce high peak stresses in the tension reinforcement.

The extension beyond the theoretical curtailment point should be not less than the effective depth of the beam d or twelve times the size of the bar, whichever is the greater as shown in Fig. 9.11.

If the bar stops in a tension zone further checks will be necessary.

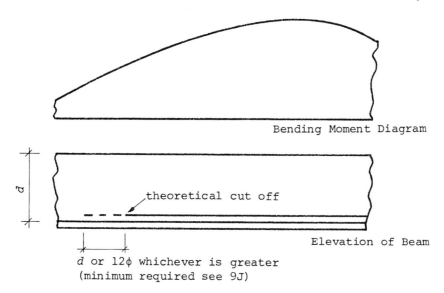

Bending Moment Diagram

theoretical cut off

Elevation of Beam

d or 12ϕ whichever is greater
(minimum required see 9J)

Fig. 9.14

QUESTION 9.7

Determine the minimum extension of a bar beyond the theoretical cut-off point, for 20 mm diameter bars in a beam of effective depth 300 mm.

(Answer: 300 mm)

.J. EXTENSION IN THE TENSION ZONE (cl.3.11.7.1(CP110))

ecause large cracks are more likely to develop in a tension zone leading to a eduction of shear and bending strength, reinforcement should not be stopped n a tension zone unless ONE of the conditions shown in Fig. 9.15 is satisfied. n no case must the extension beyond the theoretical curtailment point be less han d or 12ϕ as described in 9.1.

e application of these rules is best demonstrated by means of an example.

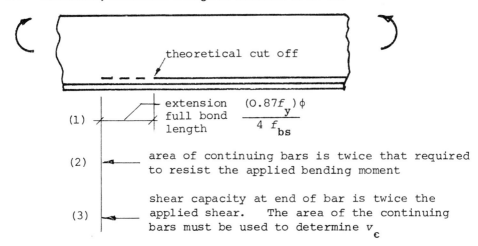

Fig. 9.15

EXAMPLE 9.3

The bars in Example 9.2 are Type 1 deformed bars.   Find the minimum extension required beyond the theoretical cut off point.   It may be assumed that nominal 8 mm diameter links at 280 mm pitch are included as shear reinforcement.

The minimum extension beyond the theoretical curtailment point is

$$12\phi = 12 \times 25 = 300 \text{ mm}$$
$$\text{or } d = 700 \text{ mm}$$

Therefore bars may be stopped at $4.10 - 0.7 = 3.40$ m from the end

These bars stop in a tension zone.   Therefore, they must be shown to satisfy one of the three conditions in Fig. 9.15.

(1) Extend by a full anchorage bond length

$$\frac{(0.87 \ f_y) \ \phi}{4 \ f_{bs}} = \frac{0.87 \times 425 \times 25}{4 \times 1.9} = 1216 \text{ mm}$$

Therefore the distance from the end of bar to the end of the cantilever using this rule is $4.10 - 1.22 = 2.88$ m

(2) The moment of resistance at the end of the bar is twice the applied moment

$$M_u = 235.2 \text{ kNm for 2 bars (already calculated in Example 9.}$$

Therefore if x is the distance from the end at which the bending moment is half the moment of resistance

$$\frac{28x^2}{2} = \frac{235.2}{2}$$

$$\text{Therefore} \quad x = \sqrt{\frac{235.2}{28}} = 2.90 \text{ m}$$

(3) The shear resistance at the end of the bar is twice the applied shear force (Note: it will be necessary to read Chapter 10 - Shear before the following calculation can be understood).

$$V_u = V_{concrete} + V_{links}$$

Concrete: $100 \dfrac{A_s}{bd} = 0.47$ (already calculated)

Therefore from Table 5 (CP110)

$$v_c = 0.48 \text{ N/mm}$$

$$V_c = 0.48 \times 300 \times 700 \times 10^{-3} = 100.8 \text{ kN}$$

Links:

$$V_{links} = \dfrac{d}{s_v} \dfrac{A_{sv}}{} \dfrac{f_{yv}}{1.15}$$

$$= \dfrac{700}{} \cdot \dfrac{101}{280} \cdot \dfrac{425}{1.15} \times 10^{-3}$$

$$= 93.3 \text{ kN}$$

Therefore $V_u = 100.8 + 93.3 = 194.1 \text{ kN}$

The shear force diagram is given in Fig. 9.16. Therefore if the applied shear force is half the shear resistance at distance x from the end of the cantilever

$$28x = 0.5 \times 194.1$$

$$x = 3.47 \text{ m}$$

From conditions 1, 2 and 3 the condition which gives the greatest economy is 3. Condition 3 is satisfied within the minimum extension length d beyond the theoretical curtailment point. Two bars may, therefore, be cut off at 3.40 m from the end of the cantilever. It should be noted that condition 1 is the easiest to apply and in this case leads to bars 0.5m longer. Use of this rule only saves time and leads to small loss of economy in most cases.

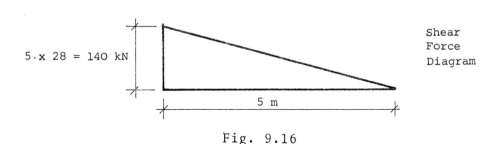

5.x 28 = 140 kN

Shear
Force
Diagram

5 m

Fig. 9.16

QUESTION 9.8

A simply supported'T'beam has a span of 8 m, a rib breadth of 300 mm an overall depth of 600 mm.   The total design ultimate load is 60 kN/m and it may be assumed that the effective breadth of the flange is 1900 mm and its thickness is 150 mm.   The main tension reinforcement is 4-32 mm Type 1 deformed bars and the shear reinforcement is 8 mm diameter stirrups at 160 mm pitch.   The strength of both reinforcements is f_y = 425 N/mm^2 and the strength of the concrete is 25 N/mm^2.   Determine the position at which two of the 32 mm diameter bars may be stopped for maximum economy.   The use of an effective depth of 544 mm gives a theoretical curtailment 1.50 m frc the support.

(Answer - for curtailment in a tension zone the three alternative conditions give the following results:

1. A full bond length extends the bars beyond the support by 60 mm.
2. The applied bending moment is half the moment of resistance at 0.67 m from the support.
3. The applied shear is half the shear resistance provided by two 32 mm bars plus links at 2.43 m from the support.

The result given by condition 3 indicates cut off at a point where the bending moment is higher than at the theoretical curtailment point.   It cannot, therefore, be used.   The curtailment position indicated by condition uses more steel than that indicated by condition 2, therefore, curtail 2 bars at 0.67 m from the support.)

9K - SIMPLIFIED RULES FOR CURTAILMENT (cl. 3.11.7.2 (CP110))

3.11.7.2 *Simplified rules for curtailment of bars in beams.* As an alternative to **3.11.7.1** for beams which support substantially uniformly distributed loads, the following simplified rules may be applied.

(1) *Simply supported beams.* At least 50 % of the tension reinforcement provided at mid-span should extend to the supports and have an effective anchorage of 12Φ past the centre of the support. The remaining 50 % should extend to within 0.08l of the support.

(2) *Cantilever beams.* At least 50 % of the tension reinforcement provided at the support should extend to the end of the cantilever. The remaining 50 % should extend a distance of $l/2$ or 45 times the bar size, whichever is the greater, from the support.

(3) *Continuous beams of equal span where the characteristic imposed load does not exceed the characteristic dead load, and which are designed in accordance with* **3.3.4.**

   a. At least 20 % of the reinforcement in tension over the supports should be made effectively continuous through the spans. Of the remainder, half should extend to a point not less than 0.25l from the support, and the other half to a point not less than 0.15l from the support, but no bar should stop at a point less than 45 times its own size from the support.

   b. At least 30 % of the reinforcement in tension at mid-span should extend to the supports. The remainder should extend to points not less than 0.15l from interior supports, and not less than 0.1l from exterior supports.

   c. At a simply supported end, the detailing should be as given in (1) above for a simply supported beam.

10 Shear in Reinforced Concrete

10.A. SHEAR FAILURE

The effects of shear forces at the ultimate limit state must be considered. Shear forces exist in beams where there is a change in bending moment along the length of the member. The shear force is equal to the rate of change of bending moment.

Shear failure is complex and may occur in several ways:-

(a) diagonal tension failure which occurs under the action of large shear forces where bending moments are low. The visual evidence is the appearance of a large diagonal crack as shown in Fig. 10.1(a).

(b) shear bending failure which occurs under a combination of bending moment and shear force. The curved crack shown in Fig. 10.1(b) starts as a vertical tension crack which becomes inclined as loading progresses. Final failure may be by extension of the crack through the compression zone as shown, or by crushing of the compression concrete.

(c) shear bond failure which occurs under a combination of bending moment and shear force. The cracks usually start near the mid height of the beam and develop in both directions. Splitting along the tension steel is common, see Fig. 10.1(c).

(d) diagonal compression failure which occurs under the action of large shear forces and is indicated by crushing of the concrete in the area shown in Fig. 10.1(d). This can only occur in beams which are

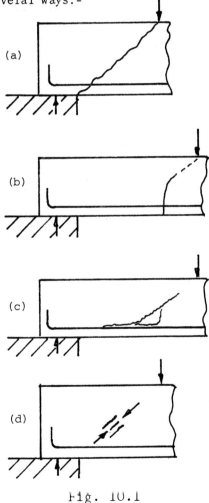

(a)

(b)

(c)

(d)

Fig. 10.1

heavily reinforced against shear.   The maximum values of shear stress given in Table 6 (CP110) are intended to guard against this type of failure.

Experimental evidence indicates that the shear force is resisted by the uncracked concrete in the compression zone, the shear force acting across the longitudinal steel (the dowel force) and the aggregate interlock as shown in Fig. 10.2.   If shear reinforcement is added then this also resists the shear force.

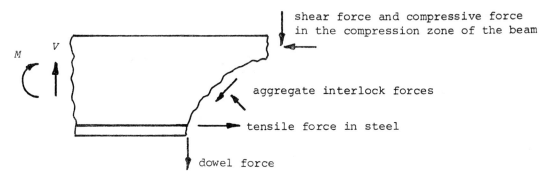

shear force and compressive force in the compression zone of the beam

aggregate interlock forces

tensile force in steel

dowel force

Forces Acting on a Beam
When Resisting Shear Forces

Fig. 10.2

10.B. SHEAR RESISTANCE OF A MEMBER WITH LONGITUDINAL STEEL ONLY (cl.3.3.6.1(CP110))

For members without shear reinforcement the resistance to shear (compression zone shear force + dowel force + aggregate interlock force) is expressed in CP110 as:-

$$V_c = \varepsilon_s v_c\, bd$$

the value of ε_s is 1.0 except where concentrated loads are applied near the supports of beams and in slabs.

The values of v_c which are related empirically to the strength of the concrete and the percentage of the longitudinal tension steel, are given in Table 5 (CP110).   It should be noted that the values of v_c not only increase for stronger concrete but also increase as the quantity of tension steel increases.
Increasing the quantity of tension reinforcement increases the available dowel force and the depth of the uncracked compression concrete, and hence the shear resistance of the concrete.

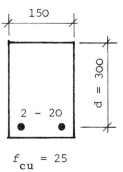

150

d = 300

2 - 20

$f_{cu} = 25$

Fig. 10.3

QUESTION 10.1

Determine the shear resistance V_c of the concrete beam reinforced with
longitudinal steel as shown in Fig. 10.3.

(Answer: 32.8 kN)

Note: The value $\dfrac{100\,A_s}{bd}$ must be calculated in order to obtain the value of
allowable shear stress v_c from Table 5 (CP110).   The rule defining the
value of A_s to be used follows Table 5 (CP110).

Table 5. Ultimate shear stress in beams

$\dfrac{100A_s}{bd}$	Concrete grade			
	20	25	30	40 or more
	N/mm²	N/mm²	N/mm²	N/mm²
0.25	0.35	0.35	0.35	0.35
0.50	0.45	0.50	0.55	0.55
1.00	0.60	0.65	0.70	0.75
2.00	0.80	0.85	0.90	0.95
3.00	0.85	0.90	0.95	1.00

The term A_s in Table 5 is that area of longitudinal tension reinforcement which continues at least an effective depth beyond the section being considered except at supports where the full area of tension reinforcement may be used in all cases provided the requirements of **3.11.7** are met.

This rule concerning the value of A_s to be used when determining v_c is of
particular importance where tension steel is curtailed (see Chapter 9).

10.C. SHEAR STRESS (cl.3.3.6.1(CP110))

When the shear stress, calculated using $v = \dfrac{V}{bd}$ exceeds the value of v_c
given in Table 5 (CP110), shear reinforcement must be added to resist the
difference $(v - v_c)$.

The value of v must not exceed the maximum values given in Table 6 (CP110)
otherwise a diagonal compression failure may occur.   If v is too high an
increase in the size of the section is required.

QUESTION 10.2

Determine the shear stress v for the sections shown in Fig. 10.4, compare
them with the values in Tables 5 and 6 (CP110), and state whether you would
add shear reinforcement or increase the size of the section or neither.

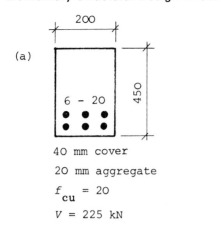

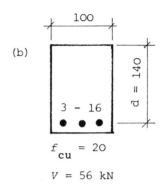

(a)

200

450

6 - 20

40 mm cover

20 mm aggregate

f_{cu} = 20

V = 225 kN

(b)

100

d = 140

3 - 16

f_{cu} = 20

V = 56 kN

Fig. 10.4

(Answers: (a) v = 2.94 N/mm^2 (Shear reinforcement required)

(b) v = 4 N/mm^2 > 3.35 (from Table 6) therefore use larger
section)

Table 6. Maximum value of shear stress in beams

Concrete grade			
20	25	30	40 or more
N/mm^2	N/mm^2	N/mm^2	N/mm^2
3.35	3.75	4.10	4.75

10.D. SHEAR REINFORCEMENT (cl.3.3.6.1(CP110))

(a) GENERAL

When shear reinforcement is necessary the shear strength of the beam is
calculated on the basis:

Total shear strength = shear resistance of beam without shear reinforcement + shear resistance of vertical shear reinforcement + shear resistance of inclined shear reinforcement

$$V = V_{concrete} + V_{links} + V_{inclined\ bars}$$

The shear resistance of the beam without shear reinforcement is calculated
in exactly the same way as in 10.B.   The shear resistance due to the shear
reinforcement can be calculated quite independently as follows in 10.Db for
vertical links and 10.Dc for inclined bars.   The theory for both types of
reinforcement is similar but they are dealt with separately for clarity.

(b) VERTICAL LINKS

Experimental evidence shows that shear cracking in the concrete is complicated. Often more than one crack appears and the angle of the cracks vary. If it is assumed that a diagonal crack is generated at an angle of 45° to the tension reinforcement for the full depth of the beam, then the theoretical shear resistance calculated using the method given below, compare reasonably well with experimental results.

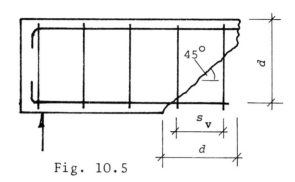

Fig. 10.5

The number of links crossing the crack, given by $\frac{d}{s_v}$, must provide the shear resistance due to vertical reinforcement.

Therefore resolving forces vertically the shear resistance provided by vertical links is:

$$\frac{d \, A_{sv}}{s_v} \frac{f_{yv}}{1.15}$$

Therefore for a beam containing tension reinforcement and vertical links:

the total shear resistance $V = V_{concrete} + V_{links}$

$$V = v_c . bd + \frac{d}{s_v} . A_{sv} . \frac{f_{yv}}{1.15}$$

rearranging

$$\frac{V}{bd} = v = v_c + \frac{A_{sv}}{s_v b} . 0.87 \, f_{yv}$$

$$\frac{A_{sv}}{s_v} = \frac{b(v - v_c)}{0.87 \, f_{yv}} \text{ which is Equation 9 (CP110)}$$

For practical use this is better rearranged thus:

$$s_v = \frac{A_{sv} . 0.87 \, f_{yv}}{b(v - v_c)}$$

EXAMPLE 10.1

A reinforced concrete beam has an effective depth
of 550 mm and a breadth of 350 mm.   It contains
4 - 32 mm bars as shown in Fig. 10.6

f_{cu} = 25 N/mm², f_{yv} = 425 N/mm²

Calculate the shear reinforcement needed for a
shear force of 400 kN.

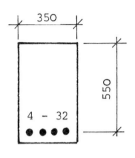

Fig. 10.6

$$100 \frac{A_s}{bd} = 100 \times \frac{3217}{350 \times 550} = 1.67$$

Therefore from Table 5(CP110) v_c = 0.78 N/mm²

From Table 6(CP110) v_{max} = 3.75 N/mm²

$$v = \frac{400 \times 10^3}{350 \times 550} = 2.08 \text{ N/mm}^2$$

0.78 < 2.08 < 3.75

Therefore provide shear reinforcement.

Assuming 10 mm links, A_{sv} = 157 mm for 2 legs and applying

$$s_v = \frac{A_{sv} \, 0.87 \, f_{yv}}{b(v - v_c)}$$

$$s_v = \frac{157 \times 0.87 \times 425}{350 \; (2.08-0.78)} = 128 \text{ mm}$$

Use 10 mm links at 120 mm pitch.

In order to anchor the links it will be necessary to provide bars in the
top of the beam which will be enclosed by the link.   They should be at
least equal in diameter to the link
but will not usually be less than
12 mm although some designers prefer
to use even larger anchor bars.   If
compression steel is provided it will
act as anchorage for the links.   The
links themselves must always enclose
all the tension reinforcement ;
they may be fully closed as in
Fig. 10.7a or open topped as in
Fig. 10.7b and 10.7c may be used.
The following quotation from CP110
is fully explanatory.

12 mm dia bars for anchorage

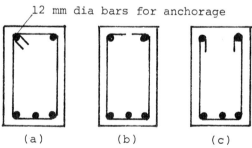

(a)   (b)   (c)

Fig. 10.7

3.11.6.4 *Anchorage of links.* A link may be considered to be fully anchored if it passes round another bar of at least its own size through an angle of 90° and continues beyond for a minimum length of eight times its own size or, through 180° and continues for a minimum length of four times its own size. In no case should the radius of any bend in the link be less than twice the radius of a test bend guaranteed by the manufacturer of the bar.

Pitch and size of links

In the above example the spacing obtained from the calculation is 128 mm but 120 mm is used.   This figure may need to be modified for one of two reasons:

(1) In deriving the theory it was assumed that the number of links crossing a crack was given by $\dfrac{d}{s_v}$, the answer to this is rarely a whole number

but this is not significant unless $\dfrac{d}{s_v}$ is less than 1.0.   In that case

it becomes possible for a shear crack to develop between adjacent links and the links are inoperative.   So that such a failure cannot occur, the maximum link spacing is restricted to 0.75 d both in the direction of the span and at right angles to it.   It is also good practice to ensure that the spacing of the legs of links does not exceed 300 mm.

(2) Links are frequently used to prevent compression reinforcement from buckling, in which case the pitch must not exceed twelve times the size of the smallest compression bar and the size must not be less than one quarter of the size of the largest compression bar (cl.3.11.4.3(CP110)).   In most building works the largest size of bar used for links will be 10 mm but for very large beams in buildings and bridges larger sizes may be used.   One restriction on the size of bar is the radius to which it can be bent.   Large bars need large radii which causes the main steel to be displaced leading to either congested reinforcement in a narrow beam or a reduction in effective depth.   The effect is shown in Fig. 10.8.

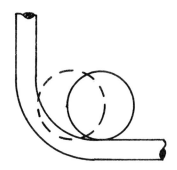

Fig. 10.8

Multiple Links

For most beams single links, for which A_{sv} equals the cross sectional area of two legs, will be sufficient.   Where compression bars are numerous and need to be tied in position, or where shear forces are large, double links

$(A_{sv}$ based on 4 legs) or triple links $(A_{sv}$ based on 6 legs) are used.

Stresses in Links

For the design of links f_{yv} is usually taken as the characteristic strength
of the steel, but if the characteristic strength exceeds 425 N/mm^2
f_{yv} = 425 N/mm^2

QUESTION 10.3

Determine the spacing of 10 mm single
links for the section shown in Fig. 10.9.
Assume f_{cu} = 20, f_{yv} = 425 N/mm^2 and
V = 225 kN.

(Answer: 137 mm say 130 mm)

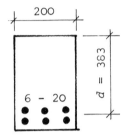

Fig. 10.9

(c) BENT UP (INCLINED) BARS

Where all the longitudinal tension reinforcement is not required to resist
bending, some may be bent up to resist the shear forces as shown in
Fig. 10.10. The bars are shown at different levels in Fig. 10.10 for ease

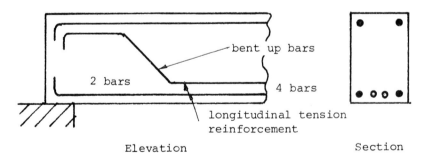

Fig. 10.10

in identification, the bars forming the upper layer would normally occupy
the position shown by the open circles in the cross section.

In practice bent up bars will only be used where it is difficult or
impossible to provide adequate shear resistance using vertical links alone.

They are difficult to use because there are usually an insufficient number
of bars available to provide a reasonable length of shear resistance.   Bent
up bars are always used in conjunction with vertical links in such a way
that the shear resistance of the links is at least equal to half the shear
force to be carried by shear reinforcement.   When bars are bent up to form

shear reinforcement they can no longer be included when ^{A}s/bd is calculated.
The shear resistance of the singly reinforced concrete section is therefore
reduced.

The shear resistance is calculated by first assuming a hypothetical pin
jointed truss in which the diagonal tension members are the inclined bars
and the compression members are formed in the concrete.   In the same way as
for stirrups the cracks are assumed to occur at 45° to the tension steel and
therefore the compression members must be parallel to the cracks.   The
arrangement is shown in Fig. 10.11 in which the solid lines represent the
tension members and the broken lines represent the compression members.

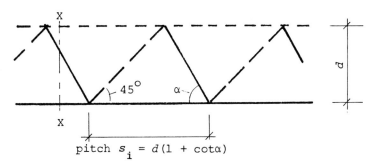

pitch $s_i = d(1 + \cot\alpha)$

Fig. 10.11

Resolving vertically on section XX

shear resistance due to inclined bars

$$V_i = A_i f_{yi} \frac{\sin \alpha}{1.15}$$

If the pitch s_i of the inclined bars is less than $d(1 + \cot \alpha)$ then it is
assumed that the strength is increased in inverse proportion to the pitch

$$\text{Therefore } V_i = A_i f_{yi} \frac{\sin \alpha}{1.15} \frac{d(1 + \cot \alpha)}{s_i}$$

which can be reduced to

$$v_i = \frac{V_i}{bd} = \frac{A_i f_{yi}}{bs_i} \frac{(\sin \alpha + \cos \alpha)}{1.15}$$

if $\alpha = 45^o$ which is a common choice

$$v_1 = \frac{V_i}{bd} = 1.41 \frac{A_i f_{yi}}{bs_i 1.15}$$

if α = 60

$$v_i = \frac{V_i}{bd} = 1.37 \frac{A_i}{bs_i} \frac{f_{yi}}{1.15}$$

When bent up bars are used they must be bent up in such a way that they and the remaining flexural reinforcing bars are symmetrically disposed in the beam cross section.   If bars can be bent up at one place only the maximum length over which they are effective is $d(1 + \cot \alpha)$.   The value of α should never be less than 45°.

EXAMPLE 10.2

For the beam of Example 10.1 two
of the main tension bars are to be
bent up at 45° near the end of the
span.   The shear force diagram is
shown in Fig. 10.12

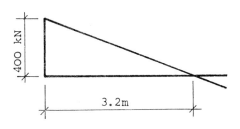

Calculate the shear resistance of
the bent up bars and the additional
links needed to provide the
required shear strength.

f_{yi} = 425 N/mm^2

Fig. 10.12

$$v = \frac{V}{bd} = \frac{400 \times 10^3}{350 \times 550} = 2.08 \text{ N/mm}^2$$

for two continuing 32 mm bars

$$\frac{100 A_s}{bd} = 0.83$$

therefore from Table 5 (CP110)

$$v_c = 0.60 \text{ N/mm}^2$$

therefore shear resistance to be provided by shear reinforcement

$$= 2.08 - 0.60 = 1.48 \text{ N/mm}^2$$

two 32 mm bars are bent up at one place only, the pitch

$$s_i = d(1 + \cot \alpha) = 550 \times (1+1) = 1100 \text{ mm}$$

therefore shear resistance of inclined bars

$$v_i = \frac{1.41 \times 1608}{350 \times 1100} \cdot \frac{425}{1.15} = 2.18$$

Theoretically the inclined bars can carry all the shear but at least half the shear force carried by steel must be carried by links.

Therefore shear force on links $= 0.5 \times 1.48\,bd = 0.74\,bd$

Assuming 8 mm links

$$s_v = \frac{101 \times 0.87 \times 425}{350 \times 0.74} = 144$$

Use pitch of 140 mm. (less than 0.75d)

Since only two bars can be bent up and these must be bent up at the same place all the shear reinforcement beyond the bent up bars must be in the form of links. Additionally the bent up bars must be arranged so that the hypothetical compression member is supported as shown in Fig. 10.11.

Shear force at 1000 mm from the face of the support is $\frac{2.2}{3.2} \times 400 = 275$ kN (see Fig. 10.12)

$$v = \frac{275 \times 10^3}{350 \times 550} = 1.43 \text{ N/mm}^2$$

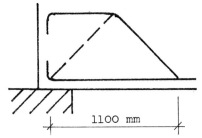

1100 mm

Fig. 10.13

Therefore provide shear reinforcement for

$$v = 1.43 - 0.78 = 0.65 \text{ N/mm}^2$$

Assuming 8 mm links

$$s_v = \frac{101 \times 0.87 \times 425}{350 \times 0.65} = 164 \text{ mm}$$

Note: the inclined bars must be properly anchored as shown in Fig. 10.13

QUESTION 10.4

For the cross section shown in Fig. 10.14 the upper four of the eight tension reinforcement bars are to be bent up in pairs at 45° to resist the shear force, such that $s_i = 250$ mm.

Determine the spacing of double vertical 8 mm dia. links to resist the remaining shear force.

Assume 8 - 12 mm dia bars, $f_{cu} = 30 \text{ N/mm}^2$,

$$f_{yv} = f_{yi} = 410 \text{ N/mm}^2, \quad V = 346.75 \text{ kN}$$

(Answer: 189 mm say 180 mm)

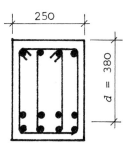

250

$d = 380$

Fig. 10.14

10.E. MINIMUM SHEAR REINFORCEMENT (cl.3.11.4.3(CP110))

Even though calculations show that a beam has adequate shear strength
without shear reinforcement, it is good practice to provide a small
quantity.   The reason for the nominal reinforcement is that tensile forces
may be introduced into a member through shrinkage or restraint, which
reduces the shear resistance of the concrete in the compression zone.   The
following rules are given in CP110.

No links need be provided in members of minor structural importance
(e.g. lintels) or where $v < 0.5\ v_c$.

In all other members nominal links should be provided such that

$$\frac{A_{sv}}{s_v} = 0.0012\ b_t \quad \text{for high yield links.}$$

$$\frac{A_{sv}}{s_v} = 0.002\ b_t \quad \text{for mild steel links.}$$

b_t is the breadth of the beam at the level of the reinforcement. s_v is the
spacing of the links which should not be greater than $0.75d$.

QUESTION 10.5

Using the rules of CP110 for the section shown in
Fig. 10.15

(a) Determine the magnitude of the shear force
    where no links are required i.e. where
    $v = \frac{1}{2}\ v_c$.

    (Answer: 16.3 kN)

(b) The size and spacing of nominal vertical
    links.

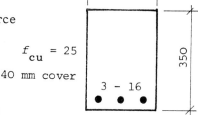

$f_{cu} = 25$

40 mm cover

3 - 16

Fig. 10.15

(Answer: high yield 6mm single at 220 mm pitch based on $s_v < 0.75d$
         mild steel 6 mm single at 190 mm pitch.)

10.F. SHEAR RESISTANCE OF FLANGED AND DOUBLY REINFORCED BEAMS

(a) FLANGED ('T' or 'L') BEAMS (cl.3.3.6.1(CP110))

Shear reinforcement is generally required in T beams and should be designed as shown in 10.D. When considering the shear resistance of flanged beams only the rib area $b_w d$ is assumed to be effective.

EXAMPLE 10.3

The beams shown in Fig. 10.16 are subjected to a shear force of 180 kN. Determine the shear stress and compare with the allowable value as given in Table 5 (CP110) if $f_{cu} = 25$ N/mm^2

(i) the shear stress $\qquad v = \dfrac{180 \times 10^3}{450 \times 300} = 1.33$ N/mm^2

$\dfrac{100\ A_s}{bd} = \dfrac{100 \times 1964}{450 \times 300} = 1.45$; $v_c = 0.74$ N/mm^2 which is less than 1.33, therefore shear reinforcement is required.

(ii) the shear stress $\qquad v = \dfrac{180 \times 10^3}{360 \times 200} = 2.50$ N/mm^2

$\dfrac{100\ A_s}{bd} = \dfrac{100 \times 1473}{360 \times 200} = 2.05$; $v_c = 0.85$ N/mm^2 which is less than 2.50, therefore shear reinforcement is required.

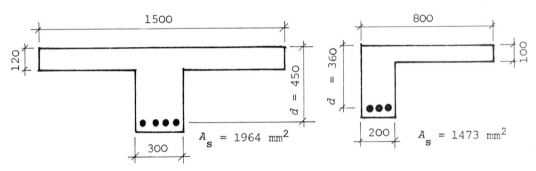

$A_s = 1964$ mm^2 $\qquad$ $A_s = 1473$ mm^2

Fig. 10.16

(b) DOUBLY REINFORCED BEAMS

When considering doubly reinforced beams, only the tension steel should be considered when calculating $\dfrac{100\ A_s}{bd}$. It may be suggested that the compression reinforcement should be included in A_s because it will provide a dowel force in addition to the dowel force due to the tension steel. Whilst it is true that there will be a dowel force it must be remembered that one of the effects of introducing compression steel is to reduce the depth of the concrete in compression, the dowel force on the compression steel may therefore be considered to replace the resistance due to compression concrete had the compression steel not been there. Therefore NO specific consideration of compression reinforcement need be made.

10.G. SHEAR RESISTANCE FOR CONCENTRATED LOADS NEAR SUPPORTS (cl.3.3.6.2(CP110))

Where the ratio of shear span to effective depth $\left(a_v/d\right)$ is less than 2, the shear capacity (dowel force + compression zone + aggregate interlock) is greatly increased because diagonal cracks are unlikely to develop above the line AA in Fig. 10.17 The value v_c obtained from Table 5 is therefore replaced by $v_c \left(\dfrac{2d}{a_v}\right)$, provided this does not exceed the maximum value allowed in Table 6 (CP110). Shear reinforcement is provided as previously, but for cantilever beam and corbels when $a_v/d < 0.6$, horizontal links should be provided. Special attention should also be given to anchorage of the main reinforcement. An anchorage equivalent to at least 20 times the bar size is recommended. A typical detail is shown in Fig. 10.18.

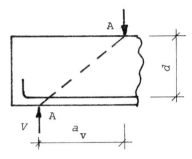

Fig. 10.17

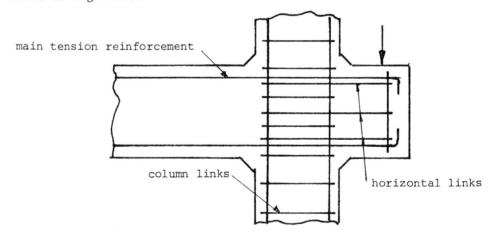

main tension reinforcement

column links

horizontal links

Fig. 10.18

QUESTION 10.6

Fig. 10.19 shows a portion of a member of short shear span.   If the shear force is 300 kN determine the size and spacing of 10 mm diameter single links.

$f_{cu} = 30 \qquad f_y = 425 \ \text{N/mm}^2$

(Answer: 105 mm say 100 mm)

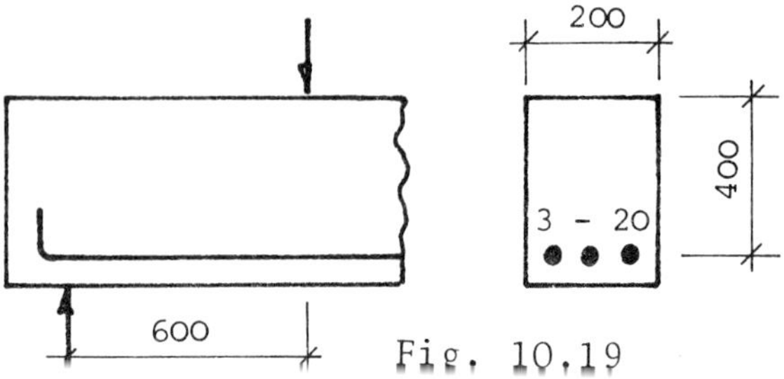

Fig. 10.19

10.H. LOCAL BOND STRESSES PRODUCED BY SHEAR FORCES
(cl.3.11.6.1(CP110))

Bond stresses are the shear stresses at the bar surface which prevent
longitudinal movement of the bar in the concrete.

Local bond failure is produced by large changes in tensile forces over
short lengths of reinforcement.   The change in tensile force is produced
by a change in bending moment.   The rate of change of bending moment is
the shear force.   The theory for the simple case of bars parallel to the
compression force is developed by considering an elemental length of beam
δx at the ultimate limit state.

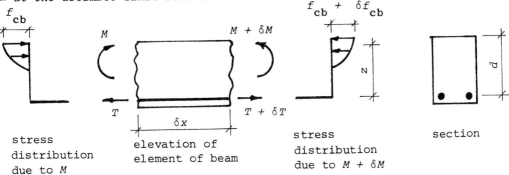

stress   elevation of   stress   section
distribution   element of beam   distribution
due to M due to $M + \delta M$

Fig. 10.20

The change in bending moment from M to $M + \delta M$ produces a change of tensile
force δT in the bars, see Fig. 10.20   This change is balanced by the bond
stresses on the surface of the bar.

$$\delta T = f_{bs} \cdot \sum u_s \cdot \delta x$$

where $\sum u_s$ is the sum of the perimeters of the bars in the tensile
reinforcement.

rearranging

$$\frac{\delta T}{\delta x} = f_{bs} \cdot \sum u_s$$

and since
$\frac{\delta T}{\delta x}$ (horizontal shear per unit length) $= \frac{V}{z}$ (vertical shear per unit depth)

$$\frac{V}{z} = f_{bs} \cdot \sum u_s$$

For simplicity the lever arm (z) has been replaced in CP110 by the
effective depth (d) and the values of f_{bs} adjusted accordingly hence

$$f_{bs} = \frac{V}{d \sum u_s}$$

The values of f_{bs} for types of bar and grades of concrete are given in Table 21 (CP110). The effective perimeter of the bars will be modified if they are used in bundles, the reduction factors are given in Table 23 (CP110), also see Chapter 9.

Local bond is most likely to need checking at the supports for simply supported beams, at points of contraflexure for continuous beams, and at positions where longitudinal reinforcement is stopped (curtailed).

Table 21. Ultimate local bond stresses

Bar type	Concrete grade			
	20	25	30	40 or more
	N/mm²	N/mm²	N/mm²	N/mm²
Plain bars	1.7	2.0	2.2	2.7
Deformed bars*	2.1	2.5	2.8	3.4

Where there would be an advantage, and the deformed reinforcement to be used is Type 2, as defined in **E.1** of Appendix E, the values of bond stress for deformed bars may be increased by 20 %.

Appendix E

Classification of reinforcement as deformed bars suitable for use with normal or enhanced bond stresses

E.1 Geometrical classification of deformed bars

For the purposes of this Code there are two types of deformed bar, namely:

Type 1: a plain square twisted bar or a plain chamfered square twisted bar, each with a pitch of twist not greater than 18 times the nominal size of the bar.

Type 2: a bar with transverse ribs with a substantially uniform spacing not greater than 0.8Φ (and continuous helical ribs where present), having a mean area of ribs (per unit length) above the core of the bar projected on a plane normal to the axis of the bar not less than 0.15Φ mm² per mm, where Φ is the nominal bar size.

QUESTION 10.7

(a) Determine the local bond stress for the section shown in Fig. 10.21

(b) If this value is not acceptable (see Table 21, CP110) how would you modify the design,

(Answers: (a) 2.98 > 2.52 N/mm² not satisfactory

(b) change to 3-10, f_{bs} = 2.39, or increase strength of concrete to f_{cu} = 40)

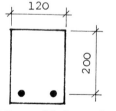

120

200

2-12 mm (deformed type 2)

f_{cu} = 20

V = 45 kN

Fig. 10.21

11 Torsion in Reinforced Concrete

11.A. INTRODUCTION

Modern methods of design and construction of monolithic reinforced concrete structures tend to introduce torsional moments into members which cannot be ignored in design.   It is not however a problem that is likely to be common and should only be taken into account when it is also included in the analysis of the structure which means that the analysis of the whole or part of the structure must be in three dimensions.

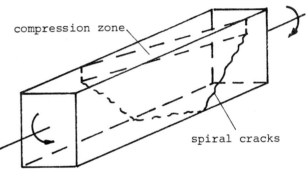

compression zone

spiral cracks

Fig. 11.1

Visual evidence of torsional failure is spiral cracking commencing on one face and extending to form a compression zone on the opposite face.   The angle of the cracks varies depending on the relative values of the bending, shear and torsion forces.

Many theories have been presented which show interaction between these forces but full understanding has not yet been achieved.   A simple method similar to that for shear is given in CP110.   The essence of the method is to determine a torsional shear stress, if this exceeds a given value then additional links and longitudinal reinforcement are added to take all the torsion.   Torsion like shear may therefore be considered separately from bending.

11.B. STIFFNESS OF A MEMBER IN TORSION (cl.3.3.7(CP110))

The analysis of a structure to determine the forces in a member is carried out assuming the structure behaves in a linear elastic manner.   This involves the stiffness of a member in bending EI/L and where torsion forces need to be considered the torsional stiffness $\dfrac{GC}{L}$

where G = elastic shear modulus in torsion and is equal to $0.4E$ according to CP110.

L = length of member between joint centres.

C = torsional constant equal to half the St. Venant value calculated for plain concrete.

The value of C for a rectangular cross section may be expressed as $\frac{1}{2} Khb^3$

The values of K related to $\frac{h}{b}$ are given in Table 11.1.

Table 11.1 Value of K in $C = \frac{1}{2}Khb^3$

$\frac{h}{b}$	1.0	1.5	2.0	3.0	4.0
K	0.14	0.20	0.23	0.26	0.28

QUESTION 11.1

Determine the ratio of bending stiffness $\left(\frac{EI}{L}\right)$ to the torsional stiffness $\left(\frac{GC}{L}\right)$ for a rectangular concrete section of breadth equal to half the depth.

(*Answer:* *7.25:1*)

11.C. TORSIONAL SHEAR STRESS   (cl.3.3.7(CP110))

The torsional resistance of a member with longitudinal steel is limited by its resistance to torsional cracking, measured by the torsional shear stress v_t.

The torsional shear stress v_t at any section should be calculated assuming a plastic stress distribution

$$v_t = \frac{2 T}{h_{min}^2 \left(h_{max} - \frac{h_{min}}{3}\right)} \qquad \text{(Equation 10(CP110))}$$

The application of this formula to rectangular sections is straightforward, but it may also be applied to 'T', 'L', 'I' and box sections by dividing the section shape into a number of rectangles as shown in Example 11.1.

EXAMPLE 11.1

Determine the maximum torsional shear stress v_t for the 'L' section shown in Fig. 11.2(a). The section is subject to a torsional moment of 100 kNm.

The area is subdivided into rectangles so as to maximise the function $\Sigma (h_{min}^3 h_{max})$. This is generally achieved by making the widest rectangle as long as possible, e.g. area A in Fig. 11.2(b).

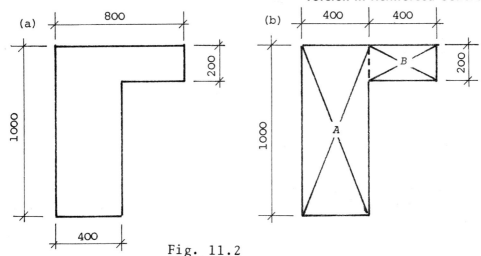

Fig. 11.2

The proportion of the torsional moment (T = 100 kNm) resisted by area A is

$$T_A = \frac{T\ (h_{min}^{\ 3}\ h_{max})}{\Sigma(h_{min}^{\ 3}\ h_{max})} = 100\ \frac{(400^3\ \text{x}\ 1000)}{(400^3\ \text{x}\ 1000 + 200^3\ \text{x}\ 400)} = 95.24\ \text{kNm}$$

The maximum torsional shear stress in rectangle A is

$$v_{tA} = \frac{2\ T_A}{h_{min}^{\ 2}\ (h_{max} - h_{min}/3)} = \frac{2\ \text{x}\ 95.24\ \text{x}\ 10^6}{400^2\ (1000 - 400/3)} = 1.37\ \text{N/mm}^2$$

QUESTION 11.2

Determine the maximum shear stress in rectangle B for the 'L' section shown in Example 11.1.

(Answer: $v_{tB} = 0.71\ N/mm^2$)

11.D. TORSIONAL RESISTANCE   (cl.3.3.7(CP110))

Where the torsion shear stress v_t exceeds the value of v_{tmin} given in Table 7 (CP110) reinforcement should be provided to take all of the torsion. This is in contrast to shear reinforcement where the (concrete + dowel force + aggregate interlock) takes part of the shear force.

To ensure that the concrete is not over-stressed in torsion and shear the sum of the shear stresses due to shear and torsion ($v+v_t$) should not exceed the value of v_{tu} as given in Table 7 (CP110).   If it does exceed the value a larger section is required.

Table 7. Ultimate torsion shear stress

	Concrete grade			
	20	25	30	40 or more
	N/mm²	N/mm²	N/mm²	N/mm²
v_{tmin}	0.30	0.33	0.37	0.42
v_{tu}	3.35	3.75	4.10	4.75

Because of anchorage problems for torsion reinforcement there is also a
limitation for small sections where the larger stirrup dimension y_1 is less
than 550 mm.   In this case v_t must not exceed $v_{tu} y_1/550$

QUESTION 11.3

Determine the torsional shear stress
for the section shown in Fig. 11.3,
and state whether torsional reinforcement
is required.

Assume f_{cu} = 25 N/mm² and T = 100 kNm.

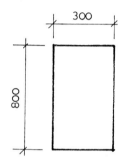

(*Answer: 3.17 N/mm², v_{tmin} = 0.33 N/mm²*

v_{tu} = 3.75 N/mm² therefore torsion
reinforcement required.)

Fig. 11.3

11.E. TORSION REINFORCEMENT (cl.3.3.7(CP110))

A complete understanding of the failure mechanism for a member subject to
bending, torsion, and shear is yet to be achieved.   The failure surface
according to many investigators has the appearance shown in Fig. 11.4.
Failure is by rotation about a skew axis in the compression zone.   The
compression zone is shown at the top but it may be at the side or at the
bottom of the beam.

For simplicity the torsional resistance may be determined by taking moments
of forces about a longitudinal axis of the member.   The stirrups intercept
the crack angle α which is assumed to be the same for each face.   The
expression is then of the form $T \simeq \dfrac{A_{sv}}{s_v} f_{yv} x_1 y_1 \tan \alpha$ where A_{sv} is the cross
sectional area of two legs of the stirrup.   In experiments the angle α
varies with bending, shear and torsional forces and the stirrups are not
always at yield.   The expression adopted in CP110 is

$$T = 0.8 \frac{A_{sv}}{s_v} \frac{f_{yv}}{1.15} x_1 y_1 \qquad \text{(Equation 11(CP110))}$$

for rectangular closed single links. These links are additional to any requirements for shear. There is some experimental evidence that part of the torsion is taken by the concrete, which is comparable with shear resistance, but this is ignored in CP110.

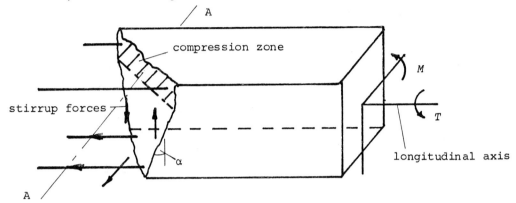

Fig. 11.4

To control cracking and to ensure that the closed vertical links intercept the cracks the spacing should not exceed the least of x_1, $y_1/2$, or 200 mm. CP110 does not clearly define the distances x_1 and y_1, but it is assumed that they are the minimum and maximum distances between the centre lines of the legs of the stirrups.

QUESTION 11.4

For the section and forces of question 11.2 determine the spacing of 10 mm dia. links. Assume f_y = 425 N/mm², and cover to the steel of 30 mm.

(Answer: s_v = 78 say 70 mm)

11.F. EXTRA LONGITUDINAL STEEL (cl.3.3.7(CP110))

The forces in the vertical links, added to resist torsion, need to be balanced for equilibrium by longitudinal forces in EXTRA longitudinal steel. This can be seen by taking moments of forces in the longitudinal steel and the stirrups about an axis AA, shown in Fig. 11.4. This axis is perpendicular to the longitudinal axis and passes through the compression zone so that the compressive forces have no moment.

$$M + \frac{A_{sl}}{2} \frac{f_{yl}}{1.15} y_1 \simeq A_s \frac{f_{yl}}{1.15} z + \frac{A_{sv}}{s_v} \frac{f_{yv}}{1.15} \frac{\tan^2\alpha}{2} (x_1 + y_1) y_1$$

where A_{sl} is the total extra area of longitudinal steel placed as four bars one at each corner.

CP110 gives a value to $\tan^2\alpha$ of 1.0 and states that

$$A_{sl} \geq \frac{A_{sv}}{s_v} \frac{f_{yv}}{f_{yl}} (x_1 + y_1)$$

(Equation 12 CP110)

It should be appreciated that the existing longitudinal steel A_s resists the applied bending moment, and that A_{sl} is extra. A_{sl} may be added as bars or by increasing the longitudinal steel supplied to resist the bending moment.   The extra longitudinal steel should be distributed evenly round the inside perimeter of the links.   The minimum requirement is a bar at each corner of a rectangular stirrup, but the clear distance between the bars should not exceed 300 mm.   It may therefore be necessary to use six or eight bars.

Because torsion cracks spiral for considerable lengths along a member torsion reinforcement should extend a distance at least equal to the largest dimension of the section beyond where it theoretically ceases to be required.   This also avoids abrupt changes of reinforcement at critical points and allows for redistribution of forces between elastic and plastic stages of behaviour.

QUESTION 11.5

Determine the extra area of longitudinal steel required for the beam of Question 11.4

Assume f_{yl} = 425 N/mm^2.

(Answer: A_{sl} = 2153   12-16 mm evenly distributed inside the stirrup)

12 Reinforced Concrete Columns

12.A. STRENGTH OF COLUMNS

The strength of all columns is dependent on the strength and elasticity of
the materials, the shape and size of the cross section, the length of the
column and the degree of positional and directional restraint of the ends
of the column.   If a compression member is very short it will fail by
compression failure of the materials which in concrete takes the form of
longitudinal splitting and spalling of the concrete.   If a compression
member is very long relative to its cross sectional dimensions the failure
will be by buckling at a load much lower than is indicated by the strength
of the material.   Most practical compression members fall somewhere
between these two extremes and failure is likely to be by a combination of
crushing of the materials and buckling.

For the purposes of design to CP110 columns are classified as *short* or
slender.   A *short* column has a slenderness ratio of not more than 12 and
its design is based on the strength of the materials and the actual applied
forces.   A *slender* column has a slenderness ratio greater than 12 and is
designed to resist the applied forces plus additional bending moments
induced because of the tendency to buckle.   The more slender the column the
greater will be the additional moments, but for slenderness ratios of twelve
or less the effect of lateral displacements due to buckling is negligible.

12.B. SLENDERNESS RATIO

Columns are classified on the basis of slenderness ratio and in the case of
slender columns the additional moments depend on the slenderness ratio.

The classic Euler* formula gives the failure load of a very slender pin
ended strut as

$$F = \frac{\pi^2 EI}{l^2}$$

which can be rearranged to give

$$F = \frac{\pi^2 EA}{\left(\frac{l}{i}\right)^2}$$

where $I = Ai^2$

* *Readers are referred to standard texts on stress analysis for the
derivation of the Euler formula.*

i being the radius of gyration of the cross section and $\frac{l}{i}$ being the slenderness ratio.   For the purpose of design of rectangular reinforced concrete columns i is roughly proportional to the breadth of the cross section and because of the variation of end fixing conditions the term *effective height* is used.   The slenderness ratio is therefore defined as the effective height divided by the breadth.

It should be noted that in laboratory testing the effective height will usually be connected with the least radius of gyration but in practical conditions the effective height relating to all possible values of slenderness ratio must be considered.   There will usually only be two values of slenderness ratio to consider which will be those corresponding to the principal axes of the cross section i.e. $l_{ex}/_h$ and $l_{ey}/_b$

12.C. EFFECTIVE HEIGHT (cl.3.5.1.4(CP110))

The effective height of a column may be defined as that height which corresponds to the height of a pin ended column which can carry the same axial load or alternatively the effective height may be considered as the height between the points of contraflexure of the buckled column.

For very slender columns to which the Euler formula may be applied the buckled shapes shown in Fig. 12.1 may be expected.   All the columns have

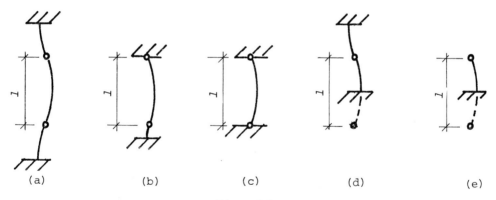

| (a) | (b) | (c) | (d) | (e) |

Fig. 12.1

the same effective height.   Fig. 12.1(c) shows the conventional pin ended strut for which the ends are held against lateral movement,i.e. a braced column but not restrained in direction at either end, in this case the effective height is equal to the actual height.   Fig. 12.1(a) shows a braced column in which the ends are rigidly restrained directionally (built in) and the bracing prevents relative lateral movement of the ends, the effective height is half the actual height.   Fig. 12(b) shows a braced column which is pinned at one end and rigidly built in at the other, it has an effective height of approximately 0.7 times the actual height.
Fig. 12.1(d) shows a column which has built in or directionally fixed ends but it is not braced against lateral movement.   Its effective height is equal to its actual height because the point of contraflexure occurs at the

mid height.   Extension of the strut by dotted lines shows the completion of the curve to correspond with the pin ended case of Fig.12.1(c).   The unbraced strut shown in Fig. 12.1(e) has a pin at one end and is rigidly built in at the other.   Lateral movement can occur because of the lack of bracing.   Extension of the strut, as shown by dotted lines indicates an effective height of twice the actual height.

Where, in Fig. 12.1, an end of a strut is shown to be rigidly built in, the effective height is given on this assumption.   In practice both pins and rigid fixity are difficult to achieve, directional restraint is usually achieved by the connection of the column to other members of the frame. Such connections cannot ensure complete rigidity because the members providing the restraint are not themselves perfectly rigid.

Table 15 (CP110) gives some guidance on the choice of effective height in practical situations.   The braced columns properly restrained in direction

Table 15. Effective column height

Type of column	Effective column height
Braced column properly restrained in direction at both ends	$0.75l_o$
Braced column imperfectly restrained in direction at one or both ends	A value intermediate between $0.75l_o$ and l_o depending upon the efficiency of the directional restraint
Unbraced or partially braced column, properly restrained in direction at one end but imperfectly restrained in direction at the other end	A value intermediate between l_o and $2l_o$ depending upon the efficiency of the directional restraint and bracing

at both ends for which an effective height of $0.75l_o$ is given corresponds to the strut in Fig. 12.1(a).   The braced column imperfectly restrained in direction at one or both ends, for which values of effective height between $0.75l_o$ and l_o are given, covers the whole range of braced struts between those shown in Figs. 12.1(a) and (c) inclusive.   The unbraced columns for which values of effective height between l_o and $2l_o$ are given includes all unbraced columns between those shown in Figs. 12.1(d) and (e) inclusive.   Table 15 (CP110) is difficult to use for the designer with limited experience and the reader is recommended to use Equations 20, 21, 22, and 23 (CP110) to calculate effective column heights.   As has been shown the effectiveness of the directional restraint will depend on the stiffness of the beams which connect to the column, and the distance between the points of contraflexure in the column will be controlled by the relative stiffness of beams and columns.   The beam and column stiffnesses are used in Equation 20, 21, 22 and 23 (CP110) to calculate effective column heights.

In cl.3.5.1.4(CP110) given below the columns are divided into braced and unbraced types, it is exceedingly important that the difference between the two is clearly understood.   For an illustration of the possible danger consider a column for which both ends are directionally restrained by stiff

For a framed structure, effective heights may alternatively be obtained from:

for a braced column, the lesser of

$$l_e = l_o[0.7+0.05(\alpha_{c1}+\alpha_{c2})] \leqslant l_o \tag{20}$$

$$l_e = l_o(0.85+0.05\alpha_{c\ min}) \leqslant l_o \tag{21}$$

for an unbraced column, the lesser of

$$l_e = l_o[1.0+0.15(\alpha_{c1}+\alpha_{c2})] \tag{22}$$

$$l_e = l_o(2.0+0.3\alpha_{c\ min}) \tag{23}$$

where l_o is the clear height between end restraints,

α_{c1} is the ratio of the sum of the column stiffnesses to the sum of the beam stiffnesses at one end of the column,

α_{c2} is the ratio of the sum of the column stiffnesses to the sum of the beam stiffnesses at the other end of the column,

α_{cmin} is the minimum of α_{c1} and α_{c2}.

When calculating α_c, only members properly framed into the end of the column in the appropriate plane of bending should be considered. The stiffness of each member should be obtained by dividing the second moment of area of its concrete section by its actual length. For flat slab construction, an equivalent beam should be taken as having the width and thickness of the slab forming the column strip. When connection between a column and its base is not designed to resist other than nominal moment, or when the beams framing into a column are designed as simply supported, α_c at such positions should be taken as 10. If a base is designed to resist the column moment, α_c may be taken as 1.0.

beams, if the column is braced the effective height is $0.75l_o$ but if it is unbraced the effective height is probably $1.5l_o$.   Using the Euler formula, the failure load is proportional to the inverse square of the effective height,   If, therefore, an unbraced column is mistakenly designed as a braced column, it may have an actual ultimate strength of one quarter of the strength it should have and collapse can be expected.

For a braced column, side sway of the frame of which it is a part is prevented by cross bracing, brick or concrete panel walls or adjacent structures.   An unbraced column is usually part of an unbraced frame which is free to deflect horizontally by flexure of the columns when horizontal forces are applied.   Braced and unbraced frames are more fully discussed in Chapter 3.   It should be noted that both axes of the column must be considered and the whole structure should be considered as a series of interlocking frames connecting to the columns at right angles.   In using the equations for slenderness ratio the *lesser* of the two values given by Equations 20 and 21 (CP110) should be used for braced columns and the *lesser* of the two values given by Equations 22 and 23 (CP110) should be used for unbraced columns.

QUESTION 12.1

Fig. 12.2 shows a column (1,2) and adjacent beams which are part of a large structure.   Determine, using Equations 20 to 23 (CP110), the slenderness ratio of the column (1,2), and hence whether the column is "short" or "slender",

(a) assuming the column is braced,

(b) assuming the column is unbraced.

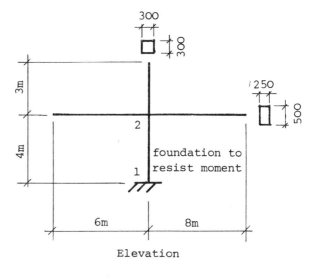

Fig. 12.2

(Answer:

(a) α_{c1} = 1.0,

α_{c2} = .52

l_e = .78 l_o,

$l_{e/b}$ = 10.3 < 12
short column

(b) l_e = 1.23 l_o,

$l_{e/b}$ = 16.4 > 12
slender column)

12.D. SIZE OF COLUMN AND REINFORCEMENT (cl.3.5.3, cl.3.5.5.2(CP110))

(a) METHOD OF DESIGN

Having determined the axial force and bending moment in the column for the ultimate limit state, using one of the methods described in Chapters 2 and 3, the size of the cross section and the area of longitudinal reinforcement may be determined by either the use of approximate formulae or by the use of design graphs. The formulae given in cl.3.5.3 and cl.3.5.4 (CP110) for the columns with only small eccentricities of load are relatively simple to use and column sections and reinforcement can be obtained easily. Approximate formulae for design of eccentrically loaded columns are given in cl.3.5.5.3 (CP110) but they are not recommended because of the difficulties involved in using them. Eccentrically loaded columns may be easily designed by the use of graphs.

(b) AXIALLY LOADED COLUMNS

Axially loaded columns fall into two categories:

(i) those in which eccentricity of load can only occur due to inaccuracies in construction for which the axial load should not exceed:

$$N = 0.4 f_{cu} A_c + 0.67 A_{sc} f_y \quad ..... \text{ Equation 25 (CP110)}$$

Such restriction on eccentricity of loading is rare and can only be expected in special structures.

(ii) the inner columns of multi-storey structures where the axial load should not exceed

$$N = 0.35 f_{cu} A_c + 0.60 A_{sc} f_y \quad ..... \text{ Equation 26 (CP110)}$$

Equation 26 (CP110) should only be used where:

(1) the beams are designed for uniformly distributed imposed loads and
(2) the beam spans do not differ by more than 15 % of the longer

(c) ECCENTRICALLY LOADED COLUMNS

Generally eccentrically loaded columns can be readily designed by the use
of graphs.   It should be appreciated that these graphs have been constructed
using a symmetrical arrangement of steel, the stress strain graphs for
concrete (see Fig. 1 (CP110)) and for steel (see Fig. 2 (CP110)) with a
linear strain distribution across the section in the same way as when
developing the equations for beams in Chapter 5.

On rearranging the equations so developed it is possible to plot M/bh^2
against N/bh for each strength of concrete and steel, and each value of d/h.
In use it is necessary to estimate the size of section required, and
determine M/bh^2 and N/bh.   Then choose a strength of concrete and steel and
d/h and from the graph determine $100 A_{sc}/bh$.   Hence obtain A_{sc}.   Columns
must always be designed for a minimum bending moment of $0.15 Nh$.   This is
built into the design graphs and is the reason for the flat top to the
curves.   A typical design graph from CP110:Pt2 which may be used to answer
the questions in this Chapter is given on page 147.

QUESTION 12.2

(a) A short braced reinforced concrete column supports an axial load of
    3000 kN at ultimate load.   Using Equation 25 (CP110) determine the size
    of the longitudinal bars required.   Assume a column 400 mm square,
    $f_y = 410 N/mm^2$, and $f_{cu} = 20 N/mm^2$.

(b) A short column supports an axial load of 1000 kN and a bending moment
    of 150 kNm at ultimate load.   Using $f_{cu} = 25 N/mm^2$, $f_y = 425 N/mm^2$,
    and $d/h = 0.9$, determine the size of longitudinal bars required using
    the graph from CP110:Pt2.   Assume a column 350 mm square.

(Answers: (a) A_{sc} = 6261 mm^2

    4 - 40 = 5026 mm^2

    4 - 20 = 1257
    _____

    6283
    _____

(b) $\dfrac{100 A_s}{bh}$ = 2.1; A_{sc} = 2573 mm^2;   6 - 25 = 2945
                                              or   4 - 32 = 3217

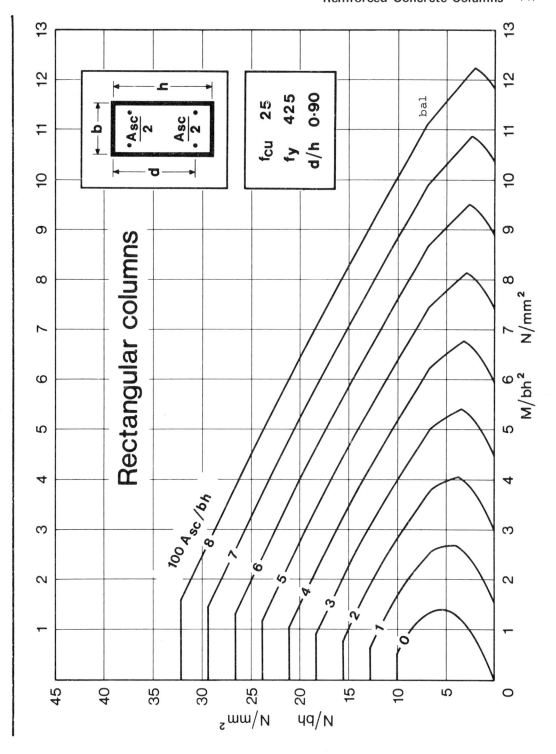

Rectangular columns

f_{cu} 25
f_y 425
d/h 0.90

100 A_{sc}/bh

M/bh^2 N/mm²

N/bh N/mm²

12.E. BIAXIAL BENDING (cl.3.5.6(CP110))

At the corner columns in a building bending moments are applied by beams connecting on two adjacent faces only which results in bending moments about both axes.   This condition can occur in other columns but is more common at the corners.   The resulting stresses are difficult to analyse by the normal methods and a simplified approach is given in cl.3.5.6(CP110).   The method

3.5.6 Short columns: biaxial bending. In those cases when it is necessary to consider biaxial bending in a short column, a section may be designed such that:

$$\left(\frac{M_x}{M_{ux}}\right)^{\alpha_n} + \left(\frac{M_y}{M_{uy}}\right)^{\alpha_n} \leqslant 1.0 \tag{31}$$

where M_x and M_y are the moments about the major and minor axes respectively, due to ultimate loads,

$\quad M_{ux}$ $\qquad$ is the maximum moment capacity assuming ultimate axial load N and bending about the major axis only,

$\quad M_{uy}$ $\qquad$ is the maximum moment capacity assuming ultimate axial load N and bending about the minor axis only, and

$\quad \alpha_n$ $\qquad$ is related to N/N_{uz} as given in Table 16

where $N_{uz} = 0.45 f_{cu} A_c + 0.75 f_y A_s'$ $\tag{32}$

Table 16. Relationship of N/N_{uz} to α_n

N/N_{uz}	α_n
$\leqslant 0.2$	1.0
0.4	1.33
0.6	1.67
$\geqslant 0.8$	2.0

is illustrated in Example 12.1.

EXAMPLE 12.1

A short column of 300 x 400 mm cross section is to carry on axial force of 600 kN with a bending moment of 95 kNm applied about the major (x-x) axis and a bending moment of 65 kNm applied about the minor (y-y) axis as shown in Fig. 12.3.   Use f_{cu} = 25 N/mm^2, f_y = 425 N/mm^2 and d/h = 0.90.

Determine suitable reinforcement.

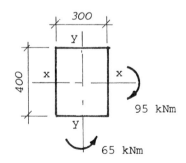

Fig. 12.3

A first estimate may be obtained by adding the two bending moments together and treating the sum as a bending moment applied about the major axis. Thus for

$$\frac{N}{bh} = \frac{600 \times 10^3}{300 \times 400} = 5.0$$

$$\frac{M}{bh^2} = \frac{(95+65) \times 10^6}{300 \times 400^2} = 3.33$$

from the design graph

$$\frac{100A_{sc}}{bh} = 1.50$$

$$\text{Therefore } A_{sc} = \frac{1.50 \times 300 \times 400}{100} = 1800$$

$$\text{Try 4-25 mm therefore } A_{sc} = 1964 \text{ mm}^2$$

$$\text{Actual } \frac{100A_{sc}}{bh} = \frac{100 \times 1964}{300 \times 400} = 1.64$$

Now find the maximum moment capacity for each axis in turn assuming full axial load to be applied.

Using the values of $\frac{N}{bh} = 5.0$ and $\frac{100A_{sc}}{bh} = 1.64$ and using the design graph backwards

$$\frac{M}{bh^2} = 3.50$$

hence

$$M_{ux} = 3.50 \times 300 \times 400^2 \times 10^{-6} = 168 \text{ kNm}$$

$$M_{uy} = 3.50 \times 400 \times 300^2 \times 10^{-6} = 126 \text{ kNm}$$

Using Equation 32 (CP110)

$$N_{uz} = (0.45 \times 25 \times 300 \times 400 + 0.75 \times 425 \times 1964) \times 10^{-3}$$
$$= 1350 + 626 = 1976 \text{ kN}$$

$$\frac{N}{N_{uz}} = \frac{600}{1976} = 0.30$$

Therefore from Table 16 (CP110)

$$\alpha_n = 1.17$$

substituting into Equation 31 (CP110)

$$\left(\frac{95}{168}\right)^{1.17} + \left(\frac{65}{126}\right)^{1.17} = 0.974 < 1.0$$

Therefore the requirements of cl.3.5.6(CP110) are satisfied.

Use 4-25 mm bars.

QUESTION 12.3

A short column is 250 mm x 350 mm in cross section and is to carry an axial force of 700 kN together with bending moments of 100 kNm and 55 kNm applied about the major and minor axes respectively.   Determine suitable reinforcement sizes assuming f_{cu} = 25 N/mm², f_y = 425 N/mm² and d/h = 0.9

(Answer: 4-32 mm, the result of Equation 31 (CP110) is 0.89).

12.F. FORCES IN SLENDER COLUMNS (cl.3.5.7(CP110))

In most structures the columns will be short, i.e. $1/b$ will be less than 12, but occasionally more slender columns will need to be designed.   In such slender columns the bending moments will need to be increased above those calculated from the applied loads.   This is because the column tends to deflect as shown in Fig. 12.4 and the axial force is applied at eccentricity e from the true centre line of the column, thus giving an additional bending moment.   The more slender the column the greater the deflection and the greater the additional bending moment.

Fig. 12.4

The bending moment which should be used in design is given by:

$$M_t = M_i + M_{add}$$

Values for M_i and M_{add} are defined in cl.3.5.7.1, cl.3.5.7.2, cl.3.5.7.3, cl.3.5.7.4 (CP110).

3.5.7.1 *Slender columns bent about a minor axis.* A slender column bent about a minor axis should be designed for its ultimate axial load N together with the moment M_t given by:

$$M_i = M_i + \frac{Nh}{1750}\left(\frac{l_e}{h}\right)^2 \left(1 - 0.0035\frac{l_e}{h}\right) \tag{33}$$

where M_i is the maximum initial moment in the column due to ultimate loads (but not less than $0.05Nh$) calculated using simple elastic analysis,

   h is the overall depth of the cross section in the plane of bending,
   l_e is the effective height either in the plane of bending or in the plane at right angles whichever is greater.

For a braced column where no transverse loads occur in its height the value of M_i may be reduced to:

$$M_i = 0.4M_1 + 0.6M_2 \tag{34}$$

where M_1 is the smaller initial end moment due to ultimate loads (assumed negative if the column is bent in double curvature),

   M_2 is the larger initial end moment due to ultimate loads (assumed positive).

In no case, however, should M_i be taken less than $0.4M_2$ or such that M_t is less than M_2.

3.5.7.2 *Slender columns bent about a major axis.* When the overall depth of its cross-section is less than three times the width, a slender column bent about a major axis should be designed for its ultimate axial load N together with the moment M_t given by:

$$M_t = M_i + \frac{Nh}{1750} \left(\frac{l_e}{b}\right)^2 \left(1 - 0.0035 \frac{l_e}{b}\right) \tag{35}$$

where M_i, l_e and h are as defined in **3.5.7.1** and

b is the width of the column cross-section at right angles to the plane of bending.

Alternatively, a column bent about its major axis may be treated as biaxially loaded with no initial moment about the minor axis.

3.5.7.3 *Slender columns bent about both axes.* A slender column bent about both axes should be designed for its ultimate axial load N together with the moments M_{tx} about its major axis and M_{ty} about its minor axis given by:

$$M_{tx} = M_{ix} + \frac{Nh}{1750} \left(\frac{l_{ex}}{h}\right)^2 \left(1 - 0.0035 \frac{l_{ex}}{h}\right) \tag{36}$$

$$M_{ty} = M_{iy} + \frac{Nb}{1750} \left(\frac{l_{ey}}{b}\right)^2 \left(1 - 0.0035 \frac{l_{ey}}{b}\right) \tag{37}$$

where M_{ix} is the initial moment due to ultimate loads about the major axis,

M_{iy} is the initial moment due to ultimate loads about the minor axis,
l_{ex} is the effective height in respect of the major axis,
l_{ey} is the effective height in respect of the minor axis,
h is the depth in respect of the major axis,
b is the width of the column.

3.5.7.4 *Adjustments to additional moments in slender columns.* In each of the equations (33), (35), (36) and (37), the second term represents the additional moment induced in the column by its deflection and this may in all cases be reduced by multiplying by the factor K, where

$$K = \frac{N_{uz} - N}{N_{uz} - N_{bal}} \leqslant 1 \tag{38}$$

where N is the ultimate axial load,

N_{uz} is the capacity of the cross-section under pure axial load which may be computed from equation (32),
N_{bal} is the axial load corresponding to the balanced condition of maximum compressive strain in the concrete of 0.0035 and tensile strain in the outermost layer of tension steel of 0.002.

The additional moments derived from the second terms of Equations 33, 35, 36 and 37 (CP110) do not take account of the variation in curvature as the ratio M/N changes. This change is considered in cl.3.5.7.4(CP110) where a multiplying factor K is defined which reduces the additional moment. The multiplying factor K cannot be determined until an estimate of column size and reinforcement has been obtained which must be done by assuming $K = 1$ which in any case will give a safe result. If it is desired to find a value of K and thus reduce the additional moment the main difficulty is in determining N_{bal}. A reasonable and safe estimate is given by the value for axial force which corresponds to the upper kink of the two kinks appearing at the extreme right hand end of the column design curves. To assist in identification of this point it has been marked bal on the 8% curve of the design graph on page 147.

QUESTION 12.4

A slender reinforced concrete column has a slenderness ratio $^{l_e}/_b = 15$.
If the column is bent about the major axis, determine the additional moment
due to deflection in the column.   The value of N = 2000 kN and h = 0.5 m.

(Answer: M_{add} = 121.8 kNm).

12.G. LIMITATIONS ON REINFORCEMENT (cl.3.11.5, cl.3.11.4.3(CP110))

To meet the practical difficulties of constructing a reinforced concrete
column the quantity of longitudinal steel must be restricted.   The maximum
permitted amounts, calculated on the basis of cross sectional area, are

       6% for vertically cast columns   )
)
       8% for horizontally cast columns)   cl.3.11.5 (CP110)
)
       10% at laps   )

The minimum longitudinal reinforcement is 1% and there should be not less
than 4 bars for a rectangular column, and 6 bars for a circular column.
For lightly loaded members the minimum area of steel is controlled by the
formula

       $A_{sc} \, f_y \geqslant 0.15N$ which will often give less than 1%.

To prevent buckling of the longitudinal bars links are used.   From
experiments the link diameter should be not less than *one quarter of the
largest longitudinal bar diameter* and the spacing should be not greater
than *12 times   the smallest longitudinal bar diameter.* (cl.3.11.4.3(CP110)).
For good practice the link spacing should not exceed the column breadth.
Every longitudinal bar must be enclosed by two legs of a link except that
each alternate bar may be considered to be anchored if it is not more than
150 mm from a fully anchored bar.   Some correct and incorrect bar and link
arrangements are shown in Fig. 12.5.

QUESTION 12.5

A vertically cast reinforced concrete column is 300 mm x 400 mm in cross
section. Determine

(a) the minimum longitudinal and tranverse steel.

(b) the maximum longitudinal and tranverse steel.

(c) the minimum longitudinal steel if N = 2000 kN and f_y = 425 N/mm^2.

(Answers: (a) 4-20 mm diameter = 1257 mm^2;   6 mm diameter link 240 mm
                spacing.

      (b) 6-32 = 6434, 8 mm diameter link, 384 mm spacing, 300 mm preferr.

      (c) 706 mm^2, 4-16 mm diameter = 804 mm^2, 6 mm diameter link
          190 mm spacing)

Link Shapes

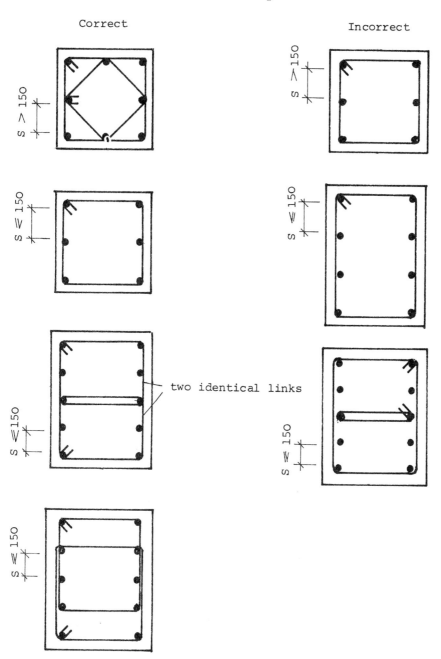

Fig. 12.5

13 Slabs and Stairs

13.A. DEFINITION

What constitutes a slab is difficult to define accurately but in this book
it is taken to be a flat plate-like element which carries its load primarily
by flexure.   In buildings slabs are generally used for floors and roofs and
are placed horizontally but they may be sloped to make ramps as used in
multi-storey car parks or similar constructions.   A staircase may be
considered to be a sloped and cranked slab.   One feature of a slab is that
its width is usually much greater than its depth whereas a beam is generally
deeper than it is wide.   Slabs may be supported by beams or by walls and
may be used as the flange of a 'T' beam.   Slabs are designed by using the same
theories of bending and shear as are used for beams.

13.B. SLABS SPANNING IN ONE DIRECTION

SIMPLY SUPPORTED SPANS

When a reinforced concrete slab is supported at two opposite sides, and has
no supports at the other two sides it is described as spanning in one
direction, a cantilever slab is a special case of a unidirectional spanning
slab.   In some structures a slab often appears to be supported on all four
sides but it is designed as though it were spanning in one direction;   the
main reinforcement then runs from one support to the other although some
subsidiary or distribution reinforcement is necessary which is placed roughly
parallel to the supported sides.

CONTINUOUS SPANS

Slabs spanning in one direction are frequently continuous over several spans,
the slab then behaves in a manner similar to a continuous beam and the
methods of analysis for continuous beams described in 2.D and Chapter 4 may
be used.

13.C. CONSTRUCTION OF SLABS

SOLID SLABS

Solid slabs, the cross section is shown in Fig. 13.1a, are the simplest to
construct and to design.   The slab is of uniform thickness and is cast on
flat formwork the design of the slab is similar to the design of a rectangular
beam.   The calculations are usually based on a width of one metre.

RIBBED SLABS

On the longer spans, say in excess of about 4 m, the dead weight of solid
slabs becomes unduly significant and the ribbed slab, shown in cross section
in Fig. 13.1b, may be more economical.   The design is similar to that of a
'T' beam but areas of solid slab may be needed near the supports where hogging
bending moments occur.   It is not usual to use compression reinforcement to
provide the necessary negative moment of resistance.

HOLLOW BLOCK SLABS

Hollow block slabs, shown in Fig. 13.1c, are intended to achieve similar
weight savings to ribbed slabs and are designed in the same way.   Although
the permanent blocks increase the cost of the construction the formwork is
simpler than for ribbed slabs and the finished slab has a flat underside or
soffit which is ready for plastering.   Slip tiles are sometimes used to
provide a better key under the concrete ribs and to help prevent pattern
staining.

VOIDED SLABS

Voided slabs, shown in Fig. 13.1d, also achieve weight savings and give a
flat soffit They are usually only used for the thicker slabs and longer
spans, design is similar to ribbed slabs.

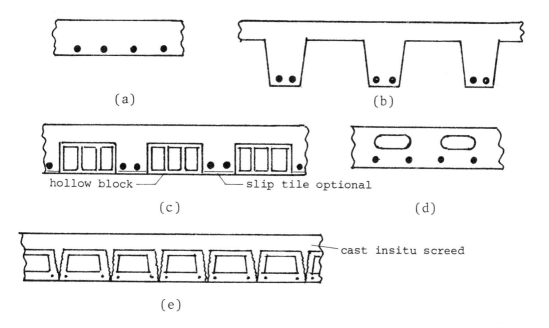

Fig. 13.1

PRECAST SLABS

Slabs are frequently built up from precast elements which may be designed as
simply supported or continuous beams.   Joints are at supports and some

continuity steel must be provided to reduce cracking of finishes even if the units are designed as simply supported beams.   The precast units may be wide or narrow or they may be narrow units widely spaced with lightweight infilling blocks between.   In any of these cases cracking of finishes along the sides of the units may occur unless it is ensured that relative movement of the units cannot occur.   Such relative movement is prevented by the provision of shear keys on the sides of the unit which are filled by cast in-situ concrete or by the use of a cast in-situ topping which may contain a light steel mesh reinforcement.   The units are designed in a similar way to rectangular or Tee beams depending on the cross section.

TOPPING THICKNESS AND RIB SPACING

To ensure that local failure of the slab is unlikely to occur and that the slab can truly be designed as a T section restrictions are placed on the topping thickness and rib spacing.   The rules are given in cl.3.7.1.2 and cl.3.7.1.3 (CP110).

3.7.1.2 *Thickness of topping.* When a topping is used to contribute to the structural strength, its thickness, after any necessary allowance has been made for wear, should be not less than:

(1) 30 mm for slabs with permanent blocks as described in **3.7.1.4** and a clear distance between ribs of not more than 500 mm,

(2) 25 mm for slabs as (1) above but with each row of blocks jointed in cement–sand mortar not weaker than 1 : 3 or 11 N/mm²,

(3) 40 mm or one-tenth of the clear distance between ribs, whichever is the greater, for all other slabs containing permanent blocks,

(4) 50 mm or one-tenth of the clear distance between ribs, whichever is the greater, for all other slabs without permanent blocks.

3.7.1.3 *Size and position of ribs.* In situ ribs should be not less than 65 mm wide. They should be spaced at centres no greater than 1.5 m apart and their depth, excluding any topping, should be not more than four times their width.

Generally ribs should be formed along each edge parallel to the span of one-way slabs. When the edge is built into a wall or rests on a beam, a rib at least as wide as the bearing should be formed along the edge.

13.D. DEFLECTION AND EFFECTIVE DEPTH (cl. 3.4.6(CP110))

Consideration of the serviceability limit state of deflection will provide a first estimate of the effective depth of the slab.   The allowable basic span/effective depth ratios are obtained in the same way as for beams using Tables 8 and 9, (CP110).   The modification factors for tension and compression reinforcement, given in Tables 10 and 11 (CP110), cannot be used until the steel has been designed and should be assumed to have a value of 1.0 initially.   The overall depth of the slab may be obtained by adding allowances for cover and bar size to the effective depth.   Values of cover related to grade of concrete and degree of exposure are given in Table 19 (CP110).   There are special requirements for cover for hollow block slabs see cl.3.7.6(CP110).

$$\frac{\text{overall}}{\text{depth}} = \frac{\text{effective}}{\text{depth}} + \tfrac{1}{2} \text{ bar dia. + cover}$$

The determination of an overall depth enables an estimate to be made of self weight from

$$\text{volume x density = self weight.}$$

13.E. MOMENT OF RESISTANCE OF SLABS (cl.3.4.4, cl.3.11.8.2, cl.3.11.8.1. (CP110))

The moment of resistance of a slab spanning in one direction may be obtained in the same way as for a singly reinforced concrete beam of rectangular or Tee section.   For convenience the slab is considered to have a width of one metre if it is solid or the rib spacing if it is ribbed.   In solid slabs and the solid parts of ribbed slabs the maximum distance between bars (cl.3.4.7, cl.3.11.8.2 (CP110)) is specified to control cracking at the serviceability limit state.   The minimum distance specified (cl.3.11.8.1(CP110)) is to enable the concrete to be properly compacted.   Fig. 5.1 summarises the requirements.

13.F. SHEAR RESISTANCE OF SLABS (cl.3.4.5(CP110))

One major difference between beams and slabs is that shear reinforcement is generally not included because of practical difficulties with shallow members. The depth of the slab must therefore be sufficient to resist the shear forces involved.

The nominal shear stress acting on a slab is $v = \dfrac{V}{bd}$

The value of v must be less than the allowable value $\varepsilon_s v_c$.   The value of ε_s is obtained from Table 14 (CP110) and depends on the depth of the slab.

Table 14. Values of ξ_s

Overall slab depth	ξ_s
mm	
300 or more	1.00
275	1.05
250	1.10
225	1.15
200	1.20
175	1.25
150 or less	1.30

The shear stress v in solid slabs less than 200 mm thick should not exceed $\xi_s v_c$.
In solid slabs at least 200 mm thick, when v is greater than $\xi_s v_c$, shear reinforcement should be provided as for a beam (see **3.3.6**) except that the space between links may be increased to d and $\xi_s v_c$ substituted for v_c in equation (9).

The value of v_c is obtained from Table 5 (CP110) and depends on the percentage tension steel.   Table 5 is the table used for beams.   The values of ε_s given in Table 14 (CP110) are obtained from test results which show that the shear strength of wide shallow members is greater than that of beams.

Shear resistance is generally not a problem in solid slabs, and therefore is often checked last.   Shear is more likely to be critical in ribbed slabs or precast units.

In special cases where shear stresses are high and shear reinforcement is used the nominal shear stress must not exceed half the appropriate value for the maximum shear stress in a beam as shown in Table 6 (CP110).

13.G. MINIMUM AREA OF SECONDARY REINFORCEMENT   (cl.3.11.4.2(CP110))

Secondary reinforcement at right angles to the main reinforcement is added in solid slabs to ensure the distribution of concentrated loads and to reduce cracking of the slab parallel to the main reinforcement.

The area of such steel expressed as a percentage of the gross cross sectional area is

0.12% for high yield reinforcement

and   0.15% for mild steel reinforcement.

To ensure the effectiveness of this reinforcement the distance between bars should not exceed five times the effective depth of the slab.

In ribbed and hollow block slabs secondary reinforcement is not obligatory but it is suggested in cl.3.7.6(CP110) that consideration should be given to the provision in the toppings of a single layer of mesh having a cross sectional area of not less than 0.12% of the topping (or flange) area, in each direction.   The pitch of the wires should be not greater than half the centre to centre distance between ribs.   The provision of such a mesh is probably not necessary where concentrated loads are unlikely to occur as in domestic or office buildings but for factory or warehouse buildings a mesh is more likely to be needed.

13.H. EXAMPLE OF DESIGN OF HOLLOW BLOCK SLAB

EXAMPLE 13.1

Fig. 13.2 gives the bending moment envelope for one span of a continuous hollow block floor slab.   The bending moments given are for a 400 mm wide strip of floor and are the values after 30% reduction at the support and 5% reduction at the centre of the span

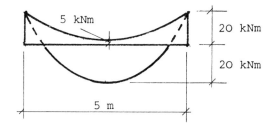

Fig. 13.2

$f_y = 410$ N/mm^2 $f_{cu} = 20$ N/mm^2.

It may be assumed that the upper curve in Fig. 13.2 is for Q_k = 24 kN and the lower curve is for F = 64 kN

From Table 8 (CP110)

Basic span/effective depth ratio = 26
Assuming factors from Tables 10 and 11 (CP110) to be 1.0

Minimum effective depth $= \dfrac{5000}{26} = 192.3$

Allowing 40 mm concrete cover and assuming a bar dia of 20 mm
Overall depth h =   250 mm

$$d = 250 - 40 - 10 = 200 \text{ mm}$$

From Equation 7.5

$$\text{putting } f_y = 410 \text{ N/mm}^2$$

$$\text{topping thickness} = h_f = 50$$

$$A_s = \frac{20 \times 10^6}{0.87 \times 410 \times (200 - \frac{50}{2})} = 321 \text{ mm}^2$$

Use 2-16 mm dia (402 mm²)

$$\frac{100 \, A_s}{bd} = \frac{100 \times 402}{400 \times 200} = 0.50$$

From Equation 13 (CP110)

$$f_s = \frac{0.58 \times 410 \times 321}{402 \times 0.95} = 200 \text{ N/mm}^2$$

From Table 10 (CP110) (interpolation is usually necessary)

Modification factor for tension reinforcement = 1.46

$$\text{Therefore } d_{min} = \frac{5000}{26 \times 0.8 \times 1.46} = 165\text{mm}$$

This seems low and a check to see if d can be further reduced should obviously be done. Such a check shows that a reduction of overall slab thickness to 225 mm is not reasonable and is liable to lead to excessive deflection.

Check that the compressive stress in the concrete is not excessive by substituting in Equation 7.2.

$$M_u = 0.4 \times 20 \times 400 \times 50 \, (200 - \frac{50}{2}) \times 10^{-6}$$

$$= 28 \text{ kNm}$$

which is greater than 20 kNm therefore the concrete strength is adequate and the neutral axis will fall within the topping.

At the supports the bending moment is also 20 kNm and for a solid slab there is no need to do special calculations. 2-16 mm bars per rib will be sufficient.

It is necessary however to calculate the strength of rib as a rectangular beam to resist hogging moment and hence determine the width of solid slab needed near the supports.

For 30% redistribution (see cl.3.2.2.3(4)(CP110))

$$x_{max} = (0.6 - 0.3) \, 200 = 60 \text{ mm}$$

Substitute in Equation 6.3 and put rib breadth = b = 100 mm

$$M_u = 0.4 \times 20 \times 100 \times 60.0 \left(200 - \frac{60.0}{2}\right) \times 10^{-6}$$

$$= 8.16 \text{ kNm}$$

The corresponding steel area is obtained by substitution in Equation 6.4.

$$M_u = 8.16 \times 10^6 = 0.87 \times 410 \times A_s \left(200 - \frac{60.0}{2}\right)$$

$$A_s = 135 \text{ mm}^2$$

1-16 mm bar continued from the support section is sufficient.

The equation of the upper BM curve is

$$M_x = -20.0 + 4.8 \left(\frac{5x}{2}\right) - \frac{4.8x^2}{2} = -8.16$$

$$x = 3.65 \text{ or } 1.35$$

Assuming clay blocks are used each 300 mm long a strip of solid slab 1.45m wide is needed at both ends of the span as shown in Fig. 13.3.

SHEAR

$$\text{Shear force at support} = 32 \text{ kN}$$

$$v = \frac{32 \times 10^3}{400 \times 200} = 0.40 \text{ N/mm}^2$$

From Tables 5 and 14 (CP110)

$$\varepsilon_s v_c = 1.10 \times 0.45 = 0.50 \text{ N/mm}^2$$

$$v < \varepsilon_s v_c$$

$$\text{Shear force at end of ribbed section} = \frac{(2.5-1.45)\ 32}{2.5} = 13.43 \text{ kN}$$

$$v = \frac{13.43 \times 10^3}{100 \times 200} = 0.67 \text{ N/mm}^2$$

$$\frac{100\ A_s}{bd} = \frac{100 \times 201}{100 \times 200} = 1.00$$

From Tables 5 and 14 (CP110)

$$\varepsilon_s v_c = 1.10 \times 0.60 = 0.66 \text{ N/mm}^2$$

$$v > \varepsilon_s v_c$$

It is necessary to continue 2-16 mm bars to provide the additional shear resistance.

The arrangement of hollow blocks and reinforcement is shown in Fig. 13.3. The positions of curtailment of reinforcement have not been calculated nor have bond stresses been checked, both calculations follow those for beams.

An alternative method for curtailment of bars is to apply the simplified rules given in cl. 3.11.7.3 (CP110)

3.11.7.3 *Simplified rules for curtailment of bars in slabs.* As an alternative to **3.11.7.1** for solid slabs spanning one way which support substantially uniformly distributed loads, the following simplified rules may be applied.

(1) *Simply supported slabs.* At least 50 % of the tension reinforcement provided at mid-span should extend to the supports and have an effective anchorage of 12Φ past the centre of the support. The remaining 50 % should extend to within 0.08l of the support.

(2) *Cantilever slabs.* At least 50 % of the tension reinforcement provided at the support should extend to the end of the cantilever. The remaining 50 % should extend a distance of $l/2$ or 45 times the bar size, whichever is the greater, from the support.

(3) *Continuous slabs of approximately equal span where the characteristic imposed load does not exceed the characteristic dead load, and which are designed in accordance with* **3.3.4.** All tension reinforcement over supports should extend a distance of 0.1l or 45 times the bar size, whichever is the greater, and at least 50 % should extend 0.3l into the span.

The tension reinforcement at mid-span of a slab should extend to within 0.2l of internal supports and within 0.1l of external supports and at least 50 % should extend into the support.

Where at an end support there is a monolithic connection between the slab and its supporting beam or wall, provision should be made for the negative moment which may arise. The negative moment to be assumed in this case depends on the degree of fixity, but it will generally be sufficient to provide tension reinforcement, equal to half that provided at mid-span, extending 0.1l or 45 times the bar size, whichever is the greater, into the span.

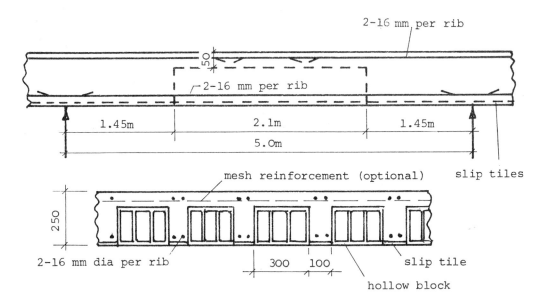

Fig. 13.3

13.1. CONCENTRATED LOADS

Concentrated loads will in general be supported by a width of slab greater than the width of the area over which the load is applied.   For simply supported solid slabs spanning in one direction the effective width of slab which may be considered to act in supporting the load is given by

$$\text{the width of the load plus } 2.4 \left(1 - \frac{x}{l}\right) x$$

where

x = the distance from the centre of the load to the nearest support

l = is the effective span

Where the concentrated load is placed nearer to an unsupported edge than

$$1.2 \left(1 - \frac{x}{l}\right) x$$

then the effective width should be reduced accordingly.

For cast insitu ribbed slabs the width of slab which may be considered to assist in supporting the load is equal to the width of the load plus four times the rib spacing.   For precast slabs formed from units which are effectively jointed together the load may be considered to be supported by a width equal to the width of the load plus the width of three units or four units where the topping is at least 30 mm thick.   In no case should the width of ribbed or precast slab taken as supporting a concentrated load exceed one quarter of the span on each side of the concentrated load.

The shear resistance of solid slabs under concentrated loads is calculated in the same way as for punching shear round a column in Chapters 14 and 15. The critical section is at a distance of 1.5 times the depth of the slab from the boundary of the loaded area, and the value of $100A_s/bd$ to be used in Table 5 (CP110) is taken as the average for strips in the two directions. The width of a strip is the width of the loaded area plus three times the depth of the slab on either side of the loaded area.   Shear reinforcement is generally not added to slabs, but is allowed where the slab thickness is greater than 200 mm.   The design of shear reinforcement in slabs is covered in Chapter 14 during the discussion on flat slabs.

13.J. STAIRCASES

The imposed loading on staircases is assumed to act vertically on the plan
area of the staircase and should be at least equal to the imposed load on the
floor to which it gives access.   The loading is more fully specified in
CP3:ChapV:PartI.

The staircase may be designed to span transversely between walls with little
or no support at the sides.   If the staircase is designed to span transversely
each tread can be treated as a separate beam as shown in Fig. 13.4a but nominal
longitudinal distribution reinforcement should be included to prevent large
cracks.   Staircases spanning as a flight may be supported by beams as shown
in Fig. 13.4b or Fig. 13.4c or a landing or another flight spanning at right
angles may provide support as shown in Fig. 13.4d.   The type of support need
not be the same at each end.   The effective span for each of the three types
is shown in Fig. 13.4b, c and d each may be treated as simply supported over
the span shown but top reinforcement should be included near the support to
prevent the formation of large cracks.   The types shown in Fig. 13.4b and c
may be made continuous with the floor slab at each end if it spans in the
same direction.   It is suggested that the reinforcement in the centre of the
span be taken as 90% of the quantity required if the flight were simply
supported and that the top reinforcement over the supports should be at least
two thirds the quantity at the centre of the span.   Fig. 13.5 is a typical
longitudinal cross section.

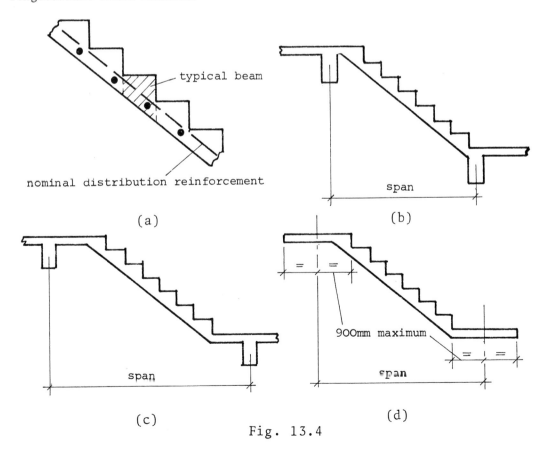

typical beam

nominal distribution reinforcement

(a)

span

(b)

span

(c)

900mm maximum

span

(d)

Fig. 13.4

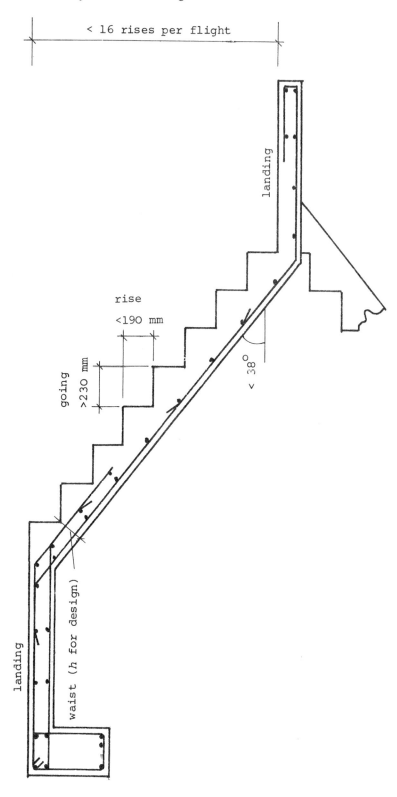

Fig. 13.5 Staircase

14 Slabs and Flat Slabs

14.A TWO WAY SPANNING SLABS   (cl.3.4(CP110))

Two way spanning slabs are supported on three or four sides and may be
simply supported or continuous on any or all sides.   Such a slab may be
considered to consist of a series of interlocking beams as shown in Fig. 14.1a
Each beam carries part of the load, the remainder of the load being carried
by the beams which span in the other direction.

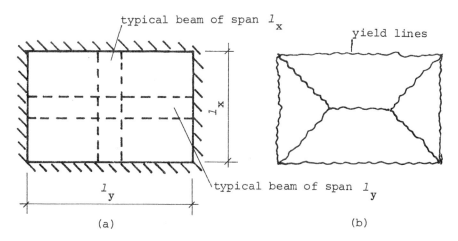

typical beam of span l_x

yield lines

l_x

l_y

typical beam of span l_y

(a)   (b)

Fig. 14.1

Elastic analysis may be based on such an assumption but it is not usual to
approach the design of a two way spanning slab by analysis from first
principles but from tables incorporating the results from the analysis of
standard cases.   Ultimate strength methods of analysis may also be used
and Johansen's yield line method assumes that a mechanism is formed
in the slab at failure with known resistance moments at the hinge lines.
A typical failure pattern is shown in Fig. 14.1b.

Tables 12 and 13 (CP110) are given to facilitate the analysis of slabs and
the part of this chapter concerned with ordinary two way spanning slabs
merely explains their derivation and the use of the tables to calculate the
forces and moments in the slab.   Once the forces and moments have been
calculated the design of the section follows that for one way spanning slabs
irrespective of whether the slab is solid, ribbed or voided.   The design
of the slab and its reinforcement is not, therefore, considered in detail

except where there are significant differences from the design of one way spanning slabs.

14.B. SIMPLY SUPPORTED SLABS (cl.3.4.3.1(CP110))

A slab which is simply supported at its edges and is not continuous over the supports tends to lift off its supports near the corners when loaded.   Such a slab is the only truly simply supported slab, if the slab is anchored down so that the corners cannot lift it has more in common with a continuous or restrained slab and is dealt with as such in both CP110 and this chapter. The following extract from cl.3.4.3.1(CP110) gives the bending moments to be used for the design of simply supported slabs.   It should be noted that the bending moments M_{sx} and M_{sy} given in Equations 14 and 15 (CP110) to be used for the design of the slab in both spans are related to the shorter span l_x.   The values of the bending moment coefficients given in Table 12 (CP110) are derived from the Grashof-Rankine formula which is based on the consideration of equating deflections of interlocking strips as explained in 14.A and illustrated in Fig. 14.1a.

$$M_{sx} = \alpha_{sx} n l_x^2 \tag{14}$$

$$M_{sy} = \alpha_{sy} n l_x^2 \tag{15}$$

where M_{sx} and M_{sy} are the maximum moments at mid-span on strips of unit width and spans l_x and l_y, respectively,

n	is the total ultimate load per unit area $(1.4g_k + 1.6q_k)$,
l_y	is the length of the longer side,
l_x	is the length of the shorter side,
α_{sx} and α_{sy}	are moment coefficients shown in Table 12.

Table 12. Bending moment coefficients for slabs spanning in two directions at right angles, simply supported on four sides

l_y/l_x	1.0	1.1	1.2	1.3	1.4	1.5	1.75	2.0	2.5	3.0
α_{sx}	0.062	0.074	0.084	0.093	0.099	0.104	0.113	0.118	0.122	0.124
α_{sy}	0.062	0.061	0.059	0.055	0.051	0.046	0.037	0.029	0.020	0.014

At least 50 % of the tension reinforcement provided at mid-span should extend to the supports. The remaining 50 % should extend to within $0.1l_x$ or $0.1l_y$ of the support, as appropriate.

QUESTION 14.1

A simply supported slab is to be designed to cover an area 6m long by 5m wide the value of n is 7.5 kN/m². Determine the bending moments to be used for the design of the slab.

(Answer: M_{sx} = 15.75 kNm; M_{sy} = 11.06 kNm)

14.C RESTRAINED SLABS (cl.3.4.3.2(CP110))

A slab may have its edges restrained to a greater or lesser degree depending whether it is continuous over its support or cast monolithically with its supporting beam.   In either case hogging, or negative, bending will occur leading to tension in the top face of the slab at the supported sides in the same way as for beams.   The bending moment coefficients for strips of unit width are given in Table 13 (CP110) and because of the support afforded by the beams running parallel to the edge strips the bending moments calculated from the coefficients need only be considered to act in the middle strips of the slab as shown in Fig.5 (CP110).   The reinforcement in the edge strips need not be based upon bending moment calculations, since the minimum quantity of main reinforcement for slabs as specified in cl.3.11.4.1(CP110) and discussed in 5.C(f) is sufficient.

Table 13 (CP110) and cl.3.4.3.2(CP110) are self explanatory and are reproduced in full to assist in identifying the case types of Table 13 (CP110) Fig. 14.2 shows four different sets of slabs with each panel marked with the corresponding case type from Table 13 (CP110).   The supporting beams are shown by broken lines.

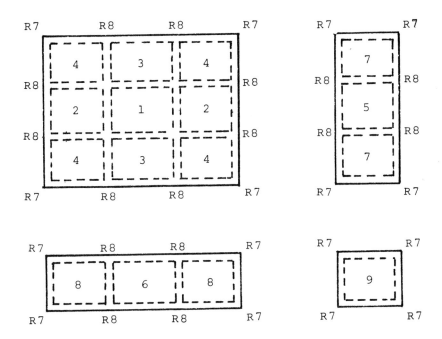

Fig. 14.2

3.4.3.2 *Restrained slabs.* In slabs where the corners are prevented from lifting, and provision for torsion is made, the maximum moments per unit width are given by the following equations:

$$M_{sx} = \beta_{sx} n l_x^2 \tag{16}$$

$$M_{sy} = \beta_{sy} n l_x^2 \tag{17}$$

where M_{sx} and M_{sy} are the maximum moments at mid-span on strips of unit width spanning l_x and l_y respectively,

n	is the total ultimate load per unit area $(1.4g_k + 1.6q_k)$,
l_y	is the length of the longer side,
l_x	is the length of the shorter side,
β_{sx} and β_{sy}	are coefficients given in Table 13.

For these slabs the following rules apply.

(1) Slabs are considered as divided in each direction into middle strips and edge strips as shown in Fig. 5, the middle strip being three-quarters of the width and each edge strip one-eighth of the width.

(2) The maximum moments calculated as above apply only to the middle strips and no redistribution should be made.

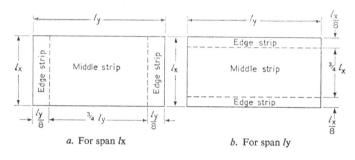

a. For span *l*x   b. For span *l*y

Fig. 5. Division of slab into middle and edge strips

(3) Tension reinforcement provided at mid-span in the middle strip should extend in the lower part of the slab to within $0.25l$ of a continuous edge, or $0.15l$ of a discontinuous edge. At least 50 % of this reinforcement should extend to within $0.15l$ of a continuous edge, and to within 50 mm of a discontinuous edge.

(4) Over the continuous edges of a middle strip, the tension reinforcement should extend in the upper part of the slab a distance of $0.15l$ from the support, and at least 50 % should extend a distance of $0.3l$.

(5) At a discontinuous edge, negative moments may arise. These depend on the degree of fixity at the edge of the slab but, in general, tension reinforcement equal to 50 % of that provided at mid-span extending $0.1l$ into the span will be sufficient.

(6) Reinforcement in an edge strip, parallel to that edge, need not exceed the minimum given in **3.11.4.1** together with the requirements for torsion described below.

(7) Torsion reinforcement should be provided at any corner where the slab is simply supported on both edges meeting at that corner. It should consist of top and bottom reinforcement, each with layers of bars placed parallel to the sides of the slab and extending from the edges a minimum distance of one-fifth of the shorter span. The area of reinforcement in each of these four layers should be three-quarters of the area required for the maximum mid-span moment in the slab.

(8) Torsion reinforcement equal to half that described in the preceding paragraph should be provided at a corner contained by edges over only one of which the slab is continuous.

(9) Torsion reinforcement need not be provided at any corner contained by edges over both of which the slab is continuous.

Where l_y/l_x is greater than 2, slabs should be designed as spanning one way only.

Table 13. Bending moment coefficients for rectangular panels supported on four sides with provision for torsion at corners

Case	Type of panel and moments considered	Short span coefficients β_{sx}								Long span coefficients β_{sy} for all values of l_y/l_x
		Values of l_y/l_x								
		1.0	1.1	1.2	1.3	1.4	1.5	1.75	2.0	
1	*Interior panels*									
	Negative moment at continuous edge	0.032	0.037	0.043	0.047	0.051	0.053	0.060	0.065	0.032
	Positive moment at mid-span	0.024	0.028	0.032	0.036	0.039	0.041	0.045	0.049	0.024
2	*One short edge discontinuous*									
	Negative moment at continuous edge	0.037	0.043	0.048	0.051	0.055	0.057	0.064	0.068	0.037
	Positive moment at mid-span	0.028	0.032	0.036	0.039	0.041	0.044	0.048	0.052	0.028
3	*One long edge discontinuous*									
	Negative moment at continuous edge	0.037	0.044	0.052	0.057	0.063	0.067	0.077	0.085	0.037
	Positive moment at mid-span	0.028	0.033	0.039	0.044	0.047	0.051	0.059	0.065	0.028
4	*Two adjacent edges discontinuous*									
	Negative moment at continuous edge	0.047	0.053	0.060	0.065	0.071	0.075	0.084	0.091	0.047
	Positive moment at mid-span	0.035	0.040	0.045	0.049	0.053	0.056	0.063	0.069	0.035
5	*Two short edges discontinuous*									
	Negative moment at continuous edge	0.045	0.049	0.052	0.056	0.059	0.060	0.065	0.069	—
	Positive moment at mid-span	0.035	0.037	0.040	0.043	0.044	0.045	0.049	0.052	0.035
6	*Two long edges discontinuous*									
	Negative moment at continuous edge	—	—	—	—	—	—	—	—	0.045
	Positive moment at mid-span	0.035	0.043	0.051	0.057	0.063	0.068	0.080	0.088	0.035
7	*Three edges discontinuous (one long edge continuous)*									
	Negative moment at continuous edge	0.057	0.064	0.071	0.076	0.080	0.084	0.091	0.097	—
	Positive moment at mid-span	0.043	0.048	0.053	0.057	0.060	0.064	0.069	0.073	0.043
8	*Three edges discontinuous (one short edge continuous)*									
	Negative moment at continuous edge	—	—	—	—	—	—	—	—	0.057
	Positive moment at mid-span	0.043	0.051	0.059	0.065	0.071	0.076	0.087	0.096	0.043
9	*Four edges discontinuous*									
	Positive moment at mid-span	0.056	0.064	0.072	0.079	0.085	0.089	0.100	0.107	0.056

Rules 7, 8 and 9 (cl.3.4.3.2(CP110)) are concerned with additional reinforcement for torsion at the corners of the slab; such torsion is only significant at corners where one or both of the sides is discontinuous and is the direct result of preventing the corners from lifting as in the simply supported slabs discussed in 14.B. The corners marked R7 or R8 in Fig. 14.2 are the corners where rule 7 or rule 8 apply.

The last part of rule 3 may be misleading, although it is permissible to stop the reinforcement 50 mm from a discontinuous edge care should be taken to ensure that the reinforcement does not stop before the support, the correct detail is shown in Fig. 14.3.

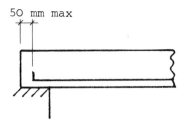

50 mm max

Fig. 14.3

EXAMPLE 14.1

A corner panel of a slab with several bays in each direction has sides 5m and 6m long. The total ultimate load is 15 kN/m^2. Design and detail all the reinforcement needed for the panel. Use f_{cu} = 20 N/mm^2 and f_y = 425 N/mm^2.

Basing the span effective depth ratio on the shorter span and its reinforcement a minimum effective depth of 192.3 mm is indicated as in Example 13.1. Further calculation shows this to be excessive and the following is based on an overall slab thickness of 175 mm.

Assuming a bar size of 20 mm and a cover of 25 mm

$$d = 175 - 25 - 10 = 140 \text{ mm}$$

$$\frac{l_y}{l_x} = \frac{6.0}{5.0} = 1.2$$

From Table 13 (CP110) for case type 4

at longer continuous edge M_{sx} = 0.060 x 15 x 5^2 = 22.5 kNm

for mid span of short span M_{sx} = 0.045 x 15 x 5^2 = 16.88 kNm

at shorter continuous edge M_{sy} = 0.047 x 15 x 5^2 = 17.63 kNm

at mid span of long span M_{sy} = 0.035 x 15 x 5^2 = 13.13 kNm

for mid span of short span

$$\frac{M}{bd^2} = \frac{16.88 \times 10^6}{1000 \times 140^2} = 0.86 \quad \text{N/mm}^2$$

from the design graph given on page 85

$$\frac{100 \ A_s}{bd} = 0.25$$

$$A_s = \frac{0.25 \times 1000 \times 140}{100} = 350 \ mm^2/m \ width$$

12 mm dia at 320 mm pitch
($353 \ mm^2/m \ width$)

Check span/effective depth ratio for the short span

from Equation 13 (CP110)

$$f_s = \frac{0.58 \times 425 \times 350}{353} = 244 \ N/mm^2$$

Note: from cl.3.11.8.2 when calculating allowable bar spacings it is suggested that the amount of redistribution at mid span when using Table 13 (CP110) should be taken at zero. Following the same practice $\beta_b = 1.0$ in Equation 13 (CP110).

$$Actual \ \frac{100 \ A_s}{bd} = \frac{100 \times 353}{1000 \times 140} = 0.25$$

from Tables 8 and 10 (CP110) for span/effective depth ratios

$$d_{min} = \frac{5000}{26 \times 1.56} = 123 \ mm < 140 \ mm$$

design reinforcement over the longer continuous edge

$$\frac{M}{bd^2} = \frac{22.5 \times 10^6}{1000 \times 140^2} = 1.15 \ N/mm^2$$

from the design graph on page 85

$$A_s = \frac{0.33 \times 1000 \times 140}{100} = 462 \ mm^2/m$$

12 mm at 240 mm pitch
($471 \ mm^2/m$)

Bar spacings in slabs with less than 0.5% reinforcement may be up to twice the spacing given in Table 24 (CP110) see cl.3.11.8.2 (CP110).

$$Max \ bar \ pitch \ for \ 12 \ mm \ bars = 2 \times 185 + 12$$

$$= 382 \ mm$$

Since the slab is less than 250 mm thick the bar spacing may be greater than the above but should not exceed three times the effective depth which is 3 x 140 = 420 mm which is greater than the 382 mm previously calculated and therefore overides it (cl.3.11.8.2 (CP110)). Therefore the bar spacing already calculated is acceptable.

Design the reinforcement for mid-span of the long span

$$d = 175 - 25 - 12 - 6 = 132 \text{ say } 130 \text{ mm}$$

$$\frac{M}{bd^2} = \frac{13.13 \times 10^2}{1000 \times 130^2} = 0.78$$

$$A_s = \frac{0.23 \times 1000 \times 130}{100} = 299 \text{ mm}^2/\text{m}$$

> 12 mm at 360 mm pitch
> ($314 \text{ mm}^2/\text{m}$)

Design the reinforcement over the shorter continuous edge

$$\frac{M}{bd^2} = \frac{17.63 \times 10^6}{1000 \times 130^2} = 1.04$$

$$A_s = \frac{0.30 \times 1000 \times 130}{100} = 390 \text{ mm}^2/\text{m}$$

> 12 mm at 280 pitch
> ($404 \text{ mm}^2/\text{m}$)

As before the maximum pitch = 3 x eff. depth = 3 x 130 = 390 mm

Local bond and shear should now be checked, but since the method is the same as for beams it is not included here.

The minimum main reinforcement for the edge strips is 0.15%

$$A_s = \frac{0.15 \times 1000 \times 140}{100} = 210 \text{ mm}^2/\text{m}$$

> 12 mm bars at 500 mm pitch
> ($226 \text{ mm}^2/\text{m}$)

The widest edge strip is $^{6000}/_8$ = 750 mm wide, therefore put two bars in each strip, see Fig. 14.4.

Torsion reinforcement is needed at three corners. For the corner with two discontinuous sides four layers are needed. In accordance with rule 7 (Cl.3.4.3.2(CP110))

$$A_s = \frac{3}{4} \times 350 = 263 \text{ mm}^2/\text{m width}$$

> 8 mm at 180 mm pitch
> ($279 \text{ mm}^2/\text{m}$)

For corners with one discontinuous edge (rule 8)

$$A_s = \frac{3}{8} \times 350 = 131 \text{ mm}^2/\text{m width}$$

> 8 mm at 360 mm pitch
> ($140 \text{ mm}^2/\text{m}$)

The arrangement of reinforcement in accordance with the rules given in cl.3.4.3.2(CP110) and practical considerations is shown in Fig. 14.4.

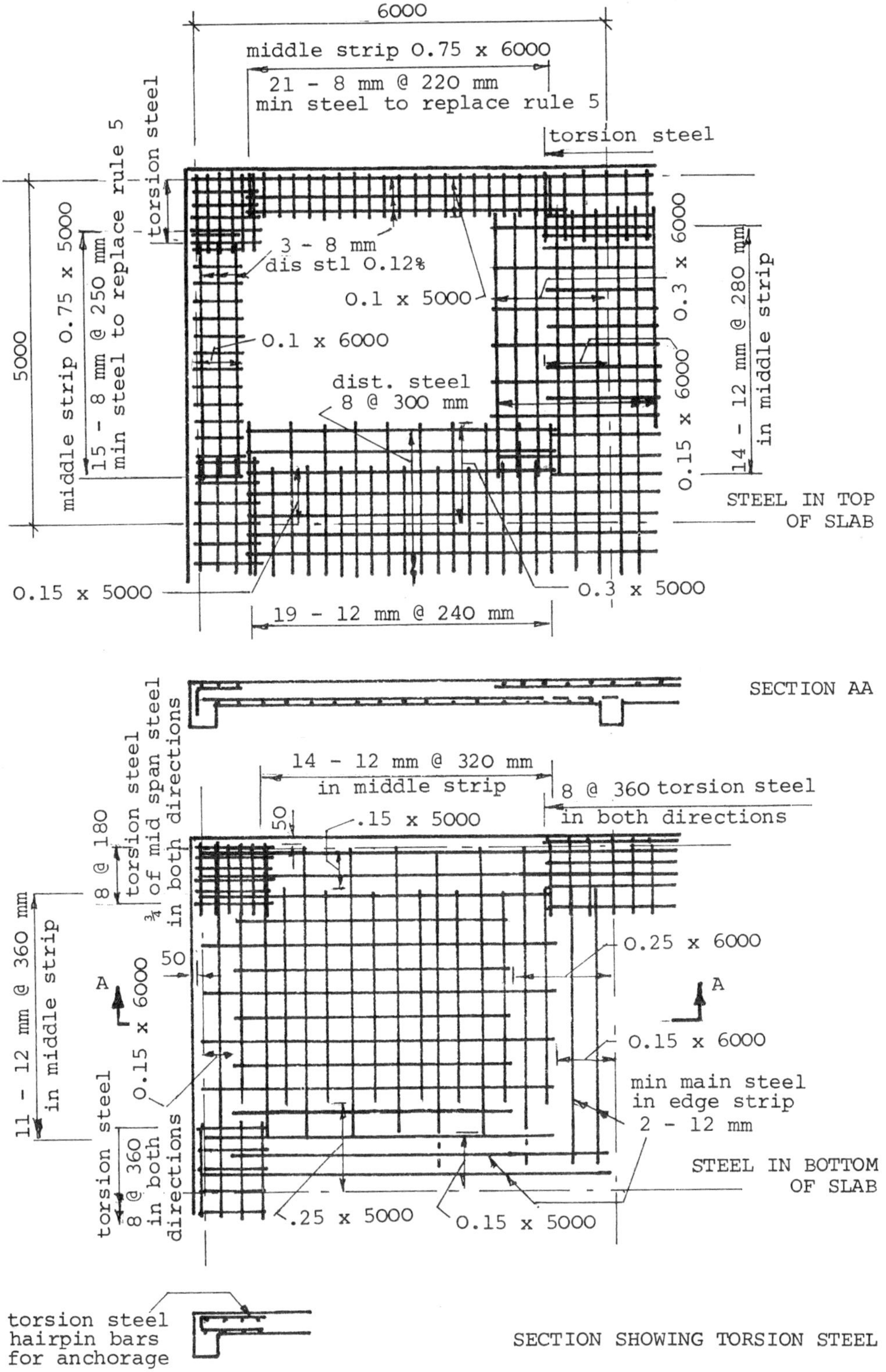

6000

middle strip 0.75 x 6000

21 - 8 mm @ 220 mm
min steel to replace rule 5

torsion steel

torsion steel

middle strip 0.75 x 5000

15 - 8 mm @ 250 mm
min steel to replace rule 5

5000

3 - 8 mm
dis stl 0.12%

0.1 x 5000

0.1 x 6000

dist. steel
8 @ 300 mm

0.3 x 6000

0.15 x 6000

14 - 12 mm @ 280 mm
in middle strip

STEEL IN TOP
OF SLAB

0.15 x 5000

19 - 12 mm @ 240 mm

0.3 x 5000

SECTION AA

14 - 12 mm @ 320 mm
in middle strip

.15 x 5000

8 @ 360 torsion steel
in both directions

50

50

torsion steel
of mid span steel
in both directions

8 @ 180

0.15 x 6000

11 - 12 mm @ 360 mm
in middle strip

torsion steel

8 @ 360
in both
directions

0.25 x 6000

A

0.15 x 6000

min main steel
in edge strip
2 - 12 mm

STEEL IN BOTTOM
OF SLAB

.25 x 5000

0.15 x 5000

torsion steel
hairpin bars
for anchorage

SECTION SHOWING TORSION STEEL

Fig. 14.4

14.D. FLAT SLABS (cl.3.6(CP110))

Flat slabs may be regarded as slabs which are supported solely by columns generally without the benefit of beams.   The soffit of the slab is therefore completely flat with consequent economies in shuttering costs. The need for false ceilings to hide services can also be avoided.   Sometimes drops are used to help reduce difficulties due to shear and high bending moment at the columns.   A drop may be regarded as a thickening of the slab extending into each span by a distance up to about a quarter of that span. Column heads, which are enlargements of the top of the column, are also used for the same reasons as drops but they work in a different way.   Neither drops nor column heads are considered in detail in this chapter.

14.E. FORCES AND MOMENTS IN FLAT SLABS (cl.3.6.5.1(CP110))

The forces and moments in flat slab structures may be obtained either by the use of empirical rules, which are set out in cl.3.6.6.2(CP110), or by considering the structure as a series of continuous frames consisting of columns and strips of slab.   The empirical rules may only be applied to certain types of structure and because of the restrictions the method is not considered in this book.

The structure should be divided longitudinally and transversely into frames which consist of the columns together with beams formed by strips of slab between the beams.   The width of the strip of slab assumed to act depends on the loading being considered and the proportions of the structure.   For vertical loads a strip of slab of width not greater than the distance between the centre lines of the panels on each side of the columns should be used. For horizontal loads the width of slab should be taken as half the width used for vertical loads.   The frames should be analysed elastically using either the complete frame or the 'one floor level subframe' as described in 2.G. and shown in Fig. 2.21 for vertical loads, and Chapter 3 for horizontal loads. Redistribution of moments may be carried out in a similar way to that described in Chapter 4 but reductions of moments are limited to 15 per cent and such reductions may only be made to the negative moments.   Even this relatively small reduction is worth while because it reduces the mass of reinforcement which is needed around the column.

14.F. DESIGN OF SLABS FOR BENDING (cl.3.6.5.2(CP110))

The bending moments obtained from the analysis should be divided between column strips and middle strips in the proportion shown in Table 17 (CP110) where the column strip has a width of one quarter of the total width of the two panels on each side of the column and the middle strip is the strip between two adjacent column strips.   The slabs are then designed in a similar way to other beams or slabs, except that negative moments greater than those occurring at a distance of $h_c/2$ from the centre line of the column need not be considered.   The deflection is controlled by using span/effective depth ratios as for beams and slabs except that an additional multiplier of 0.9 is necessary unless drops of the dimensions specified in cl.3.6.3 (CP110) are used.   The method of design is illustrated in Example 14.2.

Table 17. Distribution of moments in panels of flat slabs designed as continuous frames

| | Apportionment between column and middle strip expressed as percentages of the total negative or positive moment (see Note) | |
	Column strip	Middle strip
Negative moments	75	25
Positive moments	55	45

EXAMPLE 14.2

The analysis of two frames at right angles for a flat slab structure resulted in the bending moment envelopes given in Fig. 14.5(a) and (b) for the 5m and 6 m spans of an inner panel.   Assuming f_{cu} = 25 N/mm^2 and f_y = 425 N/mm^2 determine a suitable arrangement of reinforcement for the panel.   The columns are 400 mm diameter.

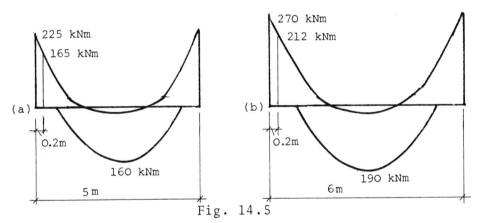

Fig. 14.5

First estimate of effective depth based on the shorter span.

$$d_{min} = \frac{5000}{26 \times 0.9} = 214 \text{ mm}$$

Assume slab thickness = 200 mm

for 5 m span upper layer of bottom steel
$$d = 200 - 20 - 1.5 \times \text{bar size}$$

$$= 200 - 20 - 1.5 \times 16 = 156 \text{ mm}$$

Bending moment at centre span = 160 kNm for column strip for 3 m wide take 55% of total bending moment see Table 17 (CP110)

$$\frac{M}{bd^2} = \frac{0.55 \times 160 \times 10^6}{3.0 \times 10^3 \times 156^2} = 1.20 \text{ N/mm}^2$$

from beam design graph on page 85

$$\frac{100 \, A_s}{bd} = 0.36$$

$$A_s = \frac{0.36 \times 3 \times 10^3 \times 156}{100} = 1685 \text{ mm}^2$$

15 - 12 mm (1695 mm^2)

for middle strip take 45% of the total bending moment

$$\frac{M}{bd^2} = \frac{0.45 \times 160 \times 10^6}{3.0 \times 10^3 \times 156^2} = 0.99 \text{ N/mm}^2$$

$$A_s = \frac{0.29 \times 3 \times 10^3 \times 156}{100} = 1357 \text{ mm}^2$$

13-12 mm (1469mm^2)

The minimum span/effective depth ratio need be calculated only for the shorter span using the average amount of steel for the span.

$$\text{Average } \frac{100 \, A_s}{bd} = \frac{100 \,(1695 + 1469)}{6000 \times 156} = 0.34$$

$$f_s = \frac{0.58 \times 425 \times (1638 + 1357)}{(1695 + 1469)} = 233$$

Min effective depth

$$d_{min} = \frac{5000}{26 \times 0.9 \times 1.52} = 141$$

It should be noted here that although there is a fair margin between the minimum effective depth of 141 mm and the actual effective depth of 156 mm repetition of this calculation for an end span would lead to a much closer result.

The bending moment at 200 mm from the centre line of the column = 165 kNm

for the column strip take 75% of the total bending moment

$$\frac{M}{bd^2} = \frac{0.75 \times 165 \times 10^6}{3000 \times 156^2} = 1.70 \text{ N/mm}^2$$

$$A_s = \frac{0.51 \times 3000 \times 156}{100} = 2387 \text{ mm}^2$$

12-16 mm dia (2412 mm^2)

for the middle strip take 25% of the total bending moment

$$\frac{M}{bd^2} = \frac{0.25 \times 165 \times 10^6}{3000 \times 156^2} = 0.57 \text{ N/mm}^2$$

$$A_s = \frac{0.16 \times 3000 \times 156}{100} = 749 \text{ mm}^2$$

$$7\text{-}12 \text{ mm dia } (792 \text{ mm}^2)$$

The smaller diameter bars are used so that the bar spacing shall not exceed $3d$. The 6 m span is now dealt with in exactly the same way leading to the following result.

Centre of span - Column strip, 16-12 mm dia; Middle strip, 14-12 mm dia.

Supports - Column strip, 15-16 mm dia; Middle strip, 5-16 mm dia.

The arrangement of the reinforcement is shown in plan in Fig. 14.6. The reinforcement in the column strip is not uniformly spaced because where h_c is less than $0.15l$, three quarters of the reinforcement in the column strip should be placed in the middle half of the column strip. The spacing is also affected by the need for the shear reinforcement to be anchored round the main tension steel.

The calculations for curtailment of reinforcement are not given because they are exactly the same as for beams.

14.G. DESIGN OF SLABS FOR SHEAR (cl.3.6.2(CP110)

The design of flat slabs for shear follows the method given in CP110 for the consideration of concentrated loads on slabs. In this case the column reaction is treated as the concentrated load. However, because the load is not always axially applied to the column, the shear stress is not uniform round the effective perimeter. To make allowance for the lack of uniformity the design shear force should be increased by 25 per cent if the ratio between adjacent spans does not exceed 1.25 and bracing or shear walls are provided to resist horizontal forces. The shear force at corner or edge columns should also be increased by 25%. In all other cases the design shear force should be increased by the factor $(1 + 12.5 (M/VL))$ or where the calculated factor is less than 1.25 the design shear force should be multiplied by 1.25. In the factor, M is the moment transmitted to the column, V is the shear force and L is the larger of the two spans in the direction in which bending is being considered.

Shear reinforcement is not permitted in slabs less than 200 mm thick and if additional shear capacity is needed for such slabs it must be obtained by increasing the slab thickness or the concrete strength or the quantity of tension reinforcement. A typical calculation is given as part of Example 14.3.

For slabs of 200 mm thickness or more, shear reinforcement in the form of vertical or inclined links is permitted, the design of such links being based on the use of Equation 19 (CP110) which is similar to Equation 9 (CP110).

$$0.4 \text{ N/mm}^2 \leqslant \frac{\sum A_{sv}(0.87f_{yv})}{u_{crit}\,d} \geqslant v - \xi_s v_c \tag{19}$$

where $\sum A_{sv}$ is the area of shear reinforcement,

f_{yv} is the characteristic strength of the shear reinforcement, which should not be taken greater than 425 N/mm²,

u_{crit} is the length of the critical perimeter.

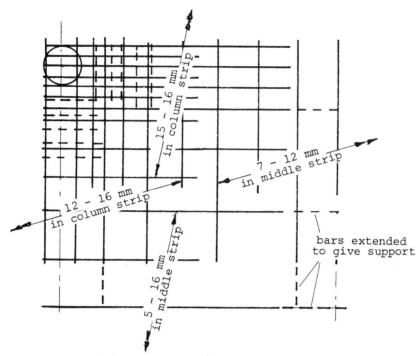

Plan on Top Reinforcement

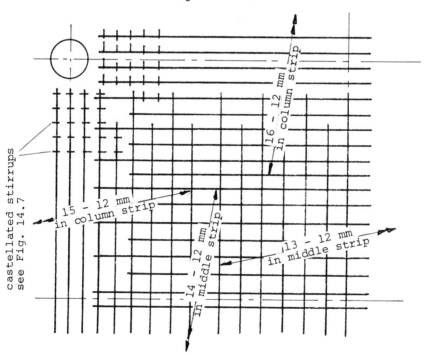

Plan on Bottom Reinforcement

Fig. 14.6

To ensure that when shear reinforcement is needed a reasonable minimum
quantity is provided Equation 19 (CP110) is organised so that the lowest
value of $v - \varepsilon_s v_c$ used is 0.4 N/mm². The use of the equation is illustrated
in Example 14.3.

EXAMPLE 14.3

The maximum shear force transmitted to each column supporting the flat slab
structure of Example 14.2 is 480 kN and n = 15 kN/m². Check the shear
strength of the slab and design any additional reinforcement needed.

For a circular column 400 mm dia and a slab 200 mm thick.

Diameter of critical perimeter for shear = 400 + 3 x 200 = 1000 mm

Design Shear Force on that perimeter = $(480 - \frac{\pi}{4} \times 1.0^2 \times 15)1.25$ = 585 kN

$$v = \frac{585 \times 10^3}{\pi \times 1000 \times 156} = 1.19 \text{ N/mm}^2$$

Note: the shear stress has been determined using the minimum value of
d = 156 mm.

The allowable shear stress v_c is determined from Tables 5 and 14 (CP110)
using the average percentage of steel for the two directions.

for 6 m span

$$\frac{100 A_s}{bd} = \frac{100 \times 3015}{2500 \times 172} = 0.70$$

for 5 m span

$$\frac{100 A_s}{bd} = \frac{100 \times 2613}{3000 \times 156} = 0.56$$

Average $= \frac{0.70 + 0.56}{2} = 0.63$

from Tables 5 and 14 (CP110)

$$\varepsilon_s v_c = 1.2 \times 0.54 = 0.65 \text{ N/mm}^2$$

The shear strength must be increased by adding additional reinforcement
either in the form of links or by increasing the quantity of tension steel.
Links are not permitted in slabs less than 200 mm thick so that they are
permitted in this case. Nevertheless an increase in tension steel may be
more convenient in some cases.

The value of v_c required from Table 5 (CP110) is

$$\frac{1.19}{1.2} = 0.99$$

hence, minimum tension steel is in excess of 3% and is therefore not reasonable

The design for links based on Equation 19(CP110) follows:

The additional shear stress to be carried by links is

$$v - \varepsilon_s v_c = 1.19 - 0.65 = 0.54 \text{ N/mm}^2$$

The design of the links should be based on the greater of 0.4 or 0.54 N/mm²

$$\Sigma A_{sv} = \frac{0.54 \times \pi \times 1000 \times 164}{0.87 \times 425} = 752 \text{ mm}^2$$

$$15 \text{ bars 8 mm dia } (754 \text{ mm}^2)$$

Use castellated link with 4 legs for each column face.

These should be placed both at 0.75h from the column face and 1.5h from the column face.

The shear resistance must also be checked at 2.25h from the column face and in steps of 0.75h until the shear resistance is adequate.

Diameter of new critical perimeter = 400 + 2 x 2.25 x 200 = 1300 mm

New Shear Force = $(480 - \frac{\pi}{4} \times 1.3^2 \times 15) 1.25 = 575$ kN

$$v = \frac{575 \times 10^3}{\pi \times 1300 \times 156} = 0.90$$

Therefore $v - \varepsilon_s v_c = 0.90 - 0.65 = 0.25 \text{ N/mm}^2$

$$\Sigma A_{sv} = \frac{0.4 \times \pi \times 1300 \times 164}{0.87 \times 425} = 725 \text{ mm}^2$$

$$15\text{-}8 \text{ mm } (754 \text{ mm}^2)$$

Provide castellated link as before.

Check again at another 0.75h step from column face.

Diameter of critical perimeter = 400 + 2 x 3.0 x 200 = 1600 mm

New Shear Force = $(480 - \frac{\pi}{4} \times 1.6^2 \times 15) 1.25 = 562$ kN

$$v = \frac{562 \times 10^3}{\pi \times 1600 \times 156} = 0.72 \text{ N/mm}^2$$

$$\Sigma A_{sv} = \frac{0.4 \times \pi \times 1600 \times 164}{0.87 \times 425} = 892 \text{ mm}^2$$

$$18\text{-}8 \text{ mm dia } (904 \text{ mm}^2)$$

Provide castellated link with 6 legs for each column face.

This calculation must be repeated for further steps of 0.75h from the face of the column until v is less than $\varepsilon_s v_c$. The next step shows that v is slightly less than $\varepsilon_s v_c$ and therefore further reinforcement is theoretically not required. The details of one quarter of the slab are shown in Fig. 14.6, including shear reinforcement at 5 x 0.75h from the face of the column. No further shear reinforcement is added beyond this stage.

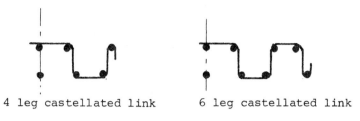

4 leg castellated link   6 leg castellated link

Fig. 14.7

14.H. COLUMNS

The bending moments and axial force for the design of the columns is derived
from the frame analyses discussed in 14.E.   The design of the column then
follows the procedures described in Chapter 12 - Columns.

In designing the slab it is assumed that the columns are of circular cross-
section, columns of rectangular cross-section may be used and for the
purposes of slab design the column diameter should be taken as that of a
column of the same cross-sectional area as the rectangular column.

15 Foundations

15.A. INTRODUCTION

A foundation is required to transmit and distribute the forces from the structure to the ground. This must be accomplished without exceeding the bearing capacity of the soil which could lead to failure or excessive settlement of the structure.

The choice of foundation type depends on:-

(a) the depth to a suitable bearing stratum

(b) the bearing capacity of the stratum

(c) the proximity of other structures and foundations

(d) access for equipment and machines

The most common types of foundation are:-

1. INDEPENDENT FOUNDATIONS

(a) Strip footing as shown in Fig. 15.1 where small forces are to be transmitted to a bearing stratum close to ground level.

    e.g. a brick wall foundation

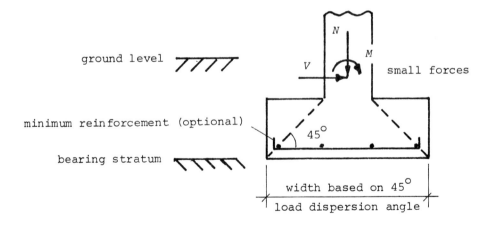

Fig. 15.1

(b) Pad footing as shown in Fig. 15.2, where large forces are to be
transmitted to a bearing stratum close to ground level.

e.g. column foundation

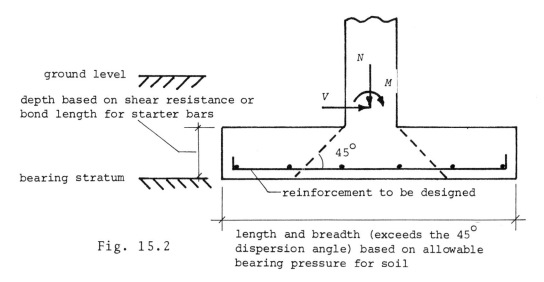

ground level

depth based on shear resistance or
bond length for starter bars

45°

bearing stratum

reinforcement to be designed

Fig. 15.2

length and breadth (exceeds the 45°
dispersion angle) based on allowable
bearing pressure for soil

(c) Pile foundation where large forces are to be transmitted to a bearing
stratum not close to ground level as shown in Fig. 15.3(b), or where
a suitable bearing stratum does not exist at a reasonable depth and
the forces are to be transmitted to the ground by friction between the
pile and the surrounding earth as shown in Fig. 15.3(a).

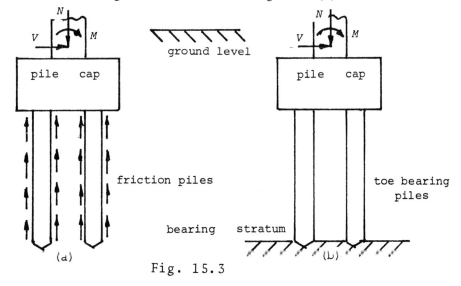

ground level

pile   cap

pile   cap

friction piles

toe bearing
piles

bearing   stratum

(a)

(b)

Fig. 15.3

2. COMBINED FOUNDATIONS

(a) A tied base similar to that shown in Fig. 15.4 is used where the forces on two adjacent foundations are acting in the same direction, e.g. the towers of a trestle or gantry.

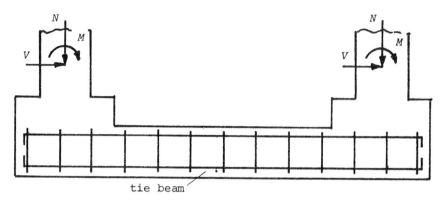

Fig. 15.4

(b) A balanced foundation is used where a site restriction e.g. an adjacent building, prevents free use of the bearing stratum for supporting the forces.   The balancing load is used to achieve reasonable uniformity of stress on the soil.   A typical arrangement is shown in Fig. 15.5.

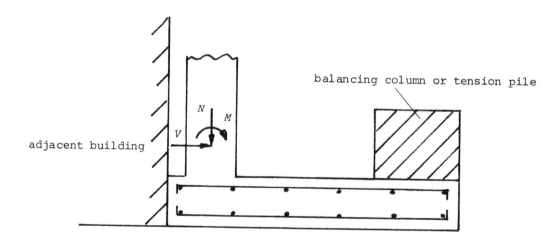

Fig. 15.5

(c) A combined foundation possibly of the shape shown in Fig. 15.6b is used where adjacent columns bases are so large that they overlap as shown in Fig. 15.6(a).

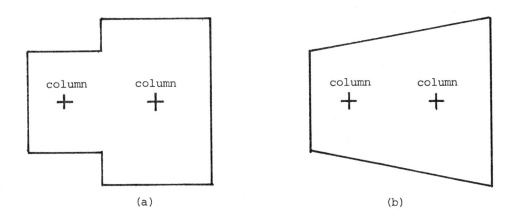

(a)   (b)

Fig. 15.6

(d) Strip foundations are used for a continuous line of loads e.g. a line of columns closely spaced in one direction.

(e) Rafts are used where individual foundations are likely to overlap or where the ground is variable in character and differential settlement must be avoided.   They carry a large number of columns on a single foundation and may be more highly developed versions of the combined foundations shown in Fig. 15.6(b).

15.B. STRESS ON THE SOIL BENEATH INDEPENDENT BASES (cl.3.10.3(CP110))

LOAD ECCENTRICITY NOT GREATER THAN $\frac{L}{6}$ THAT IS $\left(\frac{M}{N} < \frac{L}{6} \right)$

A foundation is assumed to act as a rigid body which is in equilibrium under the action of the applied forces from the structure, and the stress in the soil.   For the purpose of determining the soil stress it is commonly assumed that the soil behaves elastically, and that the stress and strain distribution in the soil immediately under the base is linear.   These assumptions allow the theory of bending to be used to determine the soil stress distribution for the axial load N and moment M, provided the stresses are always compressive.   It should be noted that this assumption is not strictly true and other assumptions can be made which do not necessarily lead to a better result.

EXAMPLE 15.1

Consider a rigid base with axial load N and a uniaxial bending moment M applied as shown in Fig. 15.7.

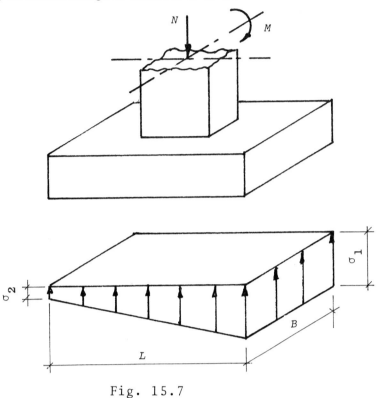

Fig. 15.7

From the theory of bending (-ve compression +ve tension)

$$\sigma_1 = -\frac{N}{BL} - \frac{M}{Z}$$

and　$$\sigma_2 = -\frac{N}{BL} + \frac{M}{Z}$$

where　$$Z = \frac{BL^2}{6}$$

The usual design process is to estimate the values of B and L and then to determine the values of σ_1 and σ_2 which are compared with the allowable soil stress. The allowable soil stress should be consistent with the limit state being considered, and would be obtained from a study of the soil properties.

Note: It is important to realise that the soil-concrete interface cannot carry tension and therefore these expressions are not applicable when $\sigma_2 > 0$ i.e. when

$$-\frac{N}{BL} + \frac{M}{Z} > 0$$

or　$$\frac{M}{N} > \frac{L}{6}$$

QUESTION 15.1

Determine the stress distribution beneath the base of a foundation 2 m wide
by 3 m long.   The values of the applied forces at the ultimate limit state
are, N = 1800 kN; M = 600 kNm applied about an axis which bisects the 3 m
length.

(*Answer: σ_1 = – 500 kN/m^2; σ_2 = – 100 kN/m^2*)

LOAD ECCENTRICITY GREATER THAN $\frac{L}{6}$ THAT IS $\left(\frac{M}{N} > \frac{L}{6} \right)$

To make effective use of the base area stresses on the soil should be
compressive over the whole area.   As the moment M increases the value of σ_2
reduces, until finally it becomes tensile.   Since it is not possible for
there to be tensile stresses the linear stress distribution for uniaxial
bending takes the form shown in Fig. 15.8.

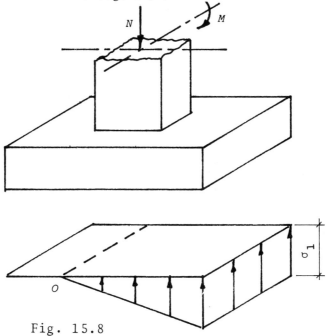

Fig. 15.8

The value of σ is determined as follows:-

The applied forces are represented as a load N at an eccentricity of
$e = M/N$ from the centroidal axis as shown in Fig. 15.9, from which

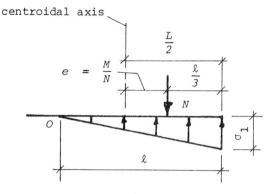

centroidal axis

$$\frac{L}{2}$$

$$e = \frac{M}{N}$$

$$\frac{\ell}{3}$$

$$N$$

$$O$$

$$\sigma_1$$

$$\ell$$

Fig. 15.9

$$\frac{L}{2} = \frac{\ell}{3} + e$$

rearranging

$$\ell = 3\left(\frac{L}{2} - e\right)$$ 15.1

Resolving forces vertically

$$N = (\ell\,\sigma_1 B)/2$$ 15.2

Combining Equations 15.1 and 15.2

$$\sigma_1 = \frac{2N}{B\ell} = \frac{2N}{3B\left[\frac{L}{2} - e\right]}$$

$$= \frac{2N}{3B\left[\frac{L}{2} - \frac{M}{N}\right]}$$

QUESTION 15.2

Determine the stress distribution beneath the base of a foundation 2m wide
by 3 m long.   The values of the applied forces at the ultimate limit state
are, N = 1800 kN; M = 1080 kNm applied about an axis which bisects the 3 m
length.

(Answer: σ_1 = 666.7 kN/m^2; ℓ = 2.7 m)

BIAXIAL BENDING

In many cases a foundation is subjected to an axial load N and moments M_x and
M_y about two axes at right angles as shown in Fig. 15.10.   If the soil
stresses are everywhere compressive they may be determined using a linear
elastic analysis based on the bending theory.

The maximum compressive stress is

$$\sigma_1 = -\frac{N}{BL} - \frac{M_x 6}{BL^2} - \frac{M_y 6}{LB^2}$$

The minimum compressive stress is

$$\sigma_2 = -\frac{N}{BL} + \frac{M_x 6}{BL^2} + \frac{M_y 6}{LB^2}$$

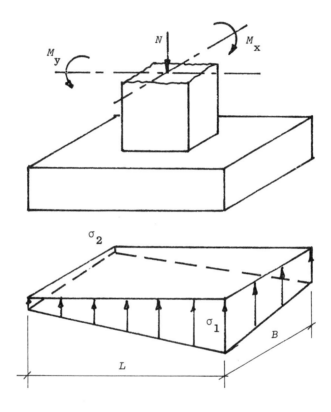

Fig. 15.10

QUESTION 15.3

Determine the maximum and minimum stresses on the soil beneath a foundation base 3 m wide and 4 m long. The values of the applied forces at the ultimate limit state are N = 2400 kN; M_x = 480 kNm applied about an axis which bisects the 4 m length, and M_y = 360 kNm applied about an axis which bisects the 3 m width.

(*Answer:* σ_1 = 320 kN/m^2, σ_2 = 80 kN/m^2)

15.C. STRESS ON THE SOIL BENEATH COMBINED FOUNDATIONS

A combined foundation supports two or more column loads as shown in
Fig. 15.11(a).   When determining the size of any foundation it is
advisable to keep the soil stress as uniform as possible.   For combined
foundations this is very important so as to minimise the possibility of
differential settlement and consequent tilting of the structure.   To do this
the resultant R of all the column forces supported by the foundation should
act as nearly as possible through the centroid of the plan area of the
foundation as in Fig. 15.11(b).   The soil stress is then determined in

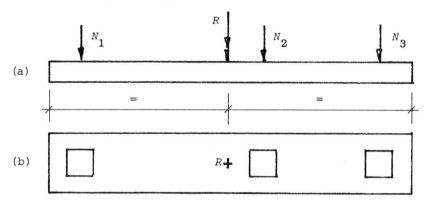

Fig. 15.11

exactly the same way as for a base supporting a single column by treating
the resultant R as a single column load.

QUESTION 15.4

Two columns, 7.2 m apart, carry axial forces of 800 kN and 1000 kN
respectively.   Due to site restrictions the combined foundation can extend
only 0.3 m beyond the centre line of the column carrying the 800 kN force.
If the allowable bearing stress on the soil is 100 kN/m^2 determine the
dimensions of a suitable rectangular foundation.

(Answer: 8.6 m by 2.1 m)

15.D. DESIGN OF INDEPENDENT COLUMN BASES

Having determined the overall plan dimensions of the column foundation it is
then necessary to consider the strength required to transmit the forces from
the column to the ground.   The base must, therefore, be designed so that
there is sufficient thickness to accommodate the bond length needed to
transmit the force in the column reinforcement to the base and the bending
and shear in the base slab must be considered so as to ensure a safe design.
All these are considered in the following.

(a) ANCHORAGE BOND LENGTH FOR COLUMN REINFORCEMENT

The thickness of isolated bases is often determined by the anchorage bond length required for the "starter bars" in compression which connect the base to the column as shown in Fig. 15.12. In combined foundations the criterion for base thickness may be bending or shear.

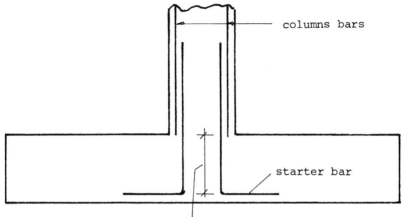

columns bars

starter bar

anchorage bond length in compression for base

Fig. 15.12

The anchorage bond length required may be determined from the expression

$$\ell = \frac{(\text{bar dia}) (\text{steel stress})}{4 (\text{bond stress})} = \frac{\phi f_{s2}}{4 f_{bs}}$$

the values of f_{bs} are given in Table 22 (CP110). The minimum depth of the base is

$$\ell + 2 \times \text{dia of main reinforcement} + \text{cover}$$

Where the dimensions of the base are large it may be more economical in concrete to adopt a stepped base of the type shown in Fig. 15.13. The

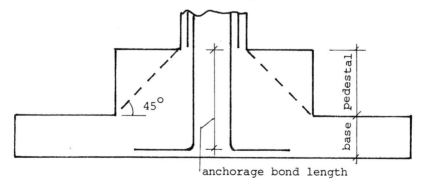

45°

pedestal

base

anchorage bond length

Fig. 15.13

anchorage length for the column starter bars can then be accommodated within the combined depth of the pedestal and the reinforced concrete base.   The pedestal must be carefully designed to ensure that tension is not induced in plain concrete although tension reinforcement may be included.   The minimum pedestal size is indicated by the 45° line shown in Fig. 15.13 but if a bending moment is to be transmitted the pedestal dimensions may need to be greater.

QUESTION 15.5

The bars in a column are 25 mm diameter and are fully stressed in compression ($0.72\ f_y$) at the ultimate limit state.   If the bars are Type 1 deformed bars for which $f_y = 410\ \text{N/mm}^2$ determine the anchorage bond length needed if the base concrete has a characteristic strength of 25 N/mm^2.

(Answer: 770 mm)

(b) BENDING IN THE BASE SLAB (cl.3.10.4.1(CP110))

Theoretically the maximum bending moment in a base occurs at the centre of the column but experiment has shown that the stresses there are not greater than the stresses at the face of the column.   It has also been shown that stresses at the face of the column can be predicted by considering the bending moment duc to all forces on one side of a section through the base taken at the face of the column.

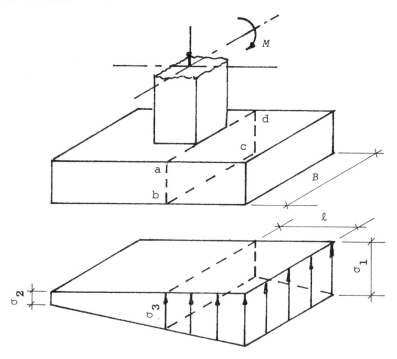

Fig. 15.14

In the base shown in Fig. 15.14 the section resisting the maximum bending moment is abcd.   The bending moment at this section is due to the earth stress on the length ℓ which varies between σ_1 and σ_3.   Consider the stress diagram as a uniform stress σ_3 and a triangular stress of $\sigma_1 - \sigma_3$.

$$M = \sigma_3 \, \ell \, B \frac{\ell}{2} + \frac{1}{2} \, (\sigma_1 - \sigma_3) \, \ell \, B \frac{2}{3} \, \ell$$

If the values of σ_1 and σ_2 are known then $\sigma_3 = \sigma_2 + \frac{(L - \ell)}{L} \, (\sigma_1 - \sigma_2)$.

The bending moment may be determined for a unit width rather than the full width B if it is so desired.   Once a value of M has been determined then M/bd^2 can be calculated and an area of tensile steel determined in the same way as for a singly reinforced concrete beam.   The value of d will already have been determined from the compression anchorage bond length of the starter bars although it may need increasing if the bending strength proves inadequate.

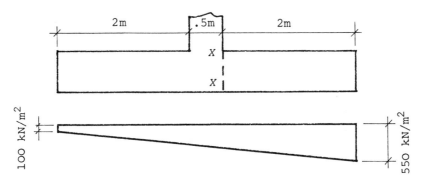

Fig. 15.15

QUESTION 15.6

Determine the bending moment per metre width at section XX, the face of the column, for the soil stress diagram in Fig. 15.15.   If $f_{cu} = 25$, $f_y = 425$ and $d = 1000$ mm, determine the area of tensile steel required.

(Answer: $M_x = 966.7$ *kNm per metre width,* $\frac{100A_s}{bd} = 0.28$ *,* $A_s = 0.3$,

$A_s = 2800$ *mm^2, 20 mm dia, 100 mm pitch = 3141 mm^2)*

(c) TRANSVERSE BENDING (cl.3.10.4.1(CP110))

The critical section for transverse bending is at the face of the column in exactly the same way as for longitudinal bending.   The total transverse bending moment acting on the section abcd shown in Fig. 15.16 is

$$M = \frac{(\sigma_1 + \sigma_2)}{2} \, \frac{L \, b^2}{2}$$

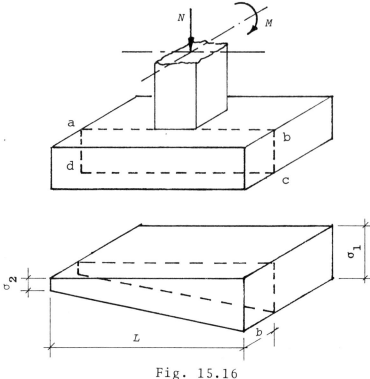

Fig. 15.16

The reinforcement should then be designed as for a singly reinforced beam but it should not be uniformly spaced along the length of the base; instead a greater amount should be concentrated under the column as indicated by the following extract from cl.3.10.4.1(CP110)

$\dfrac{2}{\beta_1 + 1}$ times total area of reinforcement is spread over a band centred on the column or support and of width equal to the short side dimension of the base.

The remainder is spread evenly over the outer parts of the section.
In the above β_1 is the ratio of the longer to the shorter side.

QUESTION 15.7

If b = 1.5m, L = 4.5m, B = 3.5 m, d = 1000mm, σ_1 = 550 and σ_2 = 100 kN/m^2 determine the total transverse bending moment and reinforcement required. Steel for longitudinal bending moment is 20 mm dia at 100 mm centres. Use f_{cu} = 25 and f_y = 425 N/mm^2

(Answer: Centre band width 3.5m, total A_s = 6750 mm^2, 5906 mm^2 in centre
            band width (19-20 mm), 427 mm^2 at each end (2-20 mm))

(d) LOCAL BOND IN THE BASE REINFORCEMENT (cl.3.10.4.3(CP110))

Local bond stresses in the tensile reinforcement must be checked at the face of the columns as for bending.   The shear force used is that which acts at section abcd as shown in Fig. 15.14.   The magnitude of this force is

$$V = \frac{(\sigma_1 + \sigma_3)}{2} B\ell$$

the local bond stress is determined from

$$f_{bs} = \frac{V}{\Sigma u_s d}$$

The allowable values of local bond stress for different types of bar and grades of concrete are given in Table 21 (CP110). Where the value of f_{bs} is greater than the allowable a reduction can be made by changing to a greater number of smaller diameter bars with the same cross sectional area.   An alternative would be to increase the allowable bond stress by changing the bar type or increasing the concrete strength.

QUESTION 15.8

Check the local bond stress for the bars given in the answer to Question 15.6 It should be assumed that the bars are deformed   Type 1.

(Answer: $v = 900$ kN per metre width; $f_{bs} = 1.43$ N/mm²;   allowable 2.5 N/mm²)

(e) SHEAR ON THE FULL WIDTH OF THE BASE (cl.3.10.4.2(CP110)

A slab base may fail in shear across the full width of the base in the same way as a beam.   Such a shear failure would generate a crack starting at

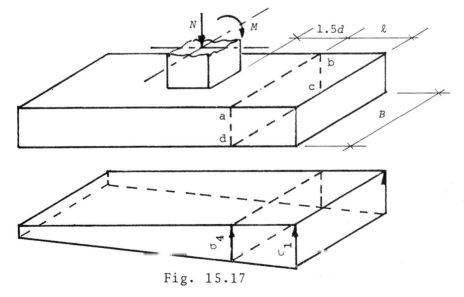

Fig. 15.17

about 1.5·d from the face of the column.   The shear force is, therefore,
checked at a distance 1.5 d from the face of the column for the ultimate limit
state.

As shown in Fig. 15.17 the shear force on the critical section abcd (Fig. 15.17
is given by

$$V = \frac{(\sigma_1 + \sigma_4)}{2} B\ell$$

The average shear stress is then determined from $v = \dfrac{V}{bd}$

This value of v must not exceed the allowable value v_c from Table 5 (CP110).
If v exceeds v_c then redesign is necessary by changing d, or f_{cu}, or A_s or
by adding stirrups.   It is not usual to add stirrups to isolated bases
because of practical difficulties.

QUESTION 15.9

Check the maximum shear stresses across the full width of the base shown in
Fig. 15.18 and compare with the allowable values.

$d = 1200$ mm, $f_{cu} = 25$ N/mm^2,

$$\frac{100 A_s}{bd} = 0.5$$

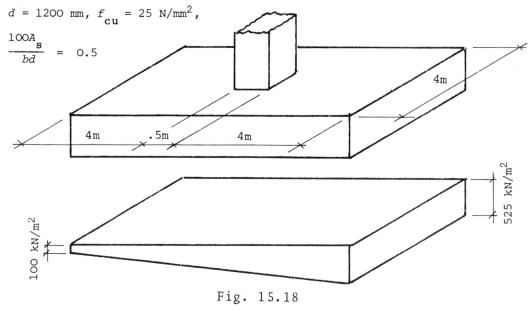

Fig. 15.18

(*Answer:*   *V = 4136 kN;   v = 0.86 N/mm²; v_c = 0.5 N/mm², therefore increase*
depth of base)

(f) PUNCHING SHEAR AROUND THE COLUMN (cl.3.10.4.2 and 3.4.5.2(CP110))

A column base may also fail in shear at the ultimate limit state along a line
at 1.5 h from the face of the column as shown in Fig. 15.19.

The shear force producing failure is the volume of the pressure diagram
outside this perimeter.   In the Fig. 15.19 for a square column of width W

$$V = \frac{(\sigma_1 + \sigma_2)\ BL}{2} - \frac{(\sigma_1 + \sigma_2)}{2} \left[4W(1.5h) + W^2 + \pi(1.5h)^2 \right]$$

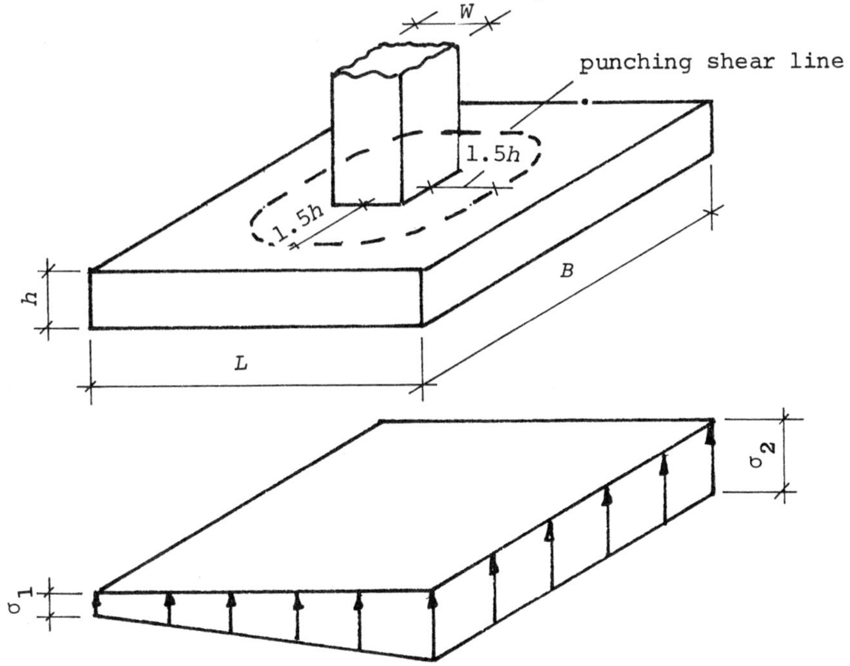

Fig. 15.19

The shear stress is

$$v = \frac{V}{[\ 4W + 2\pi\ (1.5h)\ ]\ d}$$

This is to be compared with the allowable value v_c obtained from Table 5 (CP110) modified by a thickness factor obtained from Table 14 (CP110). The thickness of a base is generally > 300 mm and therefore the factor is one. Table 5 is related to the percentage tensile reinforcement $100\ A_s/bd$. The value of A_s is the average for the two directions and should include all the steel within a column width plus three times the depth of the slab on either side of the column.

QUESTION 15.10

The uniform soil stress beneath an axially loaded column is 200 kN/m². Determine the value of the punching shear stress if the column is 400 mm square, and for the base h = 900 mm, d = 800, and the tensile reinforcement in both directions is 20 mm diameter at 100 mm centres. The base is 4 m square and concrete strength f_{cu} = 25 N/mm².

(Answer: V = 1592 kN; v = 0.20 N/mm²; v_c = 0.43 N/mm²)

15.E. DESIGN OF COMBINED FOUNDATIONS

Having determined the plan size of the foundation and the soil bearing stress
by the methods indicated in 15.C, the next step is to calculate the bending
moments and shears so that the base thickness can be determined.   Typical
Bending Moment and Shear Force diagrams for a combined foundation are shown
in Fig. 15.20   In order to calculate the soil bearing stress the individual

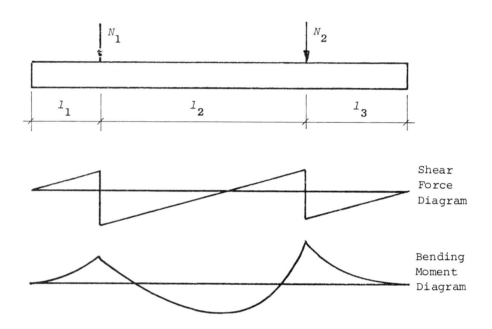

Fig. 15.20

column loads were replaced by a resultant, the resultant is now removed and
the original column loads reinstated so that bending moments and shears may
be calculated by the principles of statics.   Beginners frequently have
trouble at this stage but it initially helps if the loading diagram is turned
upside down so that the columns appear as the supports of a beam for which
the reactive forces are already known and the distributed soil bearing stress
appears as a load, the whole thing then looks much more familiar.

Once the bending moments and shear force diagrams are determined the critical
sections for bending and shear are at the column face or at a distance from
the column face in exactly the same way as for an independent foundation.
The transverse bending moment should be determined independently at each
column.

QUESTION 15.11

Draw the bending moment and shear force diagrams for the combined foundation
of Question 15.4.   Indicate on the diagrams the position and magnitude of

the critical bending moments and shear forces assuming that the columns are 300 mm square and the foundation has an effective depth of 1.2m.

(Answer: See Fig. 15.21)

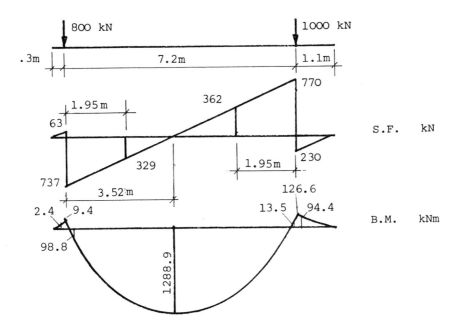

Fig. 15.21

15.F. PILE CAPS

Pile caps are used to transmit the forces from the columns to the piles. The dimensions in plan of the pile cap are based on the closest allowable spacing of the piles (approximately 1 metre), and the depth is based on the shear and/or anchorage bond stresses for the column bars in the concrete.

Each pile must be stabilised, at or near the ground surface, by connections in two directions to other piles. Three or four pile groups are, therefore, stable and do not need connecting to other pile groups but single piles or two pile groups must be connected to other piles by tie beams about 300 mm square containing 4 - 20 mm bars and nominal stirrups. If the tie beams also carry floor and wall loads they must of course be designed to carry those loads.

Pile caps are commonly designed as beams simply supported by the piles but additional reinforcement is usually added near the corners to prevent cracking. In fixing pile cap dimensions it must be remembered that piles may be up to 100 mm out of position and the pile cap made generously large to allow for this. Typical pile caps are shown in Fig. 15.22.

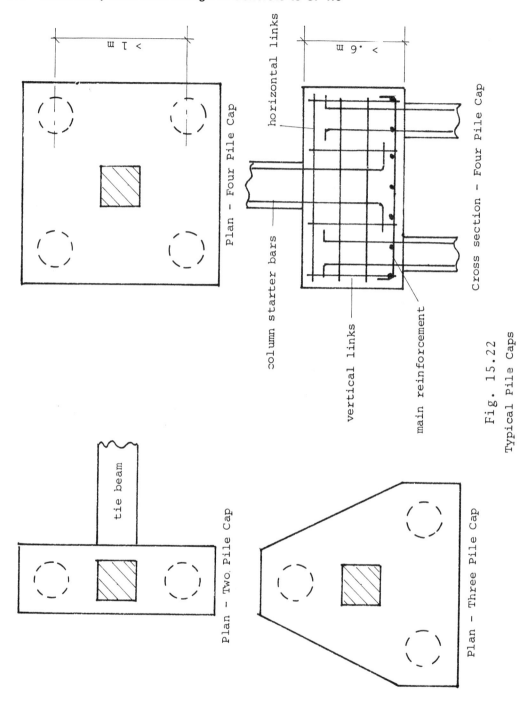

Fig. 15.22
Typical Pile Caps

16 Elastic Analysis of Prestressed Concrete

16.A. PRESTRESSED CONCRETE

In Chapter 6 it was explained that expensive steel reinforcement is used in reinforced concrete beams to solve the problem presented by the low tensile strength of the inexpensive concrete. Precompressing or prestressing concrete was conceived as another method of compensating for the low tensile strength of concrete. Since in beams both tensile and compressive stresses are induced, Fig. 16.1(a), it was suggested that if a longitudinal precompression could be introduced, Fig. 16.1(b), the final tensile stress would be zero or very small as shown in Fig. 16.1(c).

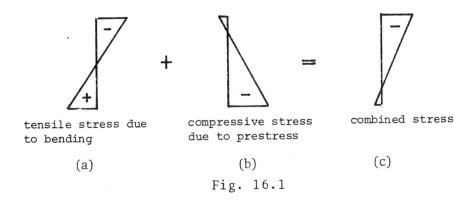

tensile stress due to bending	compressive stress due to prestress	combined stress
(a)	(b)	(c)

Fig. 16.1

In Fig. 16.1(a) it is assumed that the beam cross section is symmetrical about the horizontal centroidal axis. It may be seen that the axial precompression shown in Fig. 16.1(b) is not applied through the centroid of the cross section but at some eccentricity to give a small tensile stress at the top and a large compressive stress at the bottom. When the stresses due to precompression (prestress) are added to the bending stresses due to dead and applied loads it may be seen that the highest compressive stress is at the top and that at the bottom there may be a small tensile stress as shown in Fig. 16.1(c) or the whole section may be in compression.

The precompression is usually applied by means of wires or bars, called the tendon, threaded longitudinally through the beam. The tendon is tensioned by jacking against the concrete and then anchoring it once the right amount of prestress has been achieved. The basic principle is simple but difficulty was found in the early days because the shrinkage and creep of the low

strength concrete was sufficient to release the whole of the prestressing
force applied by means of the low strength steel bars which were then
available.   Prestressed concrete now uses high strength concrete with low
shrinkage and creep characteristics and high strength steels which allow
high initial strains, so that despite some loss of prestressing force due
to shrinkage and creep ample prestress will remain.   The wires or bars used
to provide the prestressing force may be either straight or curved depending
on the application and they may be grouped to form a single cable or
distributed to form several cables.

The terms pretensioning and post-tensioning are used, they indicate whether
the tendons are tensioned before the concrete is cast or after it has been
cured.   Pretensioned prestressed concrete is suitable for factory made
units, the wires are tensioned between rigid bulkheads and the wet concrete
is cast round them.   After the concrete has cured the tension in the wires
is released and the bond between steel and concrete causes the concrete to
be compressed.   Post-tensioned prestressed concrete is more suitable for
use on sites where the concrete is cast in-situ.   Ducts are formed in the
concrete for the cables which are tensioned after the concrete has cured.

The rest of this chapter introduces the calculations necessary to determine
the stresses due to prestress and applied bending moments in a member of
given size.   Later chapters show the design process of obtaining section
sizes to satisfy the various limit states.

16.B. BENDING MOMENT DUE TO PRESTRESS

The precompression in the concrete is most effective when it produces
bending moments of opposite sign to those produced by the dead and imposed
loads.   Fig. 16.2 shows this effect for a simply supported beam with a
straight prestressing cable.   In Fig. 16.2(a) the beam is shown with its
straight tendon carrying a prestressing force P at eccentricity e.
Alongside is shown the uniform bending moment Pe.   In Fig. 16.2(b) the beam
is shown carrying the uniformly distributed dead and imposed load w per
metre giving a parabolic bending moment diagram with a maximum value of
$wl^2/8$.   The loads and prestress are shown combined in Fig. 16.2(c) and the
final bending moment diagram is shown alongside.   It can be seen that part
of the effect of the prestressing force is to reduce the bending moment in
the beam.

If the tendon is curved its slope is usually so small that the force
parallel to the centroidal axis of the beam may be assumed to be equal to
the force in the tendon and the bending moment diagram due to the prestressing
force takes a shape similar to that of the curved cable.

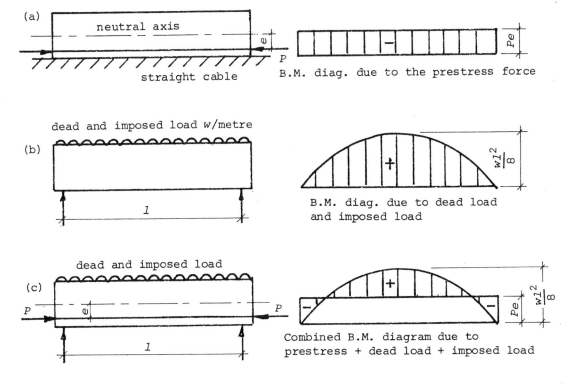

Fig. 16.2

QUESTION 16.1

If the prestressing cable is curved as shown in Fig. 16.3(a) sketch the bending moment diagram due to the prestressing force P. It may be assumed that the slope α of the cable at the ends of the beam is small.

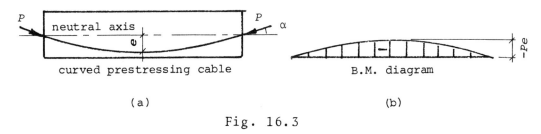

(a)   (b)

Fig. 16.3

(Answer: see Fig. 16.3(b)).

16.C. STRESS DUE TO THE PRESTRESSING FORCE

The effect of an eccentric prestressing force at a cross section is to
produce an axial stress and a bending stress.   If the cross section of
the beam is the same at every section, then the axial stress is the same at
every section.   The bending stress due to the eccentricity of the
prestressing force varies as the eccentricity varies.

EXAMPLE 16.1

Determine the stresses due to the prestressing force for the cross section
of the beam shown in Fig. 16.4(a).   The sign convention is - ve compression
and + ve tension.

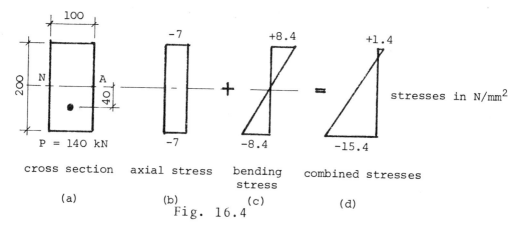

cross section   axial stress   bending   combined stresses
                                 stress

(a)   (b)   (c)   (d)

Fig. 16.4

area $A = 20 \times 10^3$ mm^2

elastic section modulus $Z = \dfrac{I}{y} = \dfrac{BD^2}{6} = \dfrac{100 \times (200)^2}{6}$ mm^3

axial stress $= -\dfrac{P}{A} = -\dfrac{140 \times 10^3}{20 \times 10^3} = -7$ N/mm^2 see Fig. 16.4(b)

bending stress $= \pm \dfrac{Pe}{Z}$ (from theory of bending $\dfrac{M}{I} = \dfrac{f}{y}$)

$= \pm \dfrac{140 \times 10^3 \times 40}{(100 \times 200^2)/6} = \pm 8.4$ N/mm^2 see Fig. 16.4(c)

These stresses are now added to give the result shown in Fig. 16.4(d).

QUESTION 16.2

If for the beam of Fig. 16.4(a) the cable is curved and the eccentricity at
another section is 20 mm below the neutral axis, determine the stresses due
to the prestressing force at this section.

(Answer: -2.8 N/mm^2, top;   -11.2 N/mm^2, bottom.)

16.D. STRESSES IN NON-RECTANGULAR SECTIONS

The best design of a prestressed concrete section frequently produces a cross section which is not rectangular.   The analysis is more difficult but the same approach is used as for the rectangular cross section.

EXAMPLE 16.2

Determine the stresses due to the prestressing force of 1600kN for the cross section of a beam shown in Fig. 16.5(a).

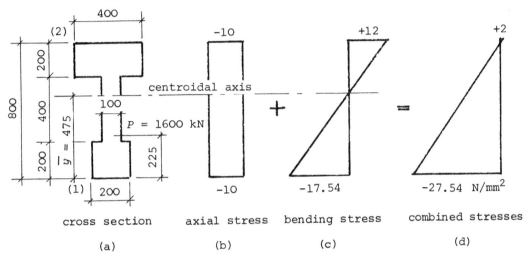

cross section	axial stress	bending stress	combined stresses
(a)	(b)	(c)	(d)

Fig. 16.5

cross sectional area A = (80 + 40 + 40) x 10^3 = 160 x 10^3 mm^2.

axial stress = $\dfrac{P}{A}$ = $\dfrac{1.6 \times 10^6}{160 \times 10^3}$ = -10 N/mm^2 (see Fig. 16.5(b)

moments of areas about the base (4 + 16 + 56) 10^6 = 160 x 10^3 $\bar{y}$

$$\bar{y} = \frac{76 \times 10^3}{160} = 475 \text{ mm}$$

second moment of area about the centroidal axis

I = $\dfrac{400 \times (325)^3}{3}$ - $\dfrac{300 \times (125)^3}{3}$ + $\dfrac{200 \times (475)^3}{3}$ - $\dfrac{100 \times 275^3}{3}$

= (4576 - 195 + 7144 - 693) x 10^6 = 10.83 x 10^9 mm^4 note: I = $\dfrac{BD^3}{3}$

elastic section modulus bottom Z_1 = 10.83 x 10^9 / 475 = 22.80 x 10^6 mm^3

"   "   "   top Z_2 = 10.83 x 10^9 / 325 = 33.32 x 10^6 mm^3

bending stress bottom $f_1 = \dfrac{Pe}{Z_1} = \dfrac{1.6 \times 10^6 \times 250}{22.80 \times 10^6} = -17.54 \text{ N/mm}^2$

"   "   top $f_2 = \dfrac{Pe}{Z_2} = \dfrac{1.6 \times 10^6 \times 250}{33.32 \times 10^6} = +12.00 \text{ N/mm}^2$

see Fig. 16.5(c)

adding stresses   stress at top $f_{1t} = -10.00 + 12.00 = +2.00 \text{ N/mm}^2$

stress at bottom $f_{2t} = -10.00 - 17.54 = -27.54 \text{ N/mm}^2$

(see Fig. 16.5(d))

QUESTION 16.3

Determine the eccentricity of the prestressing force if the stress at the
top of the section is zero for the section shown in Example 16.2.

(Answer: 208.3 mm)

16.E. LOSS OF PRESTRESSING FORCE

The magnitude of the prestressing force reduces with time from a maximum
during tensioning to a minimum after some years.   The rate of loss is high
in early life and approximately three quarters of all losses will have taken
place in the first three months.   The loss occurs due to creep and
shrinkage in the concrete, relaxation of the steel, friction etc.   Loss of
prestress will be dealt with more fully later but for the moment it should
be appreciated that the loss can vary between 10% and 40% of the initial
prestressing force.

QUESTION 16.4

Determine the stress in the beam section in Example 16.2 after a 20% loss
of prestressing force.

(Answer: $f_1 = -22.03$, $f_2 = +1.60 \text{ N/mm}^2$)

16.F. BENDING STRESSES DUE TO LOADS

The stresses produced in the concrete by the prestressing force are
modified by the stresses produced by the dead load and superimposed load.
The application of the loads will change the stress in the tendon but in
general this change is small and may be ignored.

EXAMPLE 16.3

Determine the change in bending stresses at midspan due to dead load and imposed load for a simply supported beam spanning 8m carrying an imposed load of 1.5 kN/m.   The cross section and prestress are as given in Example 16.1.   The density of the concrete is 2300 kg/m³.

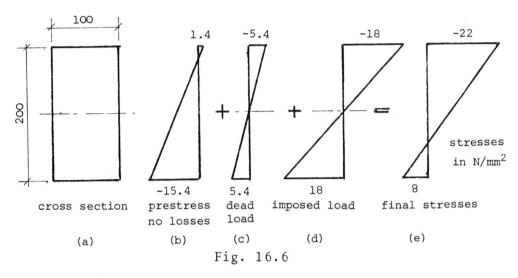

Fig. 16.6

dead load
(self weight
in this case)
$= \dfrac{100 \times 200 \times 1 \times 2{,}300 \times 9.81}{10^6} = \dfrac{2 \times 23 \times 9.81}{10^3} = 0.45 \text{ kN/m}$

At midspan

bending moment M_{DL} due to dead load $= \dfrac{wl^2}{8} = \dfrac{0.45 \times 8^2}{8} = 3.6 \text{ kNm}$

extreme fibre stresses due to dead load $\quad f_{DL} = \pm \dfrac{M}{Z} = \pm \dfrac{3.6 \times 10^6}{(100 \times 200^2)/6} = \pm 5.4 \text{ N/mm}^2$

bending moment M_{IL} due to imposed load $= \dfrac{wl^2}{8} = \dfrac{1.5 \times 8^2}{8} = 12 \text{ kNm}$

extreme fibre stresses due to imposed load $\quad f_{IL} = \pm \dfrac{M}{Z} = \pm \dfrac{12 \times 10^6}{(100 \times 200^2)/6} = \pm 18.0 \text{ N/mm}^2$

The most critical condition may be when the loss of prestress has occurred.

In the above case the maximum tensile stress at the bottom of the section would occur due to

Prestress (after losses) + Dead Load + Imposed Load

QUESTION 16.5

(a) Determine the stresses in the concrete at quarter span due to prestress and dead load and imposed load for the beam in Example 16.3, assuming that the cross section and position of the prestressing force are unchanged.   Assume no loss of prestressing force.

(b) Modify the above calculation for a 30% loss of prestressing force.

(Answers are given in Fig. 16.7(a) & (b))

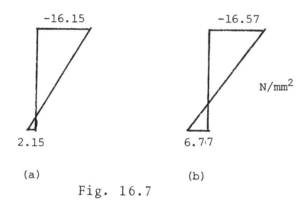

-16.15   -16.57

N/mm²

2.15   6.7'7

(a)   (b)

Fig. 16.7

QUESTION 16.6

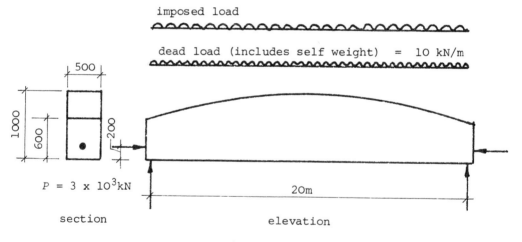

imposed load

dead load (includes self weight)   =   10 kN/m

500

1000

600

200

$P = 3 \times 10^3$ kN

20m

section   elevation

Fig. 16.8

Fig. 16.8 shows an elevation of a prestressed concrete beam for a bridge deck.   Its cross section is rectangular at any section with a width of 500 mm but its depth varies from 600 mm at the supports to 1000 mm at mid span.   The prestressing cable is straight and located as shown and applies a force of 3×10^3 kN.   The dead load, which includes self weight, may be assumed to be a uniformly distributed load of 10 kN/m.

Determine:-

(a) the stresses in the concrete at the supports of the beam due to the prestressing force assuming no loss.

(b) the stresses in the concrete at midspan due to the prestressing force and the dead load assuming no loss in prestressing force.

(c) the maximum value of the imposed uniformly distributed load in kN/m if the stress limits are f_{top} ≯ -20 N/mm², f_{bottom} ≯ $+5$ N/mm², assuming no loss of prestressing force

(d) as (c) but with 20% loss of prestressing force.

(Answers: (a) given in Fig. 16.9(a), (b) given in Fig. 16.9(b), (c) w ≯ 26.33 kN/m, (d) w ≯ 20.73 kN/m.)

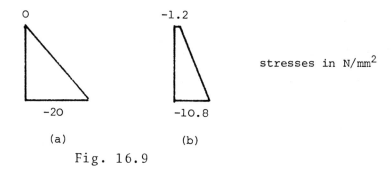

stresses in N/mm²

(a)   (b)

Fig. 16.9

QUESTION 16.7

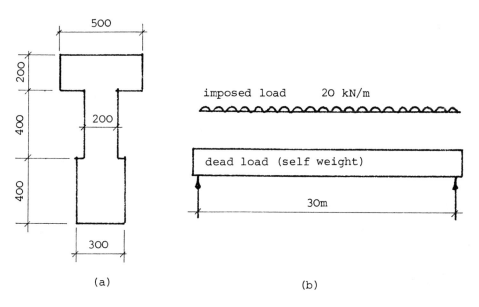

(a)   (b)

Fig. 16.10

Fig. 16.10(a) shows the cross section of a prestressed concrete beam which is simply supported over a span of 30 m.

The dead load, which acts immediately the prestressing force is applied to the member, may be taken as the self weight of the beam (assume the density of the concrete to be 2300 kg/m^3) and the imposed load is 20 kN/m run as shown in Fig. 16.10(b).

Determine the magnitude and position of the prestressing force which will ensure that the tensile stress at midspan does not exceed 5 N/mm^2.

It may be assumed that the critical load combinations at midspan are:

(1) prestress and dead load for tensile stress at the top of the section, no loss of prestressing force immediately at transfer

(2) prestress and dead load and imposed load for tensile stress at the bottom of the section with 20% loss of prestressing force.

(Answer: $\bar{y}$ = 540 mm from base, I_{NA} = 30.12 x 10^9 mm^4 P_t = 5.757 x 10^3 kN,

e = 407.4 mm)

17 Design of Prestressed Concrete for Bending

17.A. INTRODUCTION

Chapter 16 dealt with the elastic analysis of a prestressed concrete beam section in bending. The cross section was given and stresses in various critical states were considered. Familiarity with these calculations is necessary to understand the design process to determine the size and shape of a cross section for a chosen loading condition.

The simplest cross section to design is a rectangular cross section. The only problems then are the ratio of breadth to depth and the actual dimensions of the section. The rectangular cross section is not however the optimum. The optimum cross section is often an 'I' section which may involve considerable work in calculation to meet all the restraints imposed by the design.

The various parts of the 'I' cross section are generally determined from the requirements shown in the Fig. 17.1.

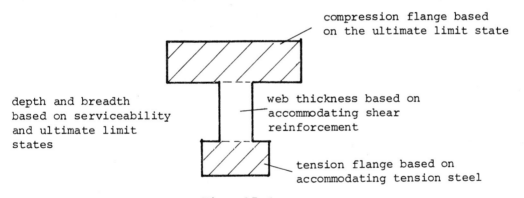

compression flange based on the ultimate limit state

depth and breadth based on serviceability and ultimate limit states

web thickness based on accommodating shear reinforcement

tension flange based on accommodating tension steel

Fig. 17.1

The design process adopted to determine the optimum cross section is often a system of trial and error.

After accommodating the spatial and architectural requirements the first trial cross section calculations require that characteristic strengths and allowable stress at the service limit state be selected.

17.B. STRESS LIMITATIONS UNDER SERVICE CONDITIONS (cl.4.3.3.2)

The selection of characteristic strengths and allowable stresses is related to method of manufacture, method of construction and site conditions. Pretensioned prestressed concrete beams are generally manufactured under well controlled factory conditions. The "long line" system is then used to great advantage for the manufacture of a number of identical beams. The system uses single straight wires which are pretensioned and anchored to the casting bed prior to casting the concrete. When the concrete has matured the final anchorage in the beam is effected by bond between the steel and concrete.

Post tensioned prestressed concrete beams are generally manufactured on site where in-situ concrete is required. After casting and when the concrete has matured the prestressing force is provided by strands or bars (curved or straight), which are anchored at the ends by wedges (or nuts on a screw thread for some bars).

Prestressed concrete has been developed to make use of high strength concrete and steel. The characteristic strength of the concrete therefore lies between 30 and 60 N/mm^2. Grade 30 concrete is not generally used except for the cast insitu part of composite construction. Grades 40, 50 and 60 are used for all other prestressed concrete work.

The characteristic strength of the steel varies between 1000 to 2000 N/mm^2 depending on the size of wire or bar. Values of strength for a wire, strand or bar are given in Tables 29, 30 and 31 (CP110). The allowable compressive stress at transfer is related to cube strength at transfer as shown in Table 36 (CP110). The allowable compressive stress at the serviceability limit states is related to the compressive characteristic strength as shown in Table 32 (CP110). It may be seen that the allowable stresses at transfer are

Table 36. Allowable compressive stresses at transfer

Nature of stress distribution	Allowable compressive stresses f_{ct}
Triangular or near triangular distribution of prestress	$0.5f_{ci}$
Uniform or near uniform distribution of prestress	$0.4f_{ci}$

Table 32. Compressive stresses in concrete for serviceability limit states

Nature of loading	Allowable compressive stresses f_{ce}
Design load in bending	$0.33f_{cu}$ In continuous beams and other statically indeterminate structures this may be increased to $0.4f_{cu}$ within the range of support moments
Design load in direct compression	$0.25f_{cu}$

4.1.4.3 *Characteristic strength of prestressing tendons.* The specified characteristic strengths of prestressing tendons are given in the appropriate British Standards and are quoted in Tables 29, 30 and 31.

Table 29. Specified characteristic strengths of prestressing wire

Nominal size	Specified characteristic strength $A_{ps} f_{pu}$	Nominal cross-sectional area A_{ps}
mm	kN	mm^2
2	6.34	3.14
2.65	10.3	5.5
3	12.2	7.1
3.25	14.3	8.3
4	21.7	12.6
4.5	25.7	15.9
5	30.8	19.6
7	60.4	38.5

Table 30. Specified characteristic strengths of prestressing strand

Number of wires	Nominal size	Specified characteristic strength $A_{ps} f_{pu}$	Nominal cross-sectional area A_{ps}
	mm	kN	mm^2
7	6.4	44.5	24.5
	7.9	69.0	37.4
	9.3	93.5	52.3
	10.9	125	71.0
	12.5	165	94.2
	15.2	227	138.7
19	18	370	210
	25.4	659	423
	28.6	823	535
	31.8	979	660

Table 31. Specified characteristic strengths of prestressing bars

Nominal size	Specified characteristic strength $A_{ps} f_{pu}$	Nominal cross-sectional area A_{ps}
mm	kN	mm^2
*20	325	314
22	375	380
*25	500	491
28	625	615
*32	800	804
35	950	961
*40	1250	1257

* Preferred sizes.

higher than at the serviceability limit states.   This is because the effects of creep and shrinkage will soon cause reduction of stress.   The stresses allowed at transfer are, therefore, short term stresses.   The stresses at the serviceability limit states are long term stresses.

Tensile stresses are allowed in monolithically cast structures but not in structures which are built up from precast blocks with mortar joints. Structures are classified according to the tensile stress as follows:

Class 1 members.   No tensile stresses are allowed except at transfer when a tensile stress of 1.0 N/mm^2 is permitted for monolithically cast members only.

Class 2 members.   Small tensile stresses are allowed but these should not produce cracks.   Values of allowable tensile stresses are given in Table 33 (CP110).

Table 33. Flexural tensile stresses for Class 2 members: serviceability limit state: cracking

	Allowable stress for concrete grade f_{te}			
	30	40	50	60
	N/mm^2	N/mm^2	N/mm^2	N/mm^2
Pre-tensioned members	—	2.9	3.2	3.5
Post-tensioned members	2.1	2.3	2.55	2.8

Class 3 members.   Cracking of the concrete is allowed but the crack width is limited.   To make work easier calculations are allowed on the basis of the uncracked section using the allowable tensile stresses given in Table 34 (CP110) which must be modified for depth of section by multiplying by the depth factor given in Table 35 (CP110).   Crack widths should not exceed 0.2 mm but in aggressive environments they should be restricted to 0.1 mm.

Table 34. Hypothetical flexural tensile stresses for Class 3 members

Group	Limiting crack width	Stress for concrete grade f_{te}		
		30	40	50 and over
	mm	N/mm^2	N/mm^2	N/mm^2
A. Pre-tensioned tendons	0.1	—	4.1	4.8
	0.2	—	5.0	5.8
B. Grouted post-tensioned tendons	0.1	3.2	4.1	4.8
	0.2	3.8	5.0	5.8
C. Pre-tensioned tendons distributed in the tensile zone and positioned close to the tension faces of the concrete	0.1	—	5.3	6.3
	0.2	—	6.3	7.3

Table 35. Depth factors for tensile stresses for Class 3 members

Depth of member (mm) 200 and under	400	600	800	1000 and over
1.1	1.0	0.9	0.8	0.7

If additional untensioned reinforcement is used in Class 3 members the tensile stress obtained from Table 4 (CP110) may be increased as indicated in the following extract from cl.4.3.3.2.2(CP110).

When additional reinforcement is contained within the tension zone and positioned close to the tension faces of the concrete, these hypothetical tensile stresses may be increased by an amount which is proportional to the cross-sectional areas of the additional reinforcement expressed as a percentage of the cross-sectional area of the concrete. For 1 % of additional reinforcement the stresses in Table 34 may be increased by 4.0 N/mm² for members in groups A and B and by 3.0 N/mm² for members in group C. For other percentages of additional reinforcement the stresses may be increased in proportion excepting that the total hypothetical tensile stress should not exceed one quarter of the characteristic cube strength of the concrete.

QUESTION 17.1

It has been decided to design a post tensioned prestressed concrete beam using 20 mm diameter bars.   It is to be constructed of precast blocks with mortar joints and will be used on a simply supported span.   The strength of the concrete on application of the prestress should be two thirds of the characteristic strength.   The prestressing force produces a triangular distribution of stress in the concrete.   Determine the maximum permitted values according to CP110 of the characteristic strengths, the allowable stresses at transfer and at the service limit state.

(Answer: f_{cu} = 60 N/mm²; $A_{ps} f_{pu}$ = 325 kN; f_{ci} = -40; f_{ct} = -20;

f_{tt} = 0; f_{ec} = -20; f_{et} = 0 N/mm²)

17.C. ULTIMATE STRENGTH OF PRESTRESSED CONCRETE BEAMS

(a) BONDED TENDONS

The design of prestressed concrete members at the ultimate limit state in bending is similar to that for reinforced concrete given in Chapters 6, 7 and 8.   The basis of the method is the equilibrium of tensile forces in the steel with the compression forces in the concrete and the equilibrium of the internal moment of resistance of a section with the external applied bending moment.   The strain distribution across the depth of the section is assumed to be linear and the stresses are obtained from the stress/strain relationships for concrete and steel shown in Figs 1, 3 and 4 (CP110).

Figs. 3 and 4 (CP110) are not reproduced in this book but they are for different types of prestressing steel. Their general form is similar to that of Fig. 2 (CP110). Graphs relating M/bd^2 against $100 A_{ps}/bd$ have been prepared using this information. The graphs also give values of x/d which can be used to determine the depth of the compression zone. Their use requires an initial estimate of b and d which may require subsequent correction. The graphs also require an estimate of the effective prestress f_{pe}, which is the initial stress in the cable (generally 70% of the characteristic strength) reduced by the loss in prestressing force of between 10% and 40% of the initial prestress in the cable. The effective stress in the cable f_{pe} should not be taken as greater than $0.6 f_{pu}$. The effective stress in the wire must be known because the strain due to the effective stress must be added to the strain from the linear strain distribution in order to find the stress in the tendon at failure.

The method in use is to determine

(a) the applied bending moment M_u at the ultimate limit state of bending including an estimate of the effect of the self weight.

(b) estimate b and d (d approx $\frac{1}{30}$ span). b is the breadth of the compression flange.

(c) calculate M_u/bd^2.

(d) choose a characteristic cube strength f_{cu} and a characteristic steel strength f_{pu}.

(e) estimate the value of $\dfrac{100 f_{pe}}{f_{pu}} = \dfrac{100\, \eta\ (\text{initial prestress})}{f_{pu}}$.

(f) from the graph (see typical graph on page 217) determine $100A_{ps}/bd$. This should generally be less than about 1.0% so as to limit x/d to less than 0.5 in order to produce a plastic failure with ample warning of collapse.

(g) check that $100A_{ps}/b_sh$ is greater 0.15% (cl.4.9.2 (CP110)) to ensure that sudden failure of the tendons does not occur when the concrete cracks.

(h) revise if necessary.

The ultimate strength approach to the design of prestressed concrete beams may indicate a greater quantity of steel than that needed to ensure that excessive cracking does not occur at the serviceability limit state. It is sometimes suggested that untensioned steel can be used for the extra strength. For the purposes of this book it is assumed that all the steel will be tensioned even though the amount of prestress is lower than that permitted. Methods for the calculation of the ultimate strength of beams containing unstressed steel are given in The Handbook on the Unified Code. The ultimate strength of prestressed concrete beams can be determined by other methods which are given in CP110.

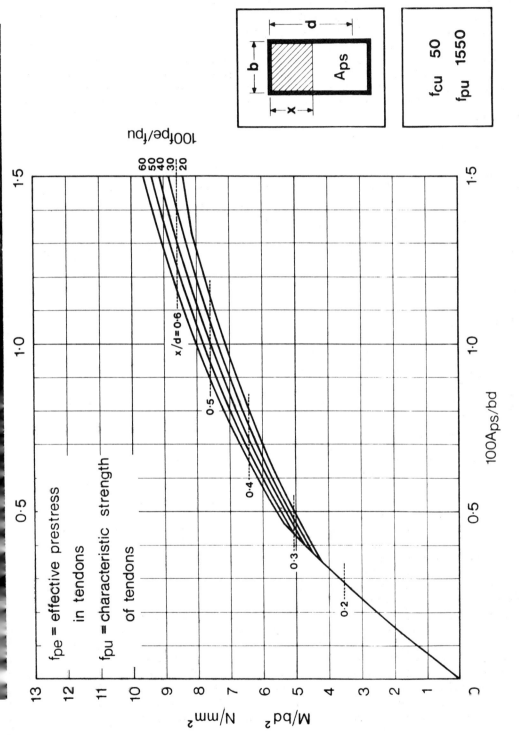

Prestressed beams Tendons of 'as drawn' wire or 'as spun' strand

(b) UNBONDED TENDONS

The foregoing methods must be revised if unbonded tendons are used.   Where
a beam with a bonded tendon is loaded to failure the effect of the bond is
to ensure that a high level of stress, approaching the ultimate is reached
in the tendon.   In an unbonded tendon the strains at each section tend to
average out over the length of the cable so that the stress in the steel
does not reach such high levels and the ultimate strength of the beam is
correspondingly low.   A method for the assessment of the strength of beams
with unbonded tendons is given in CP110, but it is not dealt with in detail
in this book.

QUESTION 17.2

Determine the area of tensile steel A_{ps} required and the depth of the
compression zone x at the ultimate limit state for a member where:

$$M_u = 1.4 \, G_k + 1.6 \, Q_k = 124 \text{ KNm}$$

Assume $b = 200$ mm, $d = 350$ mm, $f_{cu} = 50 \text{ N/mm}^2$, $f_{pu} = 1550 \text{ N/mm}^2$, $f_{pe} = 0.6 \, f_{pu}$

(use the graph given on page 217)

(Answers: $A_{ps} = 308 \text{ mm}^2$, $x = 105$ mm)

17.D. MINIMUM PRACTICAL CROSS SECTION

The consideration of the bending moment at the ultimate limit state provides
the information shown in full lines in Fig. 17.2.

The web thickness must be
sufficient to accommodate the
shear reinforcement and the
tendon if it is curved; a
thickness of 100 mm is required.
The bottom flange is often
controlled by the area required
to provide cover and spacing to
the tendon and any additional
reinforcement.   Values for
cover are the same as those for
reinforced concrete given
in Table 19 (CP110).   The

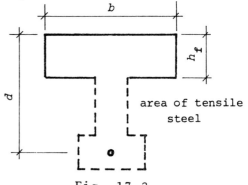

Fig. 17.2

spacing of single wires in pretensioned beams is controlled by the size of
aggregate, the use of the poker vibrator and the necessity to control
splitting along the wires at the ends of the beam.   Values of 25 mm have
been used, but if possible this should be increased.   Cable or bar spacing
should generally be greater than 100 mm.   There will of course be more than
one possible arrangement of wires or cables at each cross section, and the
final choice must be decided on a trial and error basis.

If the number of wires or cables is based on the ultimate limit state
requirement then to ensure that the wires are in tension they must all lie
outside the compression zone.

EXAMPLE 17.1

Design a suitable section for a simply supported prestressed concrete beam
to carry an imposed load of 30 kN/m on a span of 8 m. Use f_{cu} = 50 N/mm^2
and assume a self weight for the beam of 300 kg/m.

$$M_u = \frac{1.6 \times 30 \times 8^2}{8} + \frac{1.4 \times 300 \times 9.81 \times 8^2}{10^3 \qquad 8}$$

$$= 384 + 33 = 417 \text{ kNm}$$

for an effective depth d = 600 mm

and a breadth b = 400 mm

$$\frac{M}{bd^2} = \frac{417 \times 10^6}{400 \times 600^2} = 2.90$$

from the graph (CP110:Pt3) for f_{cu} = 50 N/mm and f_{pu} = 1550

$$\frac{100A_{ps}}{bd} = 0.24; \quad \text{therefore } A_{ps} = \frac{0.24 \times 400 \times 600}{100} = 576 \text{ mm}^2$$

From Table 30 (CP110) area of steel 2 - 25.4 mm 19 wire strands (alternatively
use 3 - 18 mm 19 wire strands)

x/d is less than 0.2, therefore x is less than 120 mm, hence h_f must be not
less than 120 mm.

Alternatively using approximate methods assuming a lever arm $z \simeq$ 500 mm, the
stress in the compression zone of 0.4 f_{cu} (cl.4.3.4.1(CP110)), and taking
moments about the tensile steel

$$0.4 \times 50 \times 500 \times 400 \, x = 417 \times 10^6$$

$$x = 104.3 \text{ mm}$$

Make flange 150 mm thick.

Assuming that the cable reaches its
full stress of 0.87 f_{pu} and the lever
arm is now given by

z = 600 - 104.3/2 = 547.8

Force in steel = $\dfrac{417 \times 10^6}{547.8 \times 10^3}$ = 761 kN

2 - 25.4 mm 19 wire strands

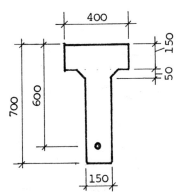

QUESTION 17.3

Using the information and answers given for
Question 17.2, determine suitable flange
thickness, web thickness, and tendon size for a
'T' beam cross section.

*(Answer: h_f = 120 mm, b_w = 100 mm, 2 - 18 mm -
19 wire strands or 1 - 25.4 mm - 19 wire strand
as shown in Fig. 17.3)*

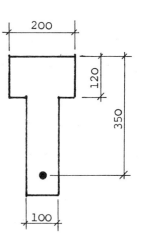

Fig. 17.3

17.E. ELASTIC ANALYSIS FOR SERVICEABILITY STRESSES

The provision of a top flange from the ultimate limit state, the web for
shear and a bottom flange to accommodate the steel presents a minimum
practical 'I' section to check for cracking at the serviceability limit
state.   One advantage of prestressed concrete over reinforced concrete is
that cracking can be prevented at the serviceability limit state.   If the
section is uncracked (or only slightly cracked) then the stresses may be
determined using an elastic analysis.

The methods of Chapter 16 make it possible to identify several critical
conditions where the stresses in the concrete may exceed the limiting values.

1. When the prestressing force is transferred to the concrete and only the
     self weight is acting.   (The dead load can be greater than the self weight
     of the beam).

2. When the dead load modifies the stresses produced by the prestressing
     force at transfer.

3. When the dead load only modifies the stresses produced by the prestressing
     force after losses (the method of calculating losses will be given later).

4. When the dead and imposed load modifies the stresses produced by the
     prestressing force after losses.

5. Handling conditions may control the design for precast units.

These conditions may be combined to produce expressions which give the
MINIMUM elastic section modulus for the section, the prestressing force and
its eccentricity.   In each case both the allowable compressive stress and
the allowable tensile stress must be considered.

The minimum cross section for a simply supported beam carrying a uniformly
distributed load must have the cable or beam shaped to give variation of the
eccentricity of the prestressing force.

Application of all the conditions which may control the design often does not give a unique position for the cable even at the position of maximum bending moment. The cable can usually be positioned anywhere within a band similar to that shown in Fig. 17.4 for a simply supported beam. It may be seen that the band width is small at the position of maximum bending moment and large where the bending moment is zero. The band width may be zero at the position of maximum bending moment if the cross section is a true minimum.

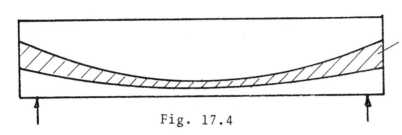

band in which prestressing cable may be placed.

Fig. 17.4

CASES 1 and 2 are similar except that the bending moments due to dead load are different (M_{min} in the following).

Referring to Fig. 17.5

at the bottom of the section

$$f_{t1} = -\frac{P_t}{A} - \frac{P_t e}{Z_1} + \frac{M_{min}}{Z_1} \qquad \ldots \ldots \ldots 17.1$$

at the top of the section

$$f_{t2} = -\frac{P_t}{A} + \frac{P_t e}{Z_2} - \frac{M_{min}}{Z_2} \qquad \ldots \ldots \ldots 17.2$$

the stress f_{t1} and f_{t2} should lie between the allowable compressive stress at transfer f_{tc} and the allowable tensile stress at transfer f_{tt}. In practice the most common situation is that f_{t1} should not exceed f_{tc}, and f_{t2} should not exceed f_{tt}.

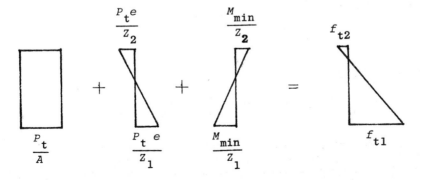

Fig. 17.5

M_{min} in Equations 17.1 and 17.2 and in Fig. 17.5 may be either the bending moment due to self weight only or it may be due to the whole or part of the dead load depending on the stage of construction at which the prestressing force is applied.

CASE 3 - Referring to Fig. 17.6

at the bottom of the section

$$f_{el} = - \frac{P_e}{A} - \frac{P_e e}{Z_1} + \frac{M_{min}}{Z_1} \qquad \ldots \ldots 17.3$$

at the top of the section

$$f_{e2} = - \frac{P_e}{A} + \frac{P_e e}{Z_2} - \frac{M_{min}}{Z_2} \qquad \ldots \ldots 17.4$$

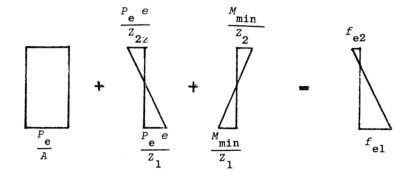

Fig. 17.6

M_{min} is usually the bending moment due to the characteristic dead load for a simply supported beam.

CASE 4 - Referring to Fig. 17.7

at the bottom of the section

$$f_{el} = - \frac{P_e}{A} - \frac{P_e e}{Z_1} + \frac{M_s}{Z_1} \qquad \ldots \ldots 17.5$$

at the top of the section

$$f_{e2} = - \frac{P_e}{A} + \frac{P_e e}{Z_2} - \frac{M_s}{Z_2} \qquad \ldots \ldots 17.6$$

M_{max} must be the true maximum bending moment at the serviceability limit states which will be due to the sum of the characteristic dead loads and the characteristic imposed loads. In both cases 3 and 4 the values of f_{el} and f_{e2} must fall between the allowable tensile stress f_{et} and the allowable compressive stress f_{ec}.

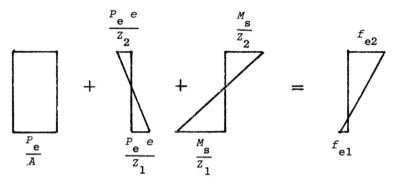

Fig. 17.7

CASE 5 cannot be covered in any general way, each case must be considered separately.

Although all the cases listed can apply for many designs the truly critical cases are 1 (or 2 or 3) and 4, that is minimum load with prestress before or after losses and maximum load with prestress after losses.

From the six equations 17.1 to 17.6 inclusive some useful design equations can be developed.

Combining equations 17.1 and 17.5 and putting

$$f_{t1} = f_{tc} \; ; \; f_{el} = f_{et} \; \text{and} \; Z_1 = Z_1'$$

$$Z_1' = \frac{M_s - \eta \, M_{min}}{f_{et} - \eta \, f_{tc}} \qquad \ldots \ldots \; 17.7$$

$$\text{where } \eta = \frac{P_e}{P_t} \qquad \ldots \ldots \; 17.8$$

Combining equations 17.2 and 17.6 and putting

$$f_{t2} = f_{tt} \; ; \; f_{e2} = f_{ec} \; \text{and} \; Z_2 = Z_2'$$

$$Z_2' = \frac{M_s - \eta \, M_{min}}{\eta \, f_{tt} - f_{ec}} \qquad \ldots \ldots \; 17.9$$

Equations 17.7 and 17.8 give the smallest allowable values for section modulus if the tensile stresses at transfer and the compressive stresses at full load and after losses control the design.   If however the losses are not too high and transfer is not made at too early an age Equation 17.3 can be combined with Equation 17.5 and Equation 17.4 can be combined with Equation 17.6, which gives

$$Z_1'' = Z_2'' = \frac{M_s - M_{min}}{f_{et} - f_{ec}} \qquad \ldots \ldots \ldots \; 17.10$$

The actual values of z_1 and z_2 must be greater than the values given by Equations 17.7, 17.8 and 17.10   If the actual values of z_1 and z_2 are very close to the theoretical minimum values the section is often found to be overstressed at some stage because the conditions of minimum load and maximum load are considered separately, both with the maximum range of stresses. A larger section may be necessary to avoid overstressing.

The cable position and the prestressing force must now be determined.   The lowest prestressing force and the lowest cable position will be given if it is assumed that the allowable tensile stresses are reached but that the compressive stresses will be within the limiting values.   To achieve this situation Equations 17.2 and 17.5 must be combined making the substitutions

$$f_{t2} = f_{tt} \quad \text{and} \quad f_{e1} = f_{et}$$

then P_{t1} $\quad = \quad \dfrac{A \, (f_{et} \, z_1 + \eta \, f_{tt} \, z_2 - M_s + \eta \, M_{min})}{- \eta \, (z_1 + z_2)}$ 17.11

and e_1 $\quad = \quad \dfrac{z_1 \, z_1 \, (f_{et} - \eta \, f_{tt}) - \eta \, M_{min} \, z_1 - M_s \, z_2}{A(f_{te} \, z_1 + \eta \, f_{tt} \, z_2 - M_s + \eta M_{min})}$ 17.12

Correspondingly the highest cable position and the highest prestressing force will be obtained if it is assumed that the maximum allowable compressive stresses are reached with the tensile stresses falling within the limit.   A pair of equations similar to Equations 17.11 and 17.12 may be obtained by combining Equations 17.1 and 17.6 and putting

$$f_{t1} = f_{tc} \quad \text{and} \quad f_{e2} = f_{ec}$$

then $P_{t2} =$ $\quad \dfrac{A \, (f_{ec} \, z_2 + \eta \, f_{tc} \, z_1 + M_s - \eta \, M_{min})}{- \eta \, (z_1 + z_2)}$ 17.13

and e_2 $\quad = \quad \dfrac{z_1 \, z_2 \, (-f_{ec} + \eta \, f_{tc}) - \eta \, M_{min} \, z_2 - M_s \, z_1}{A \, (f_{ec} \, z_2 + \eta \, f_{tc} \, z_1 + M_s - \eta \, M_{min})}$ 17.14

The use of Equations 17.7, 17.8 and 17.9 enables a quick check to be made on the section size obtained by using the methods of 17.D.   Equations 17.12 and 17.14 give the lower and upper bounds of the band within which the cable must lie.   It must be noted that if the cable is placed at an intermediate position between the positions indicated by Equation 17.12 or Equation 17.14 the magnitude of the prestressing force must be calculated by substitution of assumed values of eccentricity and allowable stresses into a suitable pair chosen from Equations 17.1 to 17.6 inclusive.

Use of the above equations does not give an absolute guarantee that allowable stresses are not exceeded. This is further discussed in 17.G.

EXAMPLE 17.2

The beam of example 17.1 is to be stressed as a Class 2 member. Determine the upper and lower cable positions and the corresponding prestressing forces. It may be assumed that the beam is post-tensioned, that there will be 22% losses and that the cube strength at transfer is 36 N/mm^2.

Cross sectional area $A = 250 \times 150 + 150 \times 700 + 2 \times 50 \times \dfrac{50}{2}$

$$= 145.0 \times 10^3 \quad mm^2$$

Taking Moments about the top

$145 \times 10^3 \times \bar{y} = 250 \times 150 \times 75 + 150 \times 700 \times 350 + 2 \times 50 \times \dfrac{50}{2}\left(150 + \dfrac{50}{3}\right)$

$\bar{y} = 275$ mm

$I = \dfrac{400 \times 275^3}{3} - \dfrac{250 \times 125^3}{3} + \dfrac{2 \times 50 \times 50}{2}\left(125 - \dfrac{50}{3}\right)^2 + \dfrac{150 \times 425^3}{3}$

$I = 6.48 \times 10^9$ mm^4

$Z_1 = \dfrac{6.48 \times 10^9}{425} = 15.25 \times 10^6 \quad mm^3$

$Z_2 = \dfrac{6.48 \times 10^9}{275} = 23.6 \times 10^6 \quad mm^3$

$M_{min} = \dfrac{0.145 \times 2400 \times 9.81}{10^3} \times \dfrac{8^2}{8} = 27.4$ kNm

$M_s = 30 \times \dfrac{8^2}{8} + 27.4 = 267.4$ kNm

$\eta = 0.78$

Substitution into Equation 17.7 gives

$Z_1' = \dfrac{(267.4 - 0.78 \times 27.4)10^6}{2.55 + 0.78 \times 18.0} = 14.8 \times 10^6$ mm^3

similarly from Equation 17.9

$Z_2' = \dfrac{(267.4 - 0.78 \times 27.4)10^6}{0.78 \times 2.55 + 16.67} = 13.2 \times 10^6$ mm^3

Alternatively from Equation 17.10

$Z_1'' = Z_2'' = \dfrac{(267.4 - 27.4) \times 10^6}{2.55 + 16.67} = 12.5 \times 10^6$ mm^3

The section appears to be satisfactory at this stage since all theoretical values of the elastic modulus are less than the practical values.
From equation 17.11 the lowest value of the prestressing force is:

$$P_{t1} = \frac{145 \times 10^3(2.55 \times 15.25 + 0.78 \times 2.55 \times 23.6 - 267.4 + 0.78 \times 27.4)10^6}{-0.78 \ (15.25 + 23.6) \times 10^6}$$

$$P_{t1} = 767 \times 10^3 \ \ N$$

From Equation 17.12 the corresponding eccentricity is:

$$e_1 = \frac{[15.25 \times 23.6(2.55 - 0.78 \times 2.55) - 0.78 \times 27.4 \times 15.25 - 267.4 \times 23.6]10^{12}}{145 \times 10^3(2.55 \times 15.25 + 0.78 \times 2.55 \times 23.6 - 267.4 + 0.78 \times 27.4)10^6}$$

$$= 277 \ mm$$

From Equation 17.13 the highest value of the prestressing force is:

$$P_{t2} = \frac{145 \times 10^3(-16.67 \times 23.6 - 0.78 \times 18.0 \times 15.25 + 267.4 - 0.78 \times 27.4)10^6}{-0.78(15.25 + 23.6)10^6}$$

$$= 1730 \times 10^3 \ \ N$$

From Equation 17.14 the corresponding eccentricity is:

$$e_2 = \frac{[15.25 \times 23.6(16.67 - 0.78 \times 18) - 0.78 \times 27.4 \times 23.6 - 267.4 \times 15.25] \ 10^{12}}{145 \ \times 10^3(-16.67 \times 23.6 - 0.78 \times 18.0 \times 15.25 + 267.4 - 0.78 \times 27.4)10^6}$$

$$= 70 \ mm$$

Hence the cable position can be anywhere between an eccentricity of 70 mm and 277 mm and the corresponding initial prestressing force will fall between 1730 kN and 767 kN.   It can be seen that the greater eccentricity leads to a lower prestressing force and greater economy in materials.

QUESTION 17.4

The beam cross section shown in Fig. 17.8 has been determined by considering the ultimate limit state and the accommodation of shear and prestressing steel.   Determine the actual and theoretical values of the moduli of section and the limits of cable eccentricity and the corresponding prestressing forces. M_s = 80 kNm;

M_{min} = 20 kNm; f_{tt} = 5 N/mm^2;
f_{tc} = -15 N/mm^2; f_{et} = 5 N/mm^2;
f_{ec} = -20 N/mm^2 and η = 0.75

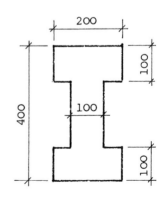

Fig. 17.8

(Answer: $Z_1 = Z_2 = 5 \times 10^6$ mm^3; $Z_1' = 4 \times 10^6$ mm^2; $Z_2' = 2.74 \times 10^6$ mm^3; $P_{t1} = 170$ kN; $e_1 = 348$ mm; $P_{t2} = 730$ kN; $e_2 = 47$ mm. Note e_1 falls outside the section and is not possible, a cable position should be chosen so that the requirements for cover are satisfied and the prestressing force worked out. The prestressing force should be the lowest possible usually obtained by considering the limiting tensile stresses at transfer and after losses.)*

17.F. CABLE SHAPE

The discussion of prestressing force and cable eccentricity has all been centred round the maximum bending moment and it has been shown that the cable position is not uniquely determined. Fig. 17.4 shows a band within which the cable may be placed. The limits of this band can be determined by substitution of the values of P_{t1} and P_{t2} into Equations 17.2 and 17.1 respectively, or Equations 17.5 and 17.6 using the values of M_s and M_{min} for sections other than that at which the maximum values occur.

In practice the position of the tendon will be fixed for the section at which the bending moment is a maximum thus the prestressing force is fixed and the limits for the cable shape can be determined.

EXAMPLE 17.3

If for the beam of Example 17.2 the cable is to be placed at 277 mm eccentricity and the initial prestressing force is 767 kN, determine the upper and lower limits for the cable position at the ends where the bending moments are zero.

The lowest cable position is the least eccentricity given by one of the following four conditions.

(i) for maximum tensile stress at the top at transfer from Equation 17.2

$$2.55 = -\frac{767}{145} + \frac{767 \times e}{23.6 \times 10^3}$$

$$\therefore \quad e = 241 \text{ mm}$$

(ii) for maximum tensile stress at the top after losses from Equation 17.4

$$2.55 = -\frac{767 \times 0.78}{145} + \frac{767 \times 0.78 \, e}{23.6 \times 10^3}$$

$$e = 263 \text{ mm}$$

(iii) for maximum compressive stress at the bottom at transfer from Equation 17.1

$$-18.0 = -\frac{767}{145} - \frac{767 \, e}{15.25 \times 10^3}$$

$$e = 253 \text{ mm}$$

(iv) for maximum compressive stress at the bottom after losses from Equation 17.3

$$-16.67 = \frac{-767 \times 0.78}{145} - \frac{767 \times 0.78 \ e}{15.25 \times 10^3}$$

$$e = 320 \ mm$$

Therefore none of the four stress limits will be exceeded if e_1 < 241 mm. For the upper limit the following two conditions should be checked.

(v) tensile stress at the bottom after loss from Equation 17.5

$$2.55 = -\frac{767 \times 0.78}{145} - \frac{767 \times 0.78 \ e}{15.25 \times 10^3}$$

$$e = -170 \ mm$$

(vi) compressive stress at the top after loss from Equation 17.6

$$-16.67 = -\frac{767 \times 0.78}{145} + \frac{767 \times 0.78 \ e}{23.6 \times 10^3}$$

$$e = -495 \ mm$$

The upper limit of cable position is e_2 = -170 mm, i.e. 170 mm above the centroidal axis.

In practice the cable position at the ends of the beam will often be determined by considerations of anchorage stresses and the physical dimensions of the anchorage.   The cable is then placed to give a smooth curve so that friction during tensioning is minimised.

QUESTION 17.5

For the beam of question 17.4 determine the limits of cable eccentricity for the section at which $M_S = M_{min}$ = 0.   Assume a final prestressing force of 235 kN and losses of 25%.

(Answer: e = ± 163 mm)

17.G. CHECK FOR STRESSES AT OTHER CONDITIONS

The procedure given in 17.E and 17.F may be used to determine the cable position and tension for certain conditions.   The conditions recommended (and used in Example 17.2) are those for dead only at transfer and full load after losses.   Nevertheless certain other conditions can arise and checks must be made to ensure that allowable stresses are not exceeded.   The additional condition most likely to occur is the application of dead load only after losses.   The dead load at this stage may not be the same as the dead load at transfer due to further construction.

It is also wise to check the stresses using the actual cable position and prestressing force in case of arithmetical error.

EXAMPLE 17.4

Determine the stresses at the likely critical load conditions for the beam of Example 17.2.   Assume P_t = 767 kN and e = 277 mm.

(i) Dead load only at transfer

$$f_{t1} = -\frac{767}{145} - \frac{767 \times 277}{15.25 \times 10^3} + \frac{27.4}{15.25} = -17.4 \text{ N/mm}^2$$

$$f_{t2} = -\frac{767}{145} + \frac{767 \times 277}{23.6 \times 10^3} - \frac{27.4}{23.6} = +2.55 \text{ N/mm}^2$$

(ii) Dead load only after losses

$$f_{e1} = -\frac{767 \times 0.78}{145} - \frac{767 \times 0.78 \times 277}{15.25 \times 10^3} + \frac{27.4}{15.25} = -13.2 \text{ N/mm}^2$$

$$f_{e2} = -\frac{767 \times 0.78}{145} + \frac{767 \times 0.78 \times 277}{23.6 \times 10^3} - \frac{27.4}{23.6} = +1.7 \text{ N/mm}^2$$

(iii) Maximum load after losses

$$f_{e1} = -\frac{767 \times 0.78}{145} - \frac{767 \times 0.78 \times 277}{15.25 \times 10^3} + \frac{267.4}{15.25} = +2.55 \text{ N/mm}^2$$

$$f_{e2} = -\frac{767 \times 0.78}{145} + \frac{767 \times 0.78 \times 277}{23.6 \times 10^3} - \frac{267.4}{23.6} = -8.4 \text{ N/mm}^2$$

All stresses are within allowable limits.

QUESTION 17.6

For the beam of Question 17.4, assuming P_t = 313 kN, e = 150 and η = 0.75 determine the stresses for the likely limiting conditions.

(Answer: At transfer f_{t1} = -10.62 N/mm^2; f_{t2} = 0.18 N/mm^2;
full load after losses
f_{e1} = 5.0 N/mm^2; f_{e2} = -12.87 N/mm^2;   dead load after losses
f_{e1} = -6.97 N/mm^2; f_{e2} = -0.87 N/mm^2)

17.H. ADJUSTMENTS TO SECTION AND CABLE POSITION

Examination of Examples 17.1 and 17.2 shows that the two sets of calculations give different quantities of prestressing steel and different effective depths.   This is common and the two sets of figures must be reconciled.   In the case of the Example the serviceability and transfer conditions indicate the smaller effective depth and a larger area of steel than the ultimate strength calculations.   The ultimate strength must be checked for the cable position arrived at by the elastic calculations.   If the new calculation shows that the neutral axis falls within the flange the section is probably suitable, otherwise a revision of the section is necessary usually by increasing the area of the compression flange.

QUESTION 17.7

It has been decided to increase the number of 7 mm diameter wires in a prestressed beam to 9, and to reduce the effective depth to 340 mm. Determine the revised moment of resistance and the depth of the compression zone at the ultimate limit state.   Determine all stresses at transfer and at the serviceability limit state if:-

b = 200 mm, h = 400 mm, f_{cu} = 50 N/mm^2, z_1 = z_2 = 5 x 10^6 mm^3

A = 60 x 10^3 mm^2, f_{pe}/f_{pu} = 0.5, M(self wt) = 20 kNm, M_s = 80 kNm.

stress in wires at transfer = 0.7 f_{pu} and there is 30% loss of prestress.

(Answers: $x \simeq$ 112 mm, M_u = 127 kNm, f_{t1} = -12.78, f_{t2} = +0.26, f_{e1} = +4.26,
           f_{e2} = -13.02 N/mm^2)

If the check calculations at the serviceability limit state show that the allowable stresses have been exceeded a complete redesign may be necessary. If, however, the excess is small the condition may be rectified as follows. Since z_1 and z_2 (practical) are greater than the theoretical values it is the allowable tensile stresses at transfer f_{tt} and at the serviceability limit state f_{et} that are most often exceeded.   This condition is generally improved by reducing the value of the cable eccentricity e and increasing the prestressing force P.   This should maintain the moment of resistance at the ultimate limit state M_u and reduce the tensile stresses at transfer at the top of the section f_{t2} and at the bottom of the section at the service limit state f_{e1} .   It will however increase the compressive stresse: and if they become excessive redesign of the section is necessary.

The design process is thus:-

(1) reduce the eccentricity e and therefore the effective depth d

(2) using the design graphs determine a revised area of tensile steel at the ultimate limit state (this must be an increase over the previous practical value)

(3) check the value of depth of compression zone x

(4) check the tensile stress f_{t2} at the top of the beam at transfer for sections at which the bending moment is a maximum or zero.

(5) check the tensile stress at the bottom of the section at the serviceability limit state f_{el}

(6) revise if necessary

(7) check all other stresses.

17.1. SERVICEABILITY LIMIT STATE OF DEFLECTION (cl.4.3.7(CP110))

(a) DEFLECTION LIMITS

Generally the deflection due to service loads should not exceed $span/250$. The limit to avoid affecting partitions and finishes is $span/350$ or $20mm$, whichever is the lesser.   If finishes are to be applied to prestressed concrete units the initial upward deflection should not exceed $span/350$ (cl.2.2.3.1(CP110)).   These limits are inevitably a matter of opinion and are therefore somewhat arbitrary.

In the above the deflection limits are applied to the deflection below the support level.   If cracking to partitions and finishes is being considered the limit is applied to that part of the deflection occurring after the construction of the partition or the application of the finishes.

Deflections in prestressed concrete members are composed of two parts

(i) elastic deflection due to dead and imposed load

(ii) long term deflection due to creep in the concrete.

For Class 1 and 2 structures and for Class 3 structures where not more than 25% of the design imposed load is acting permanently the deflection may be taken as the sum of the two parts calculated as in (b) and (c) following. For Class 3 structures permanently carrying more than 25% of the design imposed load, deflection should be controlled using the rules for reinforced concrete members.

(b) ELASTIC DEFLECTION

The part of the total deflection due to elastic deformation for a beam of uniform section can be calculated from

$$a_e = \frac{l^2}{EI} \sum kM$$

where M is the maximum bending moment in the span and k depends on the shape of the bending moment diagram as shown in Table 17.1.

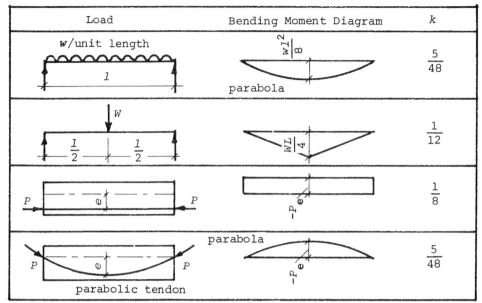

Table 17.1

(c) LONG TERM DEFLECTION

Long term deflections are generally due to creep in the concrete.   Creep is
dependent upon the stress level in the concrete and on the maturity at
first loading.   The creep effects due to transient loads are small so that
the permanent load only need be considered.   The permanent load is the
dead load plus that part of the imposed load which is permanently applied.
Each structure and its loading system must be considered separately, no
general rule can be laid down.

The long term deflection can be calculated using elastic analysis except
that a value of E derived from the values of specific creep given in
cl.4.8.2.5(CP110) should be used.   The value of E_c to be used is derived
as follows

for a beam

$$a = \iint \frac{M}{EI} \, dx, dx = \iint \frac{1}{r_b} \, dx, dx$$

The curvature $\phi = \dfrac{1}{r_b} = \dfrac{\varepsilon_2}{y}$

where for this purpose

ε_2 is the strain in the top of the beam due to creep

= specific creep x stress due to bending only

$\bar{y}$ is the distance from the top of the beam to the
centroidal axis

The stress due to bending includes the bending stress due to load and the
bending stress due to cable eccentricity, the uniform longitudinal
compression due to prestress should be ignored.

The value of E_{cc} to be used in calculating the long term deflection is given by

$$E_{cc} = \frac{\text{stress due to bending}}{\varepsilon_2} = \frac{1}{\text{specific creep}}$$

The values of specific creep from cl.4.8.2.5(CP110) are given below

For pre-tensioning at between 3 days and 5 days after concreting and for humid or dry conditions of exposure where the required cube strength at transfer is greater than 40.0 N/mm², the creep of the concrete per unit length should be taken as 48×10^{-6} per N/mm². For lower values of cube strength at transfer the creep per unit length should be assumed to be $48 \times 10^{-6} \times 40.0/f_{ci}$ per N/mm².

For post-tensioning at between 7 days and 14 days after concreting and for humid or dry conditions of exposure where the required cube strength at transfer is greater than 40.0 N/mm², the creep of the concrete per unit length should be taken as 36×10^{-6} per N/mm². For lower values of cube strength at transfer the creep per unit length should be taken as $36 \times 10^{-6} \times 40.0/f_{ci}$ per N/mm².

EXAMPLE 17.5

Calculate the deflection of the beam of example 17.4 assuming that three quarters of the imposed load is permanent and the cable is parabolic.

Elastic deflection due to dead and full imposed load (downwards)

$$a_e = \frac{5 \times 267.4 \times 10^6 \times 8^2 \times 10^6}{48 \times 34 \times 10^3 \times 6.48 \times 10^9} = 8.1 \text{ mm}$$

Elastic deflection due to prestress after losses (upwards)
Prestressing force after losses is 598 kN applied at an eccentricity of 277 mm

$$a_e = \frac{-5 \times 598 \times 10^3 \times 277 \times 8^2 \times 10^6}{48 \times 34 \times 10^3 \times 6.48 \times 10^9} = -5.0 \text{ mm}$$

Long term deflection due to bending only (downwards)

Stress at top due to prestress, dead load and three quarters imposed load

$$f_2 = \frac{598 \times 277}{23.6 \times 10^3} - \frac{(27.4 + 180)}{23.6}$$

$$= 7.0 - 8.8 = -1.8 \text{ N/mm}^2$$

For post tensioning and a cube strength of 36 N/mm² at transfer

$$\text{creep} = 36 \times 10^{-6} \times \frac{40.0}{36.0} \times 1.8 = 72.0 \times 10^{-6}$$

$$\text{therefore } E_c = \frac{10^6}{72.0} = 13.9 \times 10^3 \text{ N/mm}^2$$

$$a_c = \frac{5(207.4 \times 10^3 - 598 \times 277) 10^3 \times 8^2 \times 10^6}{48 \times 13.9 \times 10^3 \times 6.48 \times 10^9} = 3.1 \text{ mm}$$

Total deflection $\quad a = a_e + a_c = 8.1 - 5.0 + 3.1 = 6.2 \text{ mm}$

The allowable deflection $= \dfrac{8000}{250} = 32$ mm

QUESTION 17.8

If the beam described in Question 17.4 is simply supported on a span of 6m, calculate the total deflection assuming that the permanent bending moment is 50 kNm and the load uniformly distributed.   The beam is pretensioned with a straight cable at 150 mm eccentricity. $P_t = 313.3$ kN; $\eta = 0.75$ and $f_{cu} = 50$ N/mm^2; $f_{ci} = 30$ N/mm^2.

(Answer: a = 8.3 mm)

17.J. ELASTIC ANALYSIS FOR BEAMS WITH STRAIGHT CABLES

Where the beam is straight and of uniform section with a straight cable as in many pretensioned and some post-tensioned prestressed concrete beams there must occur a section at which the bending moment is zero.   For simply supported beams the position of zero bending moment is usually at the supports.   At the section of zero bending moment the dead load cannot modify the stresses due to prestress and the prestressing force must be applied in such a way that the allowable tensile and compressive stresses on the concrete are not exceeded.   The cable eccentricity may still be calculated using Equation 17.11 but M_{min} must be set to zero.   In that case when using Equations 17.7 and 17.8 M_{min} must not exceed zero (it may be negative) unless the beam itself is curved, as shown in Fig. 17.9, in order to accommodate the increased cable eccentricity needed for the centre of the span.   It is still advisable to check the stresses for other load conditions.

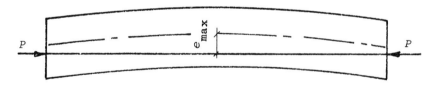

Fig. 17.9

QUESTION 17.9

If a straight beam with a straight cable had been used for the beam in question 17.4 determine the required theoretical z_1' and z_2' values for the elastic analysis at the serviceability limit state.

(Answer: $z_1' \geqslant 4.93$ x 10^6; $z_2' \geqslant 3.38$ x 10^6 mm^3.
The practical cross section is still satisfactory since $z_1 - z_2 = 5$ x $10^6 mm^3$)

18 Loss of Prestress

18.A INTRODUCTION

Early experimenters found difficulty in prestressing concrete due to loss of prestressing force with time. The rate of loss is high at first so that most of the losses occur in the first three months. Prestressed concrete is practical only if the losses in the prestressing force are reasonable. In practice the losses vary between 10 per cent and 40 per cent of the initial prestressing force.

The wires or cables are initially stressed to approximately 70 per cent of the ultimate strength of the steel. This initial stress is reduced due to:-

(a) relaxation of the steel

(b) elastic deformation of the concrete

(c) shrinkage of the concrete

(d) creep of the concrete

(e) slip at anchorages

(f) friction in ducts and at anchorages.

Each of these reasons for loss of prestress is dealt with more fully in this chapter.

In the design process the loss of prestress has initially to be estimated from past experience in order to arrive at a possible section. This is then checked more accurately and the section changed if necessary. Constants and recommendations for the calculation of the losses of prestress are given in CP110 and their use is explained in the following pages.

18.B. RELAXATION OF THE STEEL (cl.4.8.2.2(CP110))

Generally if a high tensile steel wire, bar or strand is stressed in tension to 70 per cent of its characteristic strength and anchored over a fixed length, after approximately 1000 hours the stress will have reduced by approximately 8 per cent. The fixed length is provided by the prestressed concrete member, which in reality changes slightly in length. In cases where the initial prestress is greater than 70 per cent values of the relaxation of the steel may be obtained from the appropriate British Standard (see cl.4.8.1(CP110)). In such a case the relaxation may be expected to be greater, Conversely if the initial prestressing force is lower than 70 percent of the characteristic force then the relaxation will be lower than

8 per cent.   It is suggested in CP110 that at a prestressing force of 50 per cent of the characteristic strength, the relaxation is zero and that for intermediate values the relaxation may be obtained by linear interpolation.

In the past it has been the practice to assume a reduced relaxation if the tendon was overstressed for a short time prior to anchoring.   This is not now allowed.

QUESTION 18.1

(a) If the required prestress is 70 per cent of the characteristic strength and the steel is overstressed initially, does the code allow a reduction in losses?

(b) If the initial prestress is 60% of the characteristic strength what losses should be taken for relaxation of the steel?

(Answers: (a) No.   (b) 4%)

18.C. ELASTIC DEFORMATION (cl.4.8.2.3(CP110))

In prestressed concrete, once the steel and concrete are anchored together, a change of length in the concrete causes a similar change of length in the steel.   Since the concrete behaves in part as an elastic material which reduces in length when it is compressed any steel already in the member will also be shortened.   This elastic shortening is particularly important with pretensioned members where bond is effected between the steel and the concrete whilst the steel is fully stressed and the concrete is unstressed. When the wires are released from their anchorage they tend to shorten, but because of bond they can only shorten to the stage where the compressive force in the concrete is equal to the tensile force in the steel.   The development of the compressive force in the concrete involves a shortening of the concrete and of the steel so that the final stress in the steel is lower than the stress before release from the anchorage.   The calculation for actual loss of prestress is given below.

(a) Pretensioned beams

For a pretensioned beam with a straight cable

$$\text{Strain in the concrete} = \text{strain in the steel}$$

$$\frac{f_c}{E_c} = \frac{\left[1 - \eta_e\right] f_{pi}}{E_s}$$

$$\left[1 - \eta_e\right] f_{pi} = f_c \cdot \frac{E_s}{E_c} = \alpha_e f_c$$

Expressing the loss as a percentage of the initial stress f_{pi} in the steel

$$\text{loss} = \frac{\left[1 - \eta_e\right] f_{pi} \times 100}{f_{pi}} = \frac{100 . \alpha_e f_c}{f_{pi}} \quad \text{per cent} \quad \ldots \ldots \quad 18.1$$

Method 1 for calculating f_c

Equation 18.1 has two unknown variables, the loss and f_c. A second equation can be obtained by considering the equilibrium of longitudinal forces.

Compressive force in concrete = Tensile force in steel.

$$A_c f_{cp} = A_{ps} \eta_e f_{pi}$$

$$f_{cp} = \frac{A_{ps}\left[f_{pi} - \alpha_e f_c\right]}{A_c}$$

but ignoring bending due to self weight

$$f_c = f_{cp} + \frac{A_{ps} \eta_e f_{pi} e^2}{I}$$

$$f_c = f_{cp} + A_{ps}\left[f_{pi} - \alpha_e f_c\right] \frac{e^2}{I}$$

$$f_c = \left[f_{pi} - \alpha_e f_c\right] \left(\frac{A_{ps}}{A_c} + \frac{A_{ps} e^2}{I}\right)$$

$$f_c \left[1 + \alpha_e \left(\frac{A_{ps}}{A_c} + \frac{A_{ps} e^2}{I}\right)\right] = f_{pi} \left(\frac{A_{ps}}{A_c} + \frac{A_{ps} e^2}{I}\right)$$

$$f_c = \frac{cf_{pi} \left(\frac{A_{ps}}{A_c} + \frac{A_{ps} e^2}{I}\right)}{1 + \alpha_e \left(\frac{A_{ps}}{A_c} + \frac{A_{ps} e^2}{I}\right)} \quad \ldots \ldots \quad 18.2$$

Combining equations 18.1 and 18.2

$$\text{percentage loss} = \frac{100\ \alpha_e}{f_{pi}} \cdot \frac{f_{pi}\left(\dfrac{A_{ps}}{A_c} + \dfrac{A_{ps}\ e^2}{I}\right)}{\left[1 + \alpha_e\left(\dfrac{A_{ps}}{A_c} + \dfrac{A_{ps}\ e^2}{I}\right)\right]}$$

$$= \frac{100\ \alpha_e\left(\dfrac{A_{ps}}{A_c} + \dfrac{A_{ps}\ e^2}{I}\right)}{1 + \alpha_e\left(\dfrac{A_{ps}}{A_c} + \dfrac{A_{ps}\ e^2}{I}\right)} \qquad\qquad \ldots\ldots 18.3$$

The effect of bending due to self weight has been ignored but it will tend to reduce the elastic loss in simply supported beams.   The above is, therefore, safe since the loss will be overestimated.

(ii) Method 2 for calculating f_c

If the dead load at the time of prestressing is large it is important that it should be considered when calculating the elastic loss.   The method then used is to assume that the whole of the jacking force P_k is applied to the end of the member and calculate the stress in the concrete at the level of the tendon f_c on that basis.   Equation 18.1 can then be used to obtain the loss of prestress.   This method will also tend to overestimate the loss slightly.

(b) Post-tensioned beams

In post-tensioned beams it is occasionally possible to tension and anchor the whole of the wires simultaneously, in which case there are no elastic losses. It is more usual, however, to stress and anchor the wires or strands progressively, in this case the earlier wires suffer a shortening as the later wires are stressed.   In this case the elastic loss calculated as above may be halved or alternatively, more accurate calculations may be made which take account of the sequence of stressing.   The derivation of Equation 18.3 assumes that the cable eccentricity is uniform throughout the length of the beam.   This is true for most pretensioned beams but it is rarely true for post-tensioned beams so that allowance for the variation of eccentricity must be made.   The accurate method would be integrate along the length of the beam and find a mean, but a reasonable result can be obtained by assessing a mean cable eccentricity.

QUESTION 18.2

A prestressed concrete beam has a cross sectional area of 150×10^3 mm^2 and a second moment of area of 10×10^9 mm^4.   If the characteristic strength of the concrete is 50 N/mm^2, determine the loss of prestress due to elastic shortening.

(a) if the beam is pretensioned and the cable eccentricity is 200 mm.

(b) if the beam is post-tensioned and the mean cable eccentricity is 140 mm.

In both cases the steel area is 1500 mm². The answer should be given as a percentage of the initial prestressing force. Use Equation 18.3 and assume E_s = 200 kN/mm².

(Answer: (a) 10.4% (b) 4.13%)

18.D. SHRINKAGE OF THE CONCRETE (cl.4.8.2.4(CP110))

Shrinkage is due to the evaporation of the water which is in excess of that required by the chemical reaction. The extra water is needed to lubricate the mix and assist in compaction. The amount of excess water should be kept as low as possible to minimise the shrinkage. A typical shrinkage - time relationship is shown in Figure 18.1. It may be assumed that half the total shrinkage takes place in the first month after transfer, and three quarters in the first six months after transfer.

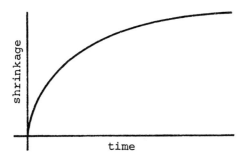

Fig. 18.1

If shrinkage is expressed as a strain then

strain in the steel = strain in the concrete

$$\varepsilon_s = \varepsilon_{cs} \qquad \cdots\cdots\cdots \text{ 18.4}$$

For a linear relationship between stress and strain in the steel

$$E_s = \frac{(1 - \eta_s)\, f_s}{\varepsilon_s} \qquad \cdots\cdots\cdots \text{ 18.5}$$

combining Equations 18.4 and 18.5

$$(1 - \eta_s)f_s = E_s\, \varepsilon_{cs} \qquad \cdots\cdots\cdots \text{ 18.6}$$

Expressed as a percentage of the initial prestressing force f_{pi}

$$\text{percentage loss} = \frac{(1 - \eta_s)\, f_s \times 100}{f_{pi}} = \frac{E_s \cdot \varepsilon_{cs} \times 100}{f_{pi}} \quad \text{percent}$$

Values of ε_{cs} are given in Table 41 (CP110).   It will be noticed that the amount of shrinkage is dependent upon the humidity of the environment and the method of prestressing.   Really the method of prestressing is irrelevant but the age of the concrete is important.

Table 41. Shrinkage of concrete

System	Shrinkage per unit length	
	Humid exposure (90 % r.h.)	Normal exposure (70 % r.h.)
Pre-tensioning: transfer at between 3 days and 5 days after concreting	100×10^{-6}	300×10^{-6}
Post-tensioning: transfer at between 7 days and 14 days after concreting	70×10^{-6}	200×10^{-6}

QUESTION 18.3

Determine the loss of prestress for a pretensioned beam (transfer at 4 days after concreting) which is kept in an atmosphere of 70% relative humidity. The initial prestress is 70% of the characteristic strength, where f_{pu} = 1850 N/mm^2 and E_s = 200 kN/mm^2.   Express the answer as a stress and a percentage.

(Answer: 60 N/mm^2, 4.63%)

18.E. CREEP OF CONCRETE (cl.4.8.2.5(CP110))

The nature of creep is not fully understood and various writers give different explanations.   In general it may be accepted that creep is due to internal movement of free or loosely bound water and to the change of size and shape of minute voids in the cement paste.   The creep-time curve is similar to the shrinkage-time curve shown in Fig. 18.1.   The creep strain is also dependent on the stress in the concrete adjacent to the tendons.   As previously the strain in the concrete is assumed equal to the strain in the steel.   Hence in the same way as before

$$(1 - \eta_c) f_s = E_s \cdot \varepsilon_{cc}$$

Values of ε_{cc} are given in cl.4.8.2.5(CP110) which are dependent on the ratio of the stress in the adjacent concrete to the cube strength at transfer f_{ci} and the method of prestressing.

For pretensioning where transfer is effected at 3 to 5 days after concreting the creep strain should be taken as $48 \times 10^{-6} \times 40.0/f_{ci}$ per N/mm^2 of the stress in the concrete at the level of the centroid of the tendon.   The concrete stress is calculated for the time at which transfer occurs.   For post-tensioning at 7 days to 14 days after concreting the creep strain should be taken as $36 \times 10^{-6} \times 40.0/f_{ci}$ per N/mm^2.   In both cases, if transfer takes place at a cube strength greater than 40.0 N/mm^2, f_{ci} should be assumed to have a value of 40.0 N/mm^2.

The above assumes that the stress in the section will nowhere exceed $f_{ci}/3$. If the maximum stress in the section is $f_{ci}/2$ the creep strain should be multiplied by 1.25. For stresses at transfer between $f_{ci}/3$ and $f_{ci}/2$ the multiplication factor may be assumed to vary linearly between 1.00 and 1.25

For a pretensioned beam

$$\text{percentage loss} = \frac{48}{10^6} \times \frac{40}{f_{ci}} \times f_c \times \frac{E_s}{f_{pi}} \times 100$$

and for a post-tensioned beam

$$\text{percentage loss} = \frac{36}{10^6} \times \frac{40}{f_{ci}} \times f_c \times \frac{E_s}{f_{pi}} \times 100$$

QUESTION 18.4

Transfer is to be effected at 4 days after casting for a pretensioned beam. The cube strength, f_{ci}, at transfer is 30 N/mm^2 and the initial stress in the concrete adjacent to the tendon is 10 N/mm^2. Determine the loss of prestress if $f_{pi} = 0.7f_{pu}$, $f_{pu} = 1850$ N/mm^2 and $E_s = 200$ kN/mm^2.

(Answer: 9.88%)

18.F. SLIP AT ANCHORAGE (Cl.4.8.2.6(CP110))

(a) Pretensioned prestressed concrete - if pretensioning is carried out by fixing all wires to a single cross head, then the slip that occurs during the tensioning process may be allowed for and is not regarded as a loss in prestress.

If however wires are tensioned individually or in pairs and wedges driven in before the release of the jack, then a slip of say 5 mm may occur. If this occurs over a long casting bed, say 60 m, then the loss is not large.

(b) Post-tensioned prestressed concrete - the 5 mm slip mentioned above may occur in a post-tensioned member, but in this case the length of the member may be as little as 6 m, in which case the loss of prestress will be greater and must be allowed for. From the stress-strain relationship for steel

$$E_s = \frac{(1 - \eta_a)f_s}{\varepsilon_s}$$

$$\text{and since } \varepsilon_s = \frac{\delta L}{L} \qquad \text{where } \delta L = \text{slip movement}$$

$$(1 - \eta_a)f_s = E_s \times \frac{\delta L}{L}$$

the loss in relation to the initial prestressing force f_{pi}

$$\text{percentage loss} = \frac{(1 - \eta_a)f_s \times 100}{f_{pi}} = E_s \times \frac{\delta L}{L} \times \frac{100}{f_{pi}}$$

QUESTION 18.5

The slip at the anchorages for a 10 m long post-tensioned beam is 5 mm.   If the steel is stressed initially to 60% of the characteristic strength, determine the loss in prestress.

Assume f_{pu} = 1400 N/mm^2, E_s = 175 kN/mm^2.

(Answer: 10.42%)

18.G. FRICTION IN THE DUCT

(a) DUE TO UNINTENTIONAL ERROR IN THE PROFILE (cl.4.8.3.3(CP110))

Slight variations in the line of the duct, either straight or curved, produce additional points of contact between the tendon and the sides of the duct.

The loss of prestressing force $(P_0 - P_x)$ at a distance x metres from the jack may be expressed as a percentage of the force P_0 at the jack.

$$\text{percentage loss} = \frac{100 (P_0 - P_x)}{P_0} = 100 (1 - e^{-Kx})$$

where $Kx \leqslant 0.2$, $e^{-Kx} \simeq 1 - Kx$; (e = 2.718, the base of Napierian logarithms)

$$\text{percentage loss} = \frac{100 (P_0 - P_x)}{P_0} = 100 Kx$$

K is a frictional constant which should generally be taken as not less than 33×10^{-4} per metre length, but it may be reduced for special conditions.

QUESTION 18.6

Determine the maximum loss of prestress due to unintentional variation from the profile for a member of 15 m length which is (a) jacked from one end, (b) jacked from both ends simultaneously.

(Answer: (a) 4.95%;   (b) 2.475%)

(b) DUE TO CURVATURE OF THE TENDON (cl.4.8.3.4(CP110))

When a tendon is curved, the loss of tension due to friction is dependent on the angle turned through and the coefficient of friction μ .

The loss of prestressing force $(P_o - P_x)$ along a curve of radius r_{ps} at a distance x metres from the jack may be expressed as a percentage of the force at the jack P_o which may be calculated from:

$$\text{percentage loss} = \frac{100\ (P_o - P_x)}{P_o} = 100\ (1 - e^{-\mu x/r_{ps}})$$

where $\mu x/r_{ps} \leqslant 0.2$; $\quad e^{-\mu x/r_{ps}} \simeq 1 - \dfrac{\mu x}{r_{ps}}$

$$\text{percentage loss} = \frac{100\ (P_o - P_x)}{P_o} = \frac{100\ \mu x}{r_{ps}}$$

Typical values of μ are given in CP110, e.g. 0.55 for steel on concrete
0.30 for steel on steel.

There is little error if a parabolic curve is treated as a circular curve and r_{ps} may be calculated as follows:

In Fig. 18.2 the tendon is shown as a circular curve. If the beam is simply supported and symmetrical

$$r_{ps} = \frac{L^2}{8a_t} + \frac{a_t}{2}$$

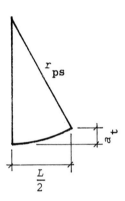

Fig. 18.2

QUESTION 18.7

Determine the loss of prestress due to curvature of the tendon where the eccentricity of the duct is 200 mm at the centre of the span and zero at the ends for a beam 20 m in length (a) if jacked from one end, (b) if jacked from both ends simultaneously. It may be assumed that the duct follows a circular curve and the steel moves over concrete.

(Answer: (a) 4.4%; (b) 2.2%)

19 Shear in Prestressed Concrete

19.A. INTRODUCTION

Experimental investigation into the effects of shear forces on prestressed concrete beams has shown that the longitudinal compression improves the shear resistance, and the following types of shear failure occur:

(a) shear cracking in the web of the beam which commences at the centroid of the cross section. Where these cracks occur flexural cracks in the tension zone of the cross section are not likely. The method of calculation for this case is given in 19.B.

(b) shear cracks which are initiated at the extreme tension side due to flexural cracking. The method of calculation for shear strength is given in 19.C.

(c) diagonal compression failure which occurs under the action of large shear stresses and is indicated by crushing of the concrete in the web. It is only likely to occur where heavy shear reinforcement is provided.

These forms of shear failure are shown in Fig. 19.1

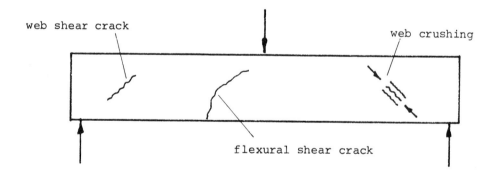

Fig. 19.1

The ultimate shear resistance, V_c, of the beam must be checked considering all types of shear failure. If the actual shear force is greater than either of the two values, V_{co} for the case in which flexural cracks are not present and V_{cr} for the case in which flexural cracks are present, then shear reinforcement must be provided. The necessary calculations are covered in the remainder of this chapter.

19.B. WEB SHEAR CRACKS AT THE ULTIMATE LIMIT STATE (cl.4.3.5.1(CP110))

Shear forces acting on a prestressed concrete member at the ultimate limit state may produce web shear cracks. Since the maximum shear stress occurs at the centroid of the cross section it is generally sufficient to check at this point only.

It is assumed that the concrete cracks when the maximum principal tensile stress exceeds a value of $f_t = 0.24\sqrt{f_{cu}}$. The stresses at the centroidal axis are:-

(a) the longitudinal stress due to the prestressing force; it is recommended in CP110 that 80% of the calculated value, $0.8f_{cp}$, is used.

(b) the maximum shear stress

$$v_c = \frac{1.5v_{co}}{bh} \qquad \cdots\cdots 19.1$$

where b is the breadth of the section, or the breadth of the web for an 'I' or 'T' section, h is the depth of the section and v_{co} is the allowable shear force on the uncracked section. The factor of 1.5 is to give the maximum shear stress for the parabolic shear stress distribution.

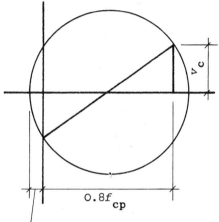

maximum principal tensile stress

Mohr's circle

Fig. 19.2

From the Mohr's circle diagram shown in Fig. 19.2 the principal tensile stress f_t may be obtained as follows

$$f_t = \sqrt{\left(\frac{1}{2} \times 0.8 f_{cp}\right)^2 + v_c^2} - \frac{1}{2} \times 0.8 f_{cp}$$

rearranging

$$v_c = \sqrt{f_t^2 + 0.8 f_{cp} f_t}$$

combining with Equation 19.1

$$V_{co} = 0.67 bh \sqrt{f_t^2 + 0.8 f_{cp} f_t} \qquad \cdots\cdots 19.2$$

Equation 19.2 is Equation 45 (CP110) where values of f_t and f_{cp} are considered positive. For design purposes put $f_t = 0.24\sqrt{f_{cu}}$

QUESTION 19.1

Determine the value of V_{co} for a beam having the cross section shown in Fig. 19.3(a) and a straight tendon.   The stresses due to the prestressing force are shown in Fig. 19.3(b).

(Answer: 280 kN)

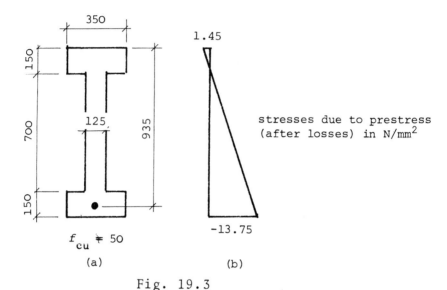

stresses due to prestress (after losses) in N/mm^2

$f_{cu} \doteq 50$

(a)

(b)

Fig. 19.3

19.C. FLEXURAL SHEAR CRACKS (cl. 4.3.5.2 (CP110))

The shear resistance V_{cr} at the ultimate limit state for sections cracked in flexure may be determined from the empirical formula, Equation 46 (CP110).

4.3.5.2 *Sections cracked in flexure.* The ultimate shear resistance of a section cracked in flexure, V_{cr}, may be calculated using equation 46:

$$V_{cr} = \left(1 - 0.55 \frac{f_{pe}}{f_{pu}}\right) v_c bd + M_0 \frac{V}{M} \qquad (46)$$

where d is the distance from the extreme compression fibre to the centroid of the tendons at the section considered,

$\quad\quad M_0$ is the moment necessary to produce zero stress in the concrete at the depth d.

$\quad\quad\quad M_0 = 0.8 f_{pt} \dfrac{I}{y}$ where f_{pt} is the stress due to prestress only at depth d and distance y from the

$\quad\quad\quad$centroid of the concrete section which has second moment of area I,

$\quad\quad f_{pe}$ is the effective prestress after all losses have occurred. For the purposes of this equation f_{pe} shall not be put greater than $0.6 f_{pu}$,

$\quad\quad v_c$ is obtained from Table 5,

$\quad\quad V$ and M are the shear force and bending moment respectively at the section considered due to ultimate loads,

$\quad\quad V_{cr}$ should be taken as not less than $0.1 bd \sqrt{f_{cu}}$.

The value of V_{cr} calculated using equation 46 at a particular section may be assumed to be constant for a distance equal to $d/2$, measured in the direction of increasing moment, from that particular section.

For a section cracked in flexure and with inclined tendons, the component of prestressing force normal to the longitudinal axis of the member should be ignored.

Experimental observations show that flexural shear cracking appears to occur at the flexural cracking load plus an additional shear force which depends on the strength of the concrete and the dimensions of the section.   If flexural cracking occurs at a moment of M_O, the shear at cracking is $(M_O'/M)V$ which is the second term in the equation.   The first term in the equation was originally determined experimentally to be $0.6\sqrt{f_c'}$.   This has been modified in CP110 and related to the shear resistance of reinforced concrete and the effective prestress.

QUESTION 19.2

Determine the value of V_{cr} for the cross section shown in Fig. 19.3.   It may be assumed that $f_{cu} = 50$ N/mm^2, $A_s = 942$ mm^2, $f_{pe} = 0.6f_{pu}$, $I = 22.5 \times 10^9$mm^4 and $M/V = 3.6$m .

(Answer: 199 kN)

19.D.   MINIMUM SHEAR REINFORCEMENT (cl.4.3.5.3(CP110))

Even if the actual shear force V is less than the allowable shear force V_c a minimum quantity of shear reinforcement should be provided.   The reinforcement provided should be in the form of links such that

$$ s_v < \frac{0.87 f_{yv} A_{sv}}{0.4b} \qquad \text{.......... 19.3} $$

s_v should not exceed $0.75d$ nor four times the web thickness.   Equation 19.3 is a rearranged form of Equation 47 (CP110).   In Equation 19.3 f_{yv} should not be taken as greater than 425 N/mm^2.

The above rules need not be applied and no shear reinforcement need be provided in the following cases as defined in cl.4.3.5.3(CP110):

(1) where V is less than $0.5V_c$,
(2) in members of minor importance,
(3) where tests, carried out in accordance with **2.4.6**, have shown that shear reinforcement is not required.

QUESTION 19.3

Determine spacing s_v for minimum reinforcement in the form of 8 mm links if $b_w = 125$ mm, $d = 935$ mm and $f_{yv} = 425$ N/mm^2.

(Answer: 500 mm based on $4b_w$)

19.E.   SHEAR REINFORCEMENT (cl.4.3.5.3(CP110))

When the shear force V applied to a section at the ultimate limit state exceeds V_c, which is the lesser of V_{co} or V_{cr}, shear reinforcement in the form of links should be provided such that

$$s_v = \frac{0.87 \, f_{yv} \, A_{sv} \, d_t}{V - V_c} \qquad \dots\dots\dots \text{19.4}$$

The development of Equation 19.4 is the same as for the reinforced concrete beam shown in Chapter 10.

When using Equation 19.4 s_v should not exceed $0.75d_t$ nor should it exceed four times the web thickness b_w. If V is greater than $1.8V_c$, s_v should not exceed $0.5d_t$ where d_t is the greater of the depths d or d_t shown in Figure 19.4.

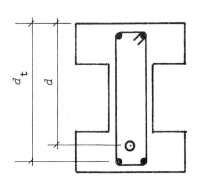

QUESTION 19.4

Determine the spacing s_V of single 10 mm diameter links at the ultimate limit state if $V = 316$ kN, $V_{cr} = 199$ kN, $d_t = 935$ mm, $f_{yv} = 425$ N/mm^2, $b_w = 125$ mm.

Fig. 19.4

(Answer: 464 say 460 mm)

19.F. MAXIMUM SHEAR FORCE (c1.4.3.5.4 (CP110)

To prevent crushing of the concrete due to diagonal compressive stress the maximum shear stress shall not exceed the values given in Table 40 (CP110), no matter how much shear reinforcement is added. The shear stresses given should be multiplied by bd to obtain the allowable maximum shear force. If the allowable maximum shear force is exceeded the breadth or the depth must be increased. Holes through the web or unfilled cable ducts reduce the shear resistance and must be allowed for.

Table 40. Maximum shear stress

	Concrete grade			
	30	40	50	60 and over
	N/mm^2	N/mm^2	N/mm^2	N/mm^2
Maximum shear stress	4.1	4.7	5.3	5.8

QUESTION 19.5

Determine the maximum shear force that may be applied to an 'I' section prestressed concrete beam where $h = 1000$, $b = 350$, $b_w = 125$, $d = 925$ mm and $f_{cu} = 50$ N/mm^2.

(Answer: 612.8 kN)

20 End Blocks

20.A ANCHORAGE ZONES FOR POST-TENSIONED CABLES

When a prestressing cable is being tensioned and after it has been anchored a large force is applied to a small area at the end of the member.   If such a force is applied to a block through a stiff plate cracks occur as shown in Fig. 20.1.   It may be considered that the wedge under the rigid plate applies forces to the block which are normal to its sides and thus cause the block to split.   The load which can be carried is dependent upon the tensile strength of the concrete of the block and the ratio of the load area to the unloaded area.   The tensile strength of the concrete is usually insufficient to resist the tensile stresses induced and reinforcement is necessary to prevent longitudinal splitting of the member. At a distance from the end plate greater than the length of side of the end plate the transverse tensile stresses need not be considered, stresses can then be calculated by the methods given in Chapters 16 and 17.

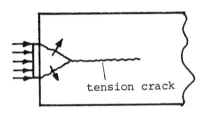

tension crack

Fig. 20.1

20.B BURSTING TENSILE FORCES FOR POST TENSIONED MEMBERS (cl.4.8.5.1(CP110))

The bursting tensile forces in the end blocks of post tensioned beams with bonded tendons should be based on the tendon jacking load P_k, since this will usually be the greater force.   For post tensioned members with unbonded cables, however, the greatest force may be at the ultimate limit state.

Table 43. Design bursting tensile forces in end blocks

y_{po}/y_o	0.3	0.4	0.5	0.6	0.7
F_{bst}/P_k	0.23	0.20	0.17	0.14	0.11

where y_o is half the side of end block,
   y_{po} is half the side of loaded area,
   P_k is the load in the tendon assessed as above,
   F_{bst} is the bursting tensile force.

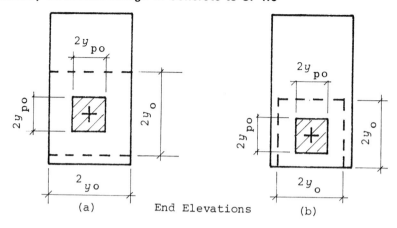

(a)   End Elevations   (b)

Fig. 20.2

The approach used in CP110 necessitates adopting a square end plate and selecting a square end section of the concrete surrounding it and centred on the tendon as shown in Fig. 20.2.   If a circular end plate is used the calculations should be based on a square plate of the same area.

Design bursting stresses are given in Table 43 (CP110) which depend on the ratios of y_{po}/y_o and F_{bst/P_k}.   Hence a value of the bursting force F_{bst} may be determined. F_{bst} is assumed to act over a length of $(2y_o - 0.2y_o)$ starting at $0.2y_o$ from the face of the end plate in contact with the concrete. Provided the cover to the steel is 50 mm this force F_{bst} is resisted by the links at the design strength.   The use of Equation 20.1 enables the pitch and size of the reinforcement to be determined.

$$F_{bst} = \frac{A_{sv}}{s_v} \frac{f_{yv}}{1.15} \ (2y_o - 0.2y_o) \qquad \ldots \ldots 20.1$$

If the cover is less than 50 mm the stress f_{yv} should correspond to a strain of 0.001 in the steel obtained from Fig. 3 or 4 (CP110).   The same reinforcement should be provided in two directions at right angles.

Where groups of anchorages occur each anchorage shall be treated separately as above.   Dimension y_o shall be calculated for each anchorage so that no overlap occurs.

QUESTION 20.1

Determine the spacing of 6 mm dia.
single links to reinforce the end
block illustrated in Fig. 20.3.

P_k = 450 kN, the end plate is

200 x 200 mm, and f_{yv} = 250 N/mm²

(Answer: 57.83 say 50 mm)

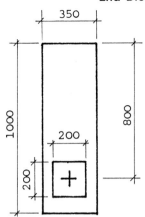

Fig. 20.3

20.C. TRANSMISSION LENGTH FOR PRE-TENSIONED BEAMS (cl.4.8.4(CP110))

In pretensioned members the forces in the wires are transmitted to the
concrete by bond between the steel and concrete.   The stress in the wires
at the end of the beam must, therefore, be zero.   The full stress in the
wires is attained at some distance from the end.   This distance is termed
the transmission length and may vary between 50 and 150 diameters.   The
true value cannot be determined by calculation with any degree of certainty
and the value used should be that known to be obtained in the plant which
is making the beams.   The main factors influencing the transmission length
are :

(a) the strength and compaction of the concrete

(b) the size and type of the tendon

(c) the surface roughness of the tendon, e.g. the crimp of the wire or the
helical groove in the surface of the strand

(d) the suddeness of the release of the tension in the wires e.g. the beams
nearest the anchorages in a long line system will probably have greater
transmission lengths than those near the middle.

Despite the difficulties some guidance is given in CP110 but the values
given must be treated with caution.

For wire which is plain or has a small degree of crimp the suggested
transmission length is 100 diameters for cube strengths not less than
35 N/mm² at transfer.   For wires with considerable crimp the transmission
length is reduced to 65 diameters.   For strand up to 18 mm diameter
values of transmission length are given in Table 42 (CP110) but similar
values are obtained by using a length of 8 $\sqrt{\phi^3}$.

20.D. ANCHORAGE ZONE STRESSES FOR PRE-TENSIONED MEMBERS

For a length at each end of a member equal to the transmission length the longitudinal compressive stresses are much reduced consequently the strength available to resist shear and bending is also reduced.   If the available strength is less than that needed to resist the ultimate loads additional reinforcement, designed as for a reinforced concrete beam, must be provided.

The transfer of the tendon force to the concrete causes bursting tensile stresses in the same way as for post-tensioned members except that because the transfer is more gradual, taking place over the transmission length, the tensile stresses are lower.   The shorter the transmission length the higher the bursting stress.   The available methods for calculation of the bursting stresses are both lengthy and unsatisfactory but since pre-tensioning is usually used for large numbers of units the cost of testing of prototypes can be readily absorbed.   Where doubt exists Guyon suggested a method of considering the load to be transferred from the tendon in a series of steps each step being treated as for post-tensioning, the tensile stresses so obtained are then added to obtain the tensile stress for design. He then suggests that the tensile stress in concrete is unlikely to be greater than 0.3 times the compressive stress in the concrete at the level of the wire.   For short runs or where difficulty is known to occur, reinforcement surrounding each wire, designed for that stress may be used.

Reinforcement may be added based on equating the bursting force to the resistance provided by the links.

$$0.3 \, f_{cu} \, b \, s = A_s \, \frac{f_{sy}}{1.15}$$

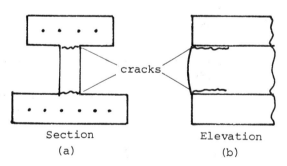
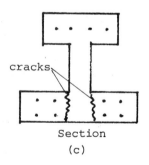

| Section | Elevation | Section |
| (a) | (b) | (c) |

Fig. 20.4

Cracks sometimes occur when wires are collected together for convenience in anchoring e.g. an I beam may have all its wires grouped in the flanges as shown in Fig. 20.4a, the abrupt changes in compression which occur locally can lead to cracks as shown in Fig. 20.4b.   Similar cracks can also occur if the wires are groups in the flanges as shown in Fig 20.4c The arrangement of wires should follow the desired stress distribution as closely as possible in order to avoid this difficulty or alternatively additional transverse reinforcement should be provided.

QUESTION 20.2

The section shown in Fig. 20.5 is
pretensioned with 13 wires in the
positions indicated.   If the maximum
force in each wire is 45 kN determine
the highest compressive stress at the
level of a prestressing wire and hence
the tensile stress using Guyon's
approximation.

(Answer: 3.18 N/mm²)

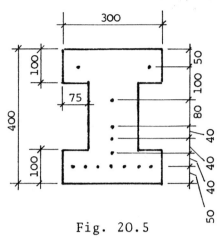

Fig. 20.5

Index